MAMMILLARIA
A Collector's Guide

MAMMILLARIA
A Collector's Guide

John Pilbeam

Photography by Bill Weightman

B. T. BATSFORD LTD · LONDON

© John Pilbeam 1981
First published 1981

All rights reserved. No part of this publication may be
reproduced, in any form or by any means, without
permission from the Publisher

ISBN 0 7134 3897 5

Typeset by Keyspools Ltd, Golborne, Lancs.
and printed in Great Britain by
The Anchor Press Ltd
Tiptree, Essex
for the publishers
B. T. Batsford Ltd.
4 Fitzhardinge Street
London W1H 0AH

CONTENTS

ACKNOWLEDGMENTS

In addition to thanking my good friend Bill Weightman for hours of patient and painstaking photography, and David Hunt for contributing the information in the chapters on classification and geography as well as valuable advice, I should like to thank the following people for their time, their opinions or the loan of their precious plants over the last several years, while this book was in its gestation period:

Jack Astley; Albert Beeching; Nellie Blowes; Bernard Bloxham; Jim Bolton; Derek Bowdery; Helmut and Christiane Broogh; Ken Burke; Bill and Joan Catchesides; Pete Chapman; Brenda Clarke; David Clarke; John Clements; Ethel Conley; John Ede; Ken and Betty Elliott; Ian Flint; Joe Gentle; Lois Glass; Eric Greenaway; Ernie Groom; Vince Hanlon; Newman Hann; Eddie Harris; Ken and Joan Harrow; Bill Hedger; Jim Hedworth; Terry Hewitt (of Holly Gate Nursery); George Hollis; Peter Holmes; Robert Holt; John Hughes; Percy Ingram; Clive Innes; Cyril Jackson; Tom and June Jenkins; Diana and Rosemary Jenner; Roy Keeler; Gus Kelley; David Lambie; Jim Laurence; Tom and Agnes Lavender; Val Loft; June Mabbs; Bill and Betty Maddams; Roger Mann; Jack and Chris Mansfield; Pat Mills; Dawn Nelson; June Norman; Doreen Oakman; Brian Oliver; Brian Oris; Michael Pilbeam; Peter Raymont; John and Mary Rayner; John Rean; Wenda Relf; Graham and Mavis Rose; Gordon Rowley; Ron Shaw; Doug Sizmur; Pat Stacey; Bill Stevens; Brian Street; Alain and Val Sutton; David and Jane Swanbrow; Pat and Meryl Sweeny; Bill and Yvonne Tree; Charlotte Walton; Joy Wheeler; Lucy Wickham; John Worral; Sydney Woolcock.

LIST OF COLOUR PLATES BETWEEN PAGES 96 AND 97

PLATE 1
M. albicans
M. candida
M. carmenae
M. dioica and *M. brandegei*
M. erythrosperma
M. elongata (various forms)

PLATE 2
M. guelzowiana
M. herrerae var. *albiflora*
M. geminispina
M. guillauminiana
M. hahniana
M. humboldtii

PLATE 3
M. lau 1186 (*M. glassii* affinity)
M. laui fa. *laui*
M. laui fa. *subducta*
M. lenta
M. longiflora fa. *longiflora*
M. pectinifera

PLATE 4
M. poselgeri
M. petterssonii

PLATE 5
M. rekoi
M. saboae fa. *saboae*

PLATE 6
M. senilis
M. ruestii

PLATE 7
M. setispina
M. slevinii

PLATE 8
M. spinosissima
M. tegelbergiana
M. solisioides
M. stella-de-tacubaya
M. tetrancistra
M. wrightii var. *wilcoxii*

I am indebted to the following for the loan of their colour photographs: Ken Burke (*M. pectinifera*), David Lambie (*M. setispina*), Betty Maddams (*M. tegelbergiana*), Pat Stacey (*M. slevinii*) and Sydney Woolcock (*M. herrerae* var. *albiflora*).

INTRODUCTION

The new discoveries of cacti are deservedly of interest to the cactus fancier, and there seems to be no end to the flow of new species and the occasional new genus from the wilds of central and south America. But there is always a keen interest among collectors in the discovery of a new species in the 'old' genus *Mammillaria*. In the last ten years several new species have been described, and some of them have been startlingly beautiful and outstanding in a genus which does not want for its beauties already.

Mammillaria, a genus set up in 1812 by Adrian Hardy Haworth, the English plantsman and botanist active in the early 1800s, has remained one of the most popular for many years with beginners to the hobby and old hands alike. The reasons are not hard to find. These cacti mostly flower readily, are undemanding of space or particularly high temperatures, and have a facility for surviving maltreatment. And they are doubly appealing in their freely produced flowers and their variety of spination. At all times of year they are attractive to the eye, and a large collection of the genus will rarely see a month go by without some flowers being produced.

This book is presented as an attempt to provide collectors with a ready guide to the species, with an indication of cultural requirements where necessary, and some idea of the classification and the geography, to indicate their affinities with each other, and to enable the collector perhaps to identify plants in his collection, or to get an idea of which other species similar to those which appeal to him most he might strive to obtain.

The names included in the commentary on the species section are those which appeared as accepted species in Craig's *Mammillaria Handbook*, published in 1945, plus those described since, or possibly some which Craig cast doubt upon, but which have since emerged as good species. David Hunt of the Royal Botanic Gardens, Kew, has published a review of the genus in successive instalments of the Mammillaria Society's journal (1967–75) and has, in addition,

published two papers in the journal of the Cactus and Succulent Society of Great Britain: 'Schumann & Buxbaum Reconciled', followed by an updating entitled 'Schumann & Buxbaum Recompiled'. These papers have been followed for classification purposes as well as for acceptance of species names. Older names, pre-Craig's *Mammillaria Handbook*, like the many synonyms of *M. magnimamma* for example, have not been included, as they would clutter the book and confuse the reader; all but a few have long since ceased to be used. If a name cannot be found here or in Craig's book, it may be that it has been described since this book went to press – new species appear in the German Society's journal or the UK or US journals from time to time, or the Mammillaria Society may be able to help with this sort of problem.

The photographs show in detail the salient characters of the species, but neither the plant pictured nor the description should be regarded too dogmatically. Species vary widely, some more than others, and the wider the distribution in the wild the more variable they become, and it is difficult to determine where one species ends and another begins.

The classification of the genus into subgenera, sections, series and groups by David Hunt enables some idea of relationships to be formed, and can be used as a guide to the possible identity of an unnamed plant – a key for such a large genus is in my opinion unworkable, and is not therefore included.

Finally may I say that I have put together a book that I have been hoping to see ever since I became interested in this fascinating and beautiful genus, nearly 30 years ago. I hope that it fulfils the reader's needs, and answers the questions that arise from collecting *Mammillaria*, but above all I hope it leads to a greater appreciation of the diversity and beauty of these plants. Bill Weightman's first-class photography shows far more than I can hope to convey in the accompanying text; I hope that at least the two are complementary.

JP 1981

CULTIVATION AND PROPAGATION

The cultivation of cacti has improved beyond belief in the last 20 years or so, because of the realisation that if potted on regularly and watered well in the growing period, cacti respond by growing well without that loss of character sometimes sombrely predicted in some of the old (and not so old) textbooks. The introduction of plastic pots has meant steadier growth because of the more constant moisture content of the potting mixture, which, with the advent of soil-less composts that seem to suit *Mammillaria* very well, has made the growing of these plants well within the capabilities of even modest collectors with no particular gardening skill.

Of course there have always been good growers who use either clay pots or soil-based composts or both, and who have stuck to them and continued to get excellent results. But the use of the newer facilities enables less able mortals to compete without necessarily having the 'green fingers' of these gardeners, in bringing these wonderful plants to maturity and flower. This is especially so with the more difficult species of *Mammillaria*.

The potting medium

The balance of the potting compost should be related to the difficulty or ease of growing the particular species: by balance I mean the amount of grit added to the basic mix. I find that many easy-going species will grow well without any grit added to the mixture at all, especially in no-soil composts. For those that are shallow rooted or a little difficult, for example some of the series *Ancistracanthae*, I add up to a third by bulk of coarse, sharp grit to the mixture. For the difficult species, like *M. wrightii*, *M. guelzowiana*, *M. herrerae* and *M. tetrancistra* to name a few, the grit content is increased to a half or two-thirds of the mixture. Whatever the balance I introduce a small amount (2 or 3 cm deep) of pure soil-less compost at the bottom of the pot to hold moisture within reach of searching roots but well away from the plant body. And for all plants I topdress with grit to keep the necks of the plants off the compost.

Crocking pots, that is putting a layer of broken pieces of pot over the drainage holes to improve the drainage, is a lingering superstition from the days of clay pots when it was difficult to know what to do with all the inevitably broken ones; it is unnecessary unless clay pots are used, in which case one shard to stop the compost falling out of the large hole in the bottom is all that is needed.

Potting on

Until the plants reach a 13 cm (5 in) pot size they should be repotted each year into a larger size pot, unless the root system has not developed sufficiently to bind together the existing potful of mixture, in which case, after carefully shaking off the surplus and inspecting the roots to ensure they have not failed, the plant can probably be put back into the same size pot. A little space can be saved in the first few years by potting successively into first shallow and then deeper pots of the same size, provided the diameter of the deeper pot does not impinge on the plant. After plants reach a 13 cm (5 in) pot, repotting can be deferred for a year or two, unless, of course, the plant continues to outgrow the larger pots. *Mammillarias* are not generally deep-rooted plants, and the clustering, hooked spined species in particular can spend their lives in quite shallow containers. Those few species which are tap-rooted quickly indicate this by pushing themselves sideways in an attempt to push through the bottom of the pot. As soon as this occurs they should be potted into a deeper pot for fear of damage to the root, which could well result in the loss of the plant.

Watering

Watering should be geared to the plants' growth. In winter and early spring, when there is little growth activity, watering should be sufficient only to keep the compost from drying out completely, and at this time of year a moisture-meter is invaluable, especially with plants in larger pots, which dry out more slowly than those in small pots. This does not mean that a teaspoonful should be given every other week – it is better to choose a bright period and give a good watering, allowing the pots to dry out over three or four weeks. If temperatures are persistently low however, the safer action is to withhold water altogether until the weather improves. Occasional spraying in periods of settled weather is beneficial too and prevents shrivelling from prolonged dryness at the root. Once buds appear in earnest, other than those species which flower in the winter or very early spring, watering can be stepped up so that the increasing drying effect of higher temperatures as the sun climbs higher in the sky is countered by increased watering, but water should still not be given each time until the compost is approaching the dry state. With smaller pots a rule of thumb can operate, with a good watering being given about once a week when the growing season is well under way (from mid-May in England), or more often in the really hot spells, but with larger pots a tentative probe in one or two will tell you their needs. At the other end of the season, from the end of September watering should be gradually reduced and none given in December and January. Always bear in mind that these plants will rarely die of underwatering; it is the hand too generous with the watering-can which reduces them to mush.

Shading

In England this genus rarely needs shade, unless the situation of the greenhouse is very exposed. And light is an important factor in connection with the production of flowers; I believe this is particularly true of the amount of winter light available to the plants. Ideally *Mammillarias* should get whatever sunshine is available in the winter months, or flowering is likely to be adversely affected, especially in the species more reluctant to flower.

Temperature

There are a few tender *Mammillaria* species which prefer higher winter temperatures, but most will tolerate 5°C (40°F) or lower if dry. Species which benefit from higher temperatures include *M. beneckei*, *guerreronis* and *nivosa* to name those which seem to have suffered in the past, but all *Mammillarias* probably do better with more warmth if available: 7 to 10°C (45–50°F) minimum.

Propagation – cuttings

Many of the clustering species are readily propagated by removal of the offsets. With some the attachment to the main stem is not strong, and they will detach if gently pulled or twisted: *M. prolifera*, *M. gracilis* and *M. yaquensis* are such species. With others a more positive attachment necessitates cutting the offsets, and this should be done at the narrowest point possible, which can often only be achieved by gently pulling the offset to one side to reveal the point of attachment. Where a plant clusters densely the first offset may well have to be sacrificed in order to reveal its neighbouring offsets' bases. A pointed, very sharp tool should be used and both cut surfaces should be dusted with a fungicide as contained in most hormone rooting powders. Sometimes necessity demands such an operation in the winter months, in order to save a piece of collapsing plant. At this time of year the cut parts should be liberally dusted with fungicide and the cuttings left to dry for a week or two.

Roots can be induced to form (if not already there) by placing the cuttings gently on dry compost – with bottom heat if temperatures are below 14°C (55°F). In the case of a collapsing plant the removed offsets should be cut back mercilessly until there is no trace of brown or orange in the tissue — look particularly at the area in the centre of the cut surface where the vascular bundle ring is often affected by the threads of the damaging fungus – if any trace is left the cutting will surely die. If the necessary cutting leaves only a small portion of stem an attempt to graft should be made, see below.

Some plants with large tubercles lend themselves to propagation by rooting individual tubercles. *M. plumosa*, some of the subgenus *Dolichothele* and many in the section *Hydrochylus* have been propagated by this means and a collapsing plant of *M. plumosa* will often be found already to have developed roots on the individual tubercles. A good dusting with fungicide should be given before placing the tubercles on sandy compost, keeping them out of sunshine and in a close atmosphere until the small roots have penetrated the soil and can swell the tubercle. Small plants develop from these rooted tubercles quite quickly, and if successful a great number of plants can be produced from the one plant. Experiments with other *Mammillarias* have shown that they are not so ready to oblige with this method of propagation, but no doubt success could be expected with some of the more advanced laboratory techniques to propagate from small parts of plants.

Propagation—seed-raising

Ideas about raising cacti from seed have changed radically over the last ten or twenty years. We now know that

plastic containers give better moisture control than clay;

darkness is not essential for germination, and is positively deleterious once germination has taken place;

a very high temperature (25°C plus) reduces the percentage of germination, as does a lower temperature than about 15°C;

the glass or plastic covering for the seed container does not need to be raised or removed as soon as germination has taken place;

nor does it need to be turned or removed each day to get rid of condensation formed.

It is many years since I sowed seed in seed trays with strips of plastic dividing the surface into squares like a seed-testing plot at a seed-trial ground, and with numbers on tiny squares of label like impersonal gravestones marking each plot. I now sow in 5cm (2 inch) individual square pots, which fit nicely into deep seed trays, with enough air space above the pots to allow the overall covering of glass or plastic to stay in place for some time. The advantages over the former method are several. The stronger growing species do not vie for space above and below ground, and can be removed to less cosseted (though still enclosed) conditions, leaving their weaker brethren in bed to gather strength without competition.

Apart from the satisfaction of seeing immediately what is coming up and what is not, when individual labels with the names on are used from the start, there is less likelihood with the individual pots of the plants invading each other's territory, especially when sowing the seed, which I find takes off like Barnes Wallis's bouncing bomb at the least opportunity.

The compost I favour is half-a-pot depth of soil-less compost topped by an equal mix of soil-less, John Innes potting compost and gritty sand. On top of this I use a coarse grit top dressing, which gives the young roots much needed protection in the first few days and helps prevent caking of the surface and moss and algae formation.

Careful tests on germination of cactus seeds have been conducted, which show that 20°C (70°F) is the optimum temperature for germination. At this temperature maximum germination is achieved; the further away from the optimum the lower the rate of success. Provided this sort of level can be maintained for a good deal of the time at least, the time of year for sowing is not crucial, except that in England the low light levels in deep winter will often lead to etiolation of the seedlings unless they are kept near to the glass. I favour March onwards for sowing, with early August about the latest time for most, in order that a good sized seedling may be obtained before winter.

There is no doubt in my mind that moisture is the major change in growing techniques over the last 20 years or so, which has led to the increase in so many and varied seedlings appearing for sale these days. The old shibboleth of removal of the glass covering soon after germination, has killed more aspiring young seedlings than any other misguided piece of advice, and some of the most successful growers now enclose their seedlings completely in polythene for the first 3, 6 or even 12 months after sowing. In any case the seedlings should not be allowed to dry out completely in the first 6 months.

An occasional watering or spray with a fungicide and a mild insecticide should prevent damping off (a fungal attack on young seedlings) and any pests, the worst of which for seedlings is the recent one to cactus growers, the Sciara or mushroom fly.

Although subdued light is all right for germination, these plants must have light immediately they have germinated, and quite strong light is necessary for strong, compact growth. Light shading from direct sunlight is ideal in England.

The seedlings may be pricked out (moved on) into shallow seed trays after about 2 or 3 months, or some growers prefer to leave them until the following spring. If pricked out early, the compost around the tiny roots should be disturbed as little as possible, and a 'friable' state of both the compost from which and to which the seedlings are being moved should be aimed at, i.e. not very wet and not very dry. They may be placed quite close together, say 2cm apart, and moved on again when they almost touch each other, usually the next spring. If a temperature of 13°C or higher can be easily maintained the seedlings may be grown on through the first winter, but otherwise they are best kept almost completely dry with an occasional overhead spray on fine days.

Grafting

Some species are very difficult to grow on their own roots, or develop extremely slowly; a few examples are *M. tetrancistra*, *M. beneckei*, *M. herrerae* and *M. egregia*. To overcome this reluctance to survive of the former two mentioned, or the slowness of development of the latter two, grafting on a more robust stock can help. This method of cultivation can be used too to grow seedlings to rapid maturity or to save small plants or parts of plants which have lost their roots.

There are several methods of effecting a union between the stock (the lower part) and the scion (the upper part), but generally nowadays flat grafting is used. A fair-sized piece of *Cereus* stock is advisable if the graft is intended to last several years, or some growers prefer to use *Echinopsis*, or for seedling grafting *Pereskiopsis* or *Eriocereus* (syn. *Harrisia*) are sometimes preferred for their narrow growing points. *Hylocereus*, popular with Japanese growers, is rarely used in England because it will not stand low temperatures below 10°C (50°F)

Whatever stock is used it should have, as should also the scion, as much sap content as possible, so that if plants with good root systems are being grafted a watering a day or two beforehand is beneficial. The cuts should be made as evenly as possible with a clean, very sharp blade, ideally in one motion, to ensure even contact of the two cut surfaces to be joined. The edges of the flat surfaces should be bevelled, taking off firstly the extreme outer ring of tissue and the lowest line of tubercles on the scion, and secondly the topmost spine clusters and areoles at the cut edge of the stock; this prevents either piece pushing against the other as they dry and tend to shrink and curl inwards. The two vascular rings, showing as lighter coloured tissue in the centre of the cut surfaces should be matched up carefully, so that they overlap each other and make contact where the rings cross each other. A light pressure should be exerted, after the two clean surfaces have been brought together, and maintained for a few days. Various means of accomplishing this delicate part of the operation have been advocated in books and journals over the years, but I have found one method satisfactory and simple. This involves using slender elastic bands, long enough to exert only gentle pressure, in cross formation over the top of the scion and beneath the pot. The smaller the scion the less pressure is needed; indeed with seedling grafting, carried out with plants only a week or two old, no pressure is required at all.

Failure of the graft is usually apparent within a month with the progressive shrivelling or detachment of the scion. Sometimes a partial union is formed, when the scion seems to take some nourishment from the stock at least for a short time, but when this happens the join is tenuous and the scion will often develop roots which push it off the stock. Otherwise, success is shown after a month or so by the steady growth of the scion, after which the graft should be watered and potted on as if for treatment of the stock plant, which is after all the part doing the growing. Offsets from the stock should be removed as soon as practicable.

Cristates and monstrose growth

A few monstrose or freak forms of *Mammillaria* species are found – *M. bocasana*, *M. gracilis*, *M. prolifera* and one or two others – with either an even greater tendency to multiply by offsetting or with an abundance of spines to each areole.

More commonly seen are cristate forms of various species. Among those I have come across have been: *M. bella*, *M. bocasana*, *M. compressa*, *M. dioica*, *M. egregia*, *M. elongata*, *M. gracilis*, *M. hahniana*, *M. lenta*, *M. pennispinosa*, *M. pseudoperbella*, *M. rhodantha*, *M. theresae*, *M. wildii* and *M. zeilmanniana*, and I am sure there are others. Some produce flowers readily, notably *M. wildii* and *M. zeilmanniana*, but most are more reluctant, seeming to be so delighted in

M. pseudoperbella (normal and cristate form together)

achieving growth in all directions at once that flowering seems unnecessary. Some make thick bands of heavy, slowly curling growth, others narrower, ribbon-like tangles.

Cristate forms will grow on their own roots, but for convenience of propagation and growth, since they sometimes tend to push themselves out of the soil, they are often grafted. A large stock should be used or looked for on purchase, as cristate forms will form a weighty clump in a short while and need strong support.

Pests and diseases

Mammillarias suffer principally from three pests: mealy-bug, root mealy-bug and red spider.

The first two are evidenced by the appearance of white cottonwool-like patches on the plants, above the soil-level for the first named, and below, on the roots, for the second. The mealy-bugs themselves (the wool is produced by them in which to lay their eggs) are apparent on close inspection: those on the body of the plant are pinkish, white meal-covered, slow-moving insects like small wood-lice (pill bugs) with a short forked tail, rarely more than 4 mm long; those on the roots are smaller, about 1 or 2 mm long and white.

Red spider is not a spider but a red-brown mite, visible only if your eyesight is very sharp and you view the plants in strong light, when the tiny creatures may just be made out on the surface or climbing up the spines on fine webbing they have produced, which runs criss-cross over the surface and between the spines. More evident of their presence is the damage they inflict, producing a yellow-brown coating on the green surface of the plant, often at the growing point, but rapidly spreading over the whole plant body.

All these pests, and a few others less bothersome or common, suck the sap of the plants they infest. If they are unchecked the plants will cease to grow, become discoloured and covered with the multiplying offspring of the first unwelcome visitors in an unbelievably short time. And in time the plants will die.

The pests' presence should always be assumed, evident or not, and regular spraying undertaken with contact and systemic insecticides. Contact insecticides, like *Malathion* or *Pyrethrum* work only if they make contact with the pest; as mealy-bugs have a waxy covering such contact is made difficult. More effective, therefore, are the systemic insecticides, which work by poisoning the sap of the plants.

The maker's instructions must be followed carefully as these chemicals are dangerous, and more than one plantsman has suffered bad health and worse through careless use of them.

Apart from these pests there are few other troubles affecting *Mammillarias*, other than fungal diseases, which all cacti are subject to. These are best combatted by regular spraying with systemic fungicides, like *Benlate*.

A regular programme of spraying (two or three

times during the growing season) against all these
troubles as a preventive is better by far than waiting
until they have struck – it is often then too late!

Summary

To grow *Mammillarias* well, pot them on each year in
the early years in compost related in its grit content to
the difficulty of the species to cultivate, and into a size
larger pot each time unless the root system has not
developed sufficiently; use shallow pots rather than
deep for most species. Water frequently in the
summer, lessening the frequency in the winter to once
a month or less according to the temperature maintained, starting again cautiously in the spring.
Ventilate well in the summer with light shading in
exposed positions, and give as much exposure to light
as possible in the winter months.

CLASSIFICATION

With the publication in 1971 of David Hunt's paper entitled 'Schumann & Buxbaum Reconciled', a giant step in the classification of *Mammillaria* was made. Subsequently he has made a number of improvements to the scheme and has recently published a revised classified list, largely followed in this book.

When a new *Mammillaria* name or combination of names is published at any level – species, variety or form – it must, to be valid, conform with the International Code of Botanical Nomenclature, which requires primarily:

Publication in printed matter distributed to the general public or at least to botanical institutions with libraries accessible to botanists generally

Use of a name complying with the provisions of the ICBN

Inclusion of a Latin description or reference to a previously published description

Deposition of plant material at a recognised herbarium of a botanical institution, such as the Royal Botanic Gardens, Kew.

If these and other rules are adhered to, the new name or combination is effective and valid; whether it is accepted by botanists and collectors only time tells.

The classification which follows, and the commentary on species reflect current thinking in this respect, which tends towards wider concepts of genera and species.

Hunt's system is broad in concept, embracing as it does the controversial fringe genera to *Mammillaria*, i.e. *Bartschella, Phellosperma, Porfiria, Chilita, Oehmea, Mammilloydia, Solisia, Dolichothele* and *Krainzia*, as well as two not completely accepted by some—*Mamillopsis* and *Cochemiea*. Of these *Chilita* and *Oehmea* have never really been seriously considered by collectors as separate, but the other names have hung on, and they are still seen in nursery lists. Other genera which have flirted with *Mammillaria* in the past, but which are not included, are *Coryphantha, Epithelantha, Escobaria, Neobesseya, Neolloydia, Cumarinia* and *Ortegocactus*.

Within the genus *Mammillaria*, Hunt recognises six subgenera based principally on flower and seed structure. Seed characters, though not easily observable without a microscope (and always supposing seeds are available), have been found to be of great value in studies of the cacti as a whole and in other related plant families. When supported by a body of clues from other parts of the plant, they are often the most telling evidence for the position of a species in the family tree. On this basis, one *Mammillaria*, *M. candida*, may not be a 'true' *Mammillaria* at all, but a pretender, given away by the minute details of its seed, and thought to be evolved from different ancestors.

Differences in the flowers are shown in the photographs accompanying the commentary on species. Apart from obvious colour differences, the shape and size of *Mammillaria* flowers vary remarkably: from the large, red or yellow flowers of the subgenera *Cochemiea, Mamillopsis* and some *Dolichothele*, through the large pink flowers of the series *Longiflorae*, the intermediate in size and variously coloured *Ancistracanthae*, and the often as large flowered *Macrothele*, to the smaller flowers of other series. See chapter on Flowers, Fruit and Seed, pages 145–147.

The subgenus *Mammillaria* itself (which contains 90% of the total species) is divided into three sections, according to whether the sap is watery or milky; this character is heavily underlined by seed characters again, and also broadly correlates with the presence or not of hooked spines.

In their turn the three sections of *Mammillaria* are each subdivided into three or more major groups of species called series; there is a total of 14 series in all. These are to a large extent regional components of their respective sections. Within each series the individual species fall into groups defined in terms of their salient characters and their geographical association. The following conspectus and synopsis show how the various subgenera, sections and series are distinguished, and lists the groups and principal species in each.

Conspectus of subgenera and sections

Seeds black, the testa cells not pitted	subgenus MAMMILLOYDIA species *M. candida*

Seeds black or brown, always pitted (though sometimes obscurely so):
  Flower-tube with a solid part between the ovary and the limb; flowers
  mostly large for the genus and yellow or orange:
    Flower salver-shaped, the tube solid up to the insertion of the
    stamens
	subgenus OEHMEA
	species *M. beneckei*

Flower funnel-shaped, the tube only solid in the lower part	subgenus DOLICHOTHELE species *M. baumii* *M. carretii* *M. heidiae* *M. longimamma* *M. melaleuca* *M. sphaerica* *M. surculosa*

Flower tube open to base:
  Flowers bright red or red or scarlet, with limb narrower than the tube
  and the stamens exserted:
    Perianth limb zygomorphic
	subgenus COCHEMIEA
	species *M. halei*
	M. maritima
	M. pondii
	M. poselgeri
	M. setispina

Perianth limb regular	subgenus MAMILLOPSIS species *M. senilis*
Flowers purplish, pink, yellowish or white, mostly without a conspicuous tube, or the tube shorter than or about equal to the diameter of the limb, stamens more or less included:	subgenus MAMMILLARIA

Sap watery, or if milky then seeds black (*M. pectinifera* and *M.*
  aureilanata); seeds black or rarely brown, the testa pitted (seen
  under strong lens); hooked spines often present
	section Hydrochylus
	(about 96 species)

Sap watery in tubercles, but usually more or less milky in stem, if only at base; seeds brown, pitted; hooked spines sometimes present	section Subhydrochylus (about 38 species)
Sap milky in tubercles and stem; seeds brown, reticulate; hooked spines absent (except *M. uncinata*)	section Mammillaria (about 61 species)

Synopsis of series in the subgenus Mammillaria

Section Hydrochylus

SERIES LONGIFLORAE
Flowers large (over 25 mm long), salver-shaped or tubular-funnel-shaped, purplish-pink with a distinct tube; fruit sunk more or less in the body of the plant; plants mostly small and clustering; central spines rarely hooked (*M. longiflora*), usually straight or absent. Six species, west Mexico.

  M. SABOAE Group: *M. goldii, M. saboae, M. theresae*
  M. LONGIFLORA Group: *M. longiflora*
  M. NAPINA Group: *M. deherdtiana, M. napina*

SERIES ANCISTRACANTHAE
Flowers mostly large, funnel-shaped, purplish-pink, creamy-yellow or white, the tube relatively short; fruit

exserted; plants often slenderly columnar or cylindric and densely clustering with relatively stout, firm textured tubercles; one or more central spines typically hooked, but some species with straight-spined forms; seeds black. About 33 species, north-west Mexico and south-west United States.

M. TETRANCISTRA Group: *M. tetrancistra*

M. GUELZOWIANA Group: *M. guelzowiana*

M. BARBATA Group: *M. barbata, M. viridiflora, M. wrightii*

M. ZEPHYRANTHOIDES Group: *M. zephyranthoides*

M. MICROCARPA Group: *M. blossfeldiana, M. boolii, M. fraileana, M. goodridgii, M. gueldemanniana, M. hutchisoniana, M. insularis, M. louisiae, M. mainiae, M. mazatlanensis, M. microcarpa, M. occidentalis, M. schumannii, M. sheldonii, M. thornberi, M. yaquensis*

M. DIOICA Group: *M. albicans, M. angelensis, M. armillata, M. capensis, M. cerralboa, M. dioica, M. estebanensis, M. multidigitata, M. neopalmeri, M. phitauiana, M. swinglei*

SERIES STYLOTHELAE
Flowers mostly small (less than 20 mm long), campanulate-funnel shaped, purplish-pink, creamy-yellow or white, the tube short; plants often globose or shortly cylindric and densely clustering with relatively thin, soft-textured tubercles; one or more central spines hooked; seeds black or rarely brown. About 26 species, central Mexico.

M. BOMBYCINA Group: *M. bombycina, M. fittkaui, M. guillauminiana, M. jaliscana, M. mathildae, M. mercadensis, M. moellerana, M. pennispinosa, M. rettigiana, M. sinistrohamata, M. stella-de-tacubaya, M. weingartiana, M. zacatecasensis, M. zeilmanniana*

M. WILDII Group: *M. aurihamata, M. bocasana, M. crinita, M. erythrosperma, M. glochidiata, M. leucantha, M. nana, M. painteri, M. pygmaea, M. wildii*

M. OTEROI Group: *M. oteroi*

M. GLASSII Group: *M. glassii*

SERIES PROLIFERAE
Flowers mostly small, campanulate funnel-shaped, creamy-white; plants low-growing, usually freely clustering, with straight central spines grading into the radials and the outermost radials often hair-like; rarely central spines lacking (*M. gracilis* var. *pulchella*), seeds black. About eight species, north-east Mexico, one (*M. prolifera*) extending to Texas and the West Indies and reported from Colombia.

M. PROLIFERA Group: *M. albicoma, M. picta, M. pilispina, M. prolifera, M. schwarzii, M. viereckii*

M. GRACILIS Group: *M. gracilis, M. vetula*

SERIES LASIACANTHAE
Flowers medium-sized or small (rarely exceeding 20 mm long), mostly pale pinkish, yellowish or white,

rarely purple or purplish-pink; central spines usually absent, rarely present and numerous but grading into the radials (*M. laui* fa. *subducta*); radials very numerous; plants mostly depressed globose and clustering, the cylindric-terete tubercles completely or nearly hidden by the spines; seeds black. About 13 species, east central Mexico.

M. LASIACANTHA Group; *M. egregia, M. lasiacantha, M. magallanii*

M. SCHIEDEANA Group: *M. carmenae, M. plumosa, M. schiedeana*

M. HUMBOLDTII Group: *M. humboldtii, M. laui*

M. LENTA Group: *M. aureilanata, M. herrerae, M. lenta*

M. PECTINIFERA Group: *M. pectinifera, M. solisioides*

SERIES SPHACELATAE
Flowers medium-sized or small, narrowly funnel-shaped, purplish; central spines straight (one hooked in *M. tonalensis*), similar to the radials; plants slender-stemmed and caespitose, with short blunt tubercles; seeds black. Three species in southern central Mexico.

M. SPHACELATA Group: *M. kraehenbuehlii, M. sphacelata, M. tonalensis*

SERIES LEPTOCLADODAE
Flowers small, campanulate, creamy-yellow or purplish; central spines straight or absent; plants slender-stemmed, densely clustering, or cylindric; seeds brown. Five species, central and northern Mexico.

M. POTTSII Group: *M. pottsii*

M. ELONGATA Group: *M. densispina, M. elongata, M. microhelia, M. mieheana*

SERIES DECIPIENTES
Flowers small, whitish, campanulate-funnel shaped; central spine straight or absent, radials ten or fewer; plants globose-stemmed and densely clustering with elongate-terete tubercles; seeds brown. Two species, eastern central Mexico.

M. DECIPIENS Group: *M. camptotricha, M. decipiens*

Section Subhydrochylus

SERIES HETEROCHLORAE
Flowers small, campanulate, purplish-pink or creamy-yellow; fruits greenish, maroon or purplish, maturing during the winter after flowering; central and radial spines sharply differentiated by colour and thickness, or radials reduced to bristles or absent; central spines not hooked, radials *not* lending the whole plant a white appearance; plants depressed-globose to stoutly columnar, mostly erect, solitary. About 13 variable species (as yet relationships are not fully determined) central Mexico, north of the volcanic belt.

M. RHODANTHA Group: *M. aureiceps, M. calacantha, M. fera-rubra, M. mollendorffiana, M. pringlei, M. rhodantha*

M. POLYTHELE Group: *M. durispina, M. kewensis, M. obconella, M. polythele*

M. DISCOLOR Group: *M. discolor, M. erectacantha, M. wiesingeri*

SERIES POLYACANTHAE

Flowers very small (less than 10 mm long) to medium-sized, deep red or purplish-red or rarely pale yellow: fruits green, maroon or purplish, maturing during the year after flowering; spines usually numerous; central spines straight or one or more hooked, radials rarely lending the whole plant a white appearance (*M. guerreronis*); plants slenderly to stoutly cylindric, erect or pendant, often clustering from the base. About 14 species, central Mexico, south of the volcanic belt.

M. SPINOSISSIMA Group: *M. backebergiana, M. matudae, M. meyranii, M. pilcayensis, M. spinosissima, M. virginis*

M. NUNEZII Group: *M. bella, M. duoformis, M. guerreronis, M. magnifica, M. nunezii, M. rekoi, M. xaltianguensis*

M. ERIACANTHA Group: *M. eriacantha*

SERIES SUPERTEXTAE

Flowers small or very small, usually purplish, rarely yellowish-pink; fruits bright red; central spines straight, curved or absent, radials usually obscuring the stem and giving the whole a white or rarely yellowish or brownish appearance; plants shortly cylindric to stoutly columnar, often clustering, tubercles relatively small. About 11 species, south Mexico, one extending to Jamaica, Colombia and Venezuela (*M. columbiana*).

M. SUPERTEXTA Group: *M. albilanata, M. columbiana, M. crucigera, M. dixanthocentron, M. haageana, M. huitzilopochtli, M. reppenhagenii, M. ruestii, M. supertexta, M. tegelbergiana, M. yucatanensis*

Section Mammillaria (syn. Galactochylus)

SERIES LEUCOCEPHALAE

Flowers small, purple, pink or whitish; central spines straight or curved, radials often numerous, white, giving the whole plant a white appearance, in one species (*M. sempervivi*) reduced or commonly absent; axillary bristles often conspicuous; plants depressed-globose with small tubercles, often branching dichotomously to form mounds. About 13 species in east and north-east central Mexico.

M. GEMINISPINA Group: *M. brauneana, M. geminispina, M. hahniana, M. klissingiana, M. morganiana, M. muehlenpfordtii, M. parkinsonii, M. perbella, M. pseudoperbella*

M. SEMPERVIVI Group: *M. chionocephala, M. formosa, M. microthele, M. sempervivi*

SERIES MACROTHELAE

Flowers medium-sized, often broadly campanulate, purplish, creamy-yellow or white, rarely bright yellow (*M. marksiana*); spines usually relatively few, these often strong, not obscuring the body, centrals straight or curved, very rarely hooked (*M. uncinata*); axillary bristles usually absent or inconspicuous; plants depressed-globose to clavate-cylindric, mostly with large gibbous or pyramidal tubercles, commonly offsetting freely to form mounds, or else solitary, massive. About 36 species, north and central Mexico, extending into the south-west United States, West Indies and northern South America.

M. MAMMILLARIS Group: *M. mammillaris, M. nivosa*

M. HEYDERI Group: *M. albiarmata, M. coahuilensis, M. gaumeri, M. grusonii, M. heyderi, M. lloydii, M. melanocentra, M. uncinata, M. wagnerana, M. zeyerana*

M. PETTERSSONII Group: *M. gigantea, M. petterssonii, M. rubrograndis*

M. STANDLEYI Group: *M. canelensis, M. hertrichiana, M. lindsayi, M. miegeana, M. standleyi, M. tayloriorum*

M. SONORENSIS Group: *M. bocensis, M. marksiana, M. scrippsiana, M. sonorensis*

M. COMPRESSA Group: *M. compressa*

M. MAGNIMAMMA Group: *M. magnimamma, M. roseo-alba, M. winterae*

M. BRANDEGEI Group: *M. brandegei, M. glareosa*

M. PETROPHILA Group: *M. baxterana, M. evermanniana, M. johnstonii, M. peninsularis, M. petrophila*

SERIES POLYEDRAE

Flowers medium-sized, usually creamy-yellow with reddish outer segments, otherwise pink or purplish; spines usually few, often unequal or radials absent; axillary bristles more or less conspicuous (absent in *M. carnea*); plants globose to short-columnar with medium-sized, conical, often angled tubercles, often offsetting or dichotomising to form clumps, rarely solitary. About 12 species, in southern Mexico, one (or two?) extending to Guatemala (*M. voburnensis* and *M. eichlamii*, closely related to each other).

M. KARWINSKIANA Group: *M. beiselii, M. collinsii, M. eichlamii, M. karwinskiana, M. knippeliana, M. nejapensis, M. voburnensis*

M. POLYEDRA Group: *M. carnea, M. polyedra*

M. MYSTAX Group: *M. mystax, M. sartorii, M. varieaculeata*

GEOGRAPHY AND DISTRIBUTION
OF SPECIES

Mammillarias occur in nature in the south-western USA and in Mexico, with a few representatives further south and in the West Indies. Their distribution is by no means at random, but in a definite pattern, reflecting their relationships one to another and their adaptation to particular conditions of climate or soil. These patterns were demonstrated by David Hunt in a series of distribution maps which accompanied his 1971 paper and later presented in more streamlined form in his 1977 Hampshire Memorial Lecture, which was printed in the journal of the National Cactus & Succulent Society later that year. The following points are based upon his paper.

Each of the subgenera, sections and series has a well-defined distribution in relation to the principal physical features of Mexico and the adjacent southern states of the USA, especially the mountain ranges on the eastern and western sides of Mexico, the transverse volcanic belt, and the upland plateau between and to the north of these ranges.

The one species of subgenus *Mammilloydia*, *M. candida*, occurs in eastern Mexico, especially in the calcareous sites east and north east of the city of San Luis Potosi. *M. beneckei*, the only species of subgenus *Oehmea*, has an unusually wide distribution on the western side, extending from Sinaloa through the Pacific coastal states as far as Oaxaca. It is found below 610 m where the climate is tropical to subtropical, and this explains why it is one of the more difficult species to grow, needing a minimum winter temperature of 10°C (50°F) or more, to be on the safe side.

As now understood, subgenus *Dolichothele* is another eastern group, with an Atlantic distribution from coastal Texas through Tamaulipas and up the river basin of the Rio Moctezuma into Hidalgo.

The subgenera *Cochemiea* and *Mamillopsis* are both western, *Cochemiea* being confined to the peninsula of Baja California and its adjacent islands (low elevations), and *Mamillopsis* to the mountains of the Sierra Madre Occidental, where it is sometimes under snow in winter.

The main subgenus, subgenus *Mammillaria* covers the entire area of the whole genus. We find that the three sections of which it is composed overlap to a large degree, and species belonging to different sections may often be found growing together in the same area. The

pattern formed by individual series, however, is not overlapping, but complementary; species of allied series do not, in general, grow in the same area. It is also rare for different species of the same series to grow in the same neighbourhood. From this pattern it seems reasonable to infer that natural mechanisms must exist to prevent the interbreeding of members of the different sections, or else the separate identity of the sections would have been lost, or never have arisen owing to hybridization. Such mechanisms probably run from simple differences of flowering time to more complex physical, chemical and genetic barriers to cross-fertilization.

Map 1 shows the distribution of the main component series of *Mammillaria* section *Hydrochylus*, which have watery sap and generally black seeds. Two groups, in *Ancistracanthae* and the *Stylothelae*, have hooked central spines, and these are complementary in their distribution. They grow characteristically in amongst non-calcareous rocks. To the east, on the calcareous rocks are two groups without hooked centrals, the *Proliferae*, with central spines, and the *Lasiacanthae*, without central spines.

The three series belonging to section *Subhydrochylus*, plus the *Leucocephalae* (section *Mammillaria*) make a neat pattern (Map 2). They all have brown seeds, but vary in sap characters. In the centre are the *M. rhodantha* group (*Heterochlorae*) and *M. spinosissima* group (*Polyacanthae*). These occur on the igneous rocks of the northern and southern flanks respectively of the volcanic belt. Then there are the two white-spined series, *Leucocuphalae* (*M. parkinsonii* etc.) on the calcareous zone to the north, and the *Supertextae* (*M. haageana* etc.) on its continuation to the south.

As defined at present, series *Macrothelae* is the most widespread of all (Map 3). It includes many species with large tubercles, like *M. magnimamma*, and all have milky sap. Like series *Supertextae* it has representatives in the West Indies and northern South America. In Mexico, south of the volcanic belt, and in central America it is replaced by series *Polyedrae* (*M. polyedra* group).

Within subgenus *Mammillaria*, each series displays its own interesting features of distribution, and numerous problems of classification which are being studied by specialists in Europe, the USA and Mexico.

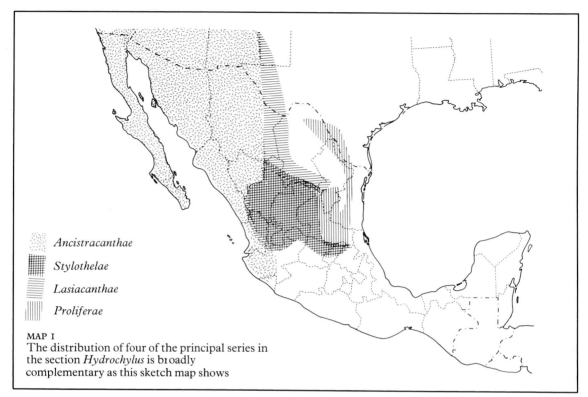

- Ancistracanthae
- Stylothelae
- Lasiacanthae
- Proliferae

MAP I
The distribution of four of the principal series in
the section *Hydrochylus* is broadly
complementary as this sketch map shows

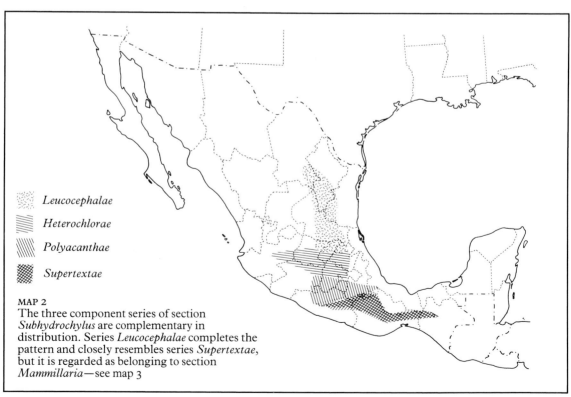

- Leucocephalae
- Heterochlorae
- Polyacanthae
- Supertextae

MAP 2
The three component series of section
Subhydrochylus are complementary in
distribution. Series *Leucocephalae* completes the
pattern and closely resembles series *Supertextae*,
but it is regarded as belonging to section
Mammillaria—see map 3

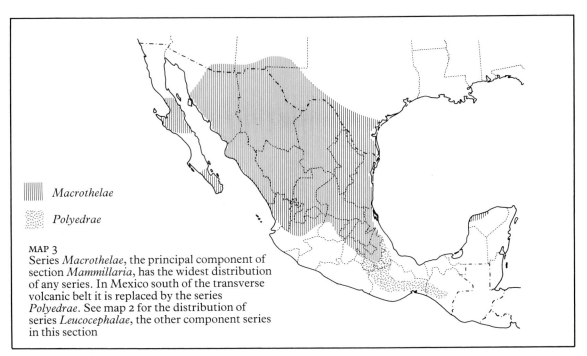

IIIII *Macrothelae*

⠿ *Polyedrae*

MAP 3
Series *Macrothelae*, the principal component of
section *Mammillaria*, has the widest distribution
of any series. In Mexico south of the transverse
volcanic belt it is replaced by the series
Polyedrae. See map 2 for the distribution of
series *Leucocephalae*, the other component series
in this section

As mentioned above, the four main elements of
section *Hydrochylus* have a complementary distribution pattern north of the volcanic belt (Map 1). In
addition there is the large-flowered group, series
Longiflorae, based on *M. longiflora* and corresponding
to the genus *Krainzia*. There are two small groups of
species involved here, widely disjunct geographically:
the *M. longiflora* and *M. saboae* groups in north-west
Mexico on the one hand, and the *M. napina* and *M.
deherdtiana* group in the south.

The two main hooked-spine series, *Ancistracanthae*
and *Stylothelae* are both complex taxonomically. In
the case of the *Ancistracanthae*, the complexity is
inherent in the plants, and intensive field work is
needed to unravel the various complexes. An excellent
start has been made with the *M. wrightii* group by Dale
and Allan Zimmerman, a father and son team working
at Western New Mexico University, whose results
have been published in the journal of the Cactus and
Succulent Society of America, in 1977.

The *M. dioica* group of Baja California appears to be
particularly interesting in that two quite distinct
members of the group are often found growing
together. There are probably two distinct groups or
even series involved, and a detailed study of their
relationships and breeding system is needed to
determine how they co-exist in the same ecological
niche and yet rarely hybridize.

The taxonomic complexity of the *Stylothelae* is,
sadly, more the fault of authorities like Boedeker, who
described innumerable species from very few, often
young, imported specimens, often too of uncertain
origin, than of the plants themselves. As a result, there

are half a dozen names for a common plant like *M.
bocasana*, and time is wasted arguing about whether
more than one species is involved.

The series *Proliferae*, with straight centrals, inter-
grades via the form of *M. schiedeana* known as *M.
dumetorum* with the *Lasiacanthae*, the species of which
have no central spines but very numerous radials.
Most of the *Proliferae* and *Lasiacanthae* have cream-
coloured flowers, and the proper classification of the
purplish-red-flowered species *M. humboldtii* and *M.
laui* is uncertain.

The series *Leptocladodae* is another problematical
group, which Buxbaum made a separate genus,
Leptocladodia, believing them to be evolved from
Escobaria stock. This is the *M. elongata* group, which
formerly included species now separated into separate
series, the *Sphacelatae*, with watery sap and black
seeds, and occurring south, not north, of the volcanic
belt.

M. decipiens (which probably takes in *M. camptotricha*) is the only species of the series *Decipientes*, and
was included in *Dolichothele* by Backeberg and given a
separate genus *Pseudomammillaria* by Buxbaum. It
occurs in eastern Mexico and has many points in
common with series *Stylothelae* and *Proliferae*, but the
fruit and seeds are different. Interestingly, there is a
hybrid in cultivation between *M. decipiens* and *M.
elongata*, usually labelled *M. kuentzii*.

The first two series in the section *Subhydrochylus*
occur on opposite flanks of the trans-Mexican volcanic
belt. The *Polyacanthae* species are on the south side,
and in collections their best-known representative is
M. spinosissima. Some of the more recently discovered

forms are also very attractive and interesting, like *M. matudae* and *M. magnifica*. The characteristic habitat of all members of the group is cliffs and ravines, where the plants are often very difficult to reach. The population in each ravine seems to be a little different from the next, and many local forms have been described as species. This seems a case where the terrain has helped to isolate the populations, resulting in rapid diversification and speciation.

The counterpart of series *Polyacanthae* on the northern flank of the volcanic belt is series *Heterochlorae*. To this group belong some familiar species like *M. rhodantha* and *M. pringlei*, with well-developed radial spines, and *M. polythele* and *M. obconella*, which have none, except when juvenile.

The true *M. rhodantha* is confined to the valley of Mexico itself. To the west it is replaced by *M. ferarubra*. The *M. polythele* group is characteristic of the drier and lower Mesquital valley to the north, and *M. pringlei* is characteristic of ravines. Where *M. pringlei* and *M. polythele* meet, natural hybridization occurs.

The mass of igneous rocks, of which the volcanic belt is composed, also separates two groups of *Mammillarias* characterized by their small tubercles and numerous white radial spines which grow in areas where the underlying rock is calcareous.

South of the belt is the territory of the *Supertextae* series, currently one of the most difficult to classify. The range of forms found in the states of Puebla and Oaxaca is very wide. The variation in habit, spination and flower colour represents a complex pattern and it is not yet possible to determine how many species should be recognized.

Some members of the series are readily identifiable, such as the coral-like *M. crucigera* and the much larger growing *M. dixanthocentron*. Further west and south other forms are found allied to *M. albilanata*, which have been called in addition to *M. albilanata*, *M. martinezii*, *M. tegelbergiana*, *M. reppenhagenii* etc.

The northern group is the series *Leucocephalae* (section *Mammillaria*) containing one species complex with whitish flowers, including *M. formosa*, *M. sempervivi*, etc., and another with darker, purplish-pink flowers which covers *M. geminispina*, *M. perbella* and the *M. hahniana* group. *M. parkinsonii*, the type of the series, is a pale-flowered exception in the second subgroup. There is one yellow-spined species in the series, *M. muehlenpfordtii*.

Taxonomic studies of the series *Macrothelae* and *Polyedrae* are at an early stage. David Hunt currently distinguishes nine species-groups amongst the *Macrothelae*, mostly distinguished by habit, spination and flower colour, and falling into definite geographical zones:

The West Indian and South American group includes the type species of the genus, *M. mammillaris*, as well as *M. nivosa* and other taxa of less certain status, such as *M. ekmanii*.

The north-east mainland group includes mainly solitary stemmed species of depressed habit, such as *M. melanocentra* and *M. winterae*, which are found in rocky habitats in the Sierra Madre Oriental. *M. gaumeri*, from the Yucatan peninsula, is similar to *M. heyderi* from south-east Texas. In this predominantly whitish-flowered group, there is the one species with hooked spines, *M. uncinata*. This is one of the most wide-ranging species, from Chihuahua and Zacatecas in the north to Puebla in the south. It is one of the very few *Mammillaria* species which crosses the trans-Mexican volcanic belt, and is also of interest in that it often grows with *M. magnimamma* yet rarely, if ever, hybridizes. The nature of their relationship merits study.

The north-west mainland groups include two complexes in the Sierra Madre Oriental, based on *M. standleyi* and *M. sonorensis*.

Other geographical groups of the *Macrothelae* series occupy central Mexico. Firstly we have *M. gigantea* and its allies. These are large solitary-growing plants, like *M. petterssonii*. Then there are the clustering species like *M. compressa* and *M. magnimamma*. One could probably spend a lifetime studying the variations and inter-relationships of these two species alone. *M. compressa* is usually in drier places than *M. magnimamma*. One population of *M. magnimamma* seen in Hidalgo contained both purplish-red and pale yellow flowered plants, possibly due to introgression between *M. magnimamma* and *M. compressa*. Further south *M. magnimamma* tends to be more solitary and pale-flowered.

Finally there are two groups of species with pale yellowish flowers in the peninsula of Baja California. These are allied to *M. brandegei* and *M. petrophila* and vary in the degree to which the plant body is exposed above ground level, depending on the nature of the soil and severity of the habitat.

Apart from *M. uncinata* and *M. gaumeri*, mentioned above, none of the *Macrothelae* occur in Mexico south of the volcanic belt. In southern Mexico, their place is taken by the group known as series *Polyedrae*. Apart from *M. polyedra* itself, this series contains a whole series of forms centred on *M. karwinskiana*, a pale yellow-flowered species, and *M. mystax*, with red flowers. These plants are usually characterized by the presence of bristles in the axils of the tubercles and their variability is pronounced. There is one species classified in the *Polyedrae* which lacks axillary bristles. It has flesh-pink flowers and for this reason is called *M. carnea*. Often it grows with *M. mystax*, though usually in deeper soil, and the inter-relationship of these species is another topic for detailed study.

THE DISCOVERY AND COLLECTION OF MAMMILLARIA SPECIES IN THE WILD

With the present-day enlightened attitude to conservation, wild-collected plants in most collections are a rarity. Indeed many nurserymen and collectors now adhere to the principle of selling and buying only nursery-raised plants. Of course when a new species is discovered a few plants must be collected if they are to be recorded properly, and a few collected for propagation. In moderation this is laudable, but all too often still when a new, choice species is found the habitat is stripped of plants within a very short time. If the species is widespread and/or plentiful it will survive the depredation, but this is by no means always the case, and what was common becomes uncommon, and what was uncommon becomes rare. It is to be hoped that what is or becomes rare never becomes non-existent in the wild.

The solution is in the hands of the nurserymen, because, like stolen art treasures, there are always willing buyers: rapid propagation by seed-raising or modern grafting techniques can produce enough plants to satisfy the demand in a matter of a year or two. *Mammillaria carmenae*, recently rediscovered, is a prime example. I gave a seedling to a friend who was a grafting wizard, Derek Desborough of Crawley, Sussex, now sadly no longer with us. Within a year he had produced nearly 100 grafted plants. Given another year he could have made it 1,000.

Laws on collecting in the USA and Mexico have been getting more and more stringent, and it is to be hoped that it will be left to the less commercially-minded collectors in future, who often spend many months travelling by mule or on foot sometimes, in pursuit of new cactus wonders. Alfred Lau has produced recently a list of his collections over the last several years in central and southern America, and since he is by far the most active collector of *Mammillarias* his collections of this genus are extracted and listed below. When they first come into cultivation they often do so merely with the collector's number, pending identification, since plants in the wild are seldom labelled. Examples are '*Lau*' (Alfred Lau's collection), '*FR*' (Friedrich Ritter), '*KK*' (Karel Knize), '*HK*' (Horst Kuenzler), '*R*' (Walther Rausch), '*H*' (David Hunt), '*Rep*' (Werner Reppenhagen). Determination of their identity is often tardy and seldom printed in easily accessible publications, so that the numbers on labels tend to stay unaltered for lack of information.

With the vast areas of Mexico still little invaded by collectors there will no doubt be more *Mammillarias* discovered. In the last 15 years or so we have seen the discovery of such lovely species as *M. theresae*, *M. saboae*, *M. goldii*, *M. haudeana*, *M. laui*, *M. magnifica*, *M. matudae*, *M. deherdtiana*, *M. dodsonii* and *M. huitzilopochtli*, to name a few. No doubt the next 15 years will see others.

Alfred Lau's collection numbers, and the species to which it is believed they relate

NO.	SPECIES	LOCALITY
001	*dioica*	Puerto Escondido, Baja California
003	*poselgeri*	Puerto Escondido, Baja California
004	*fraileana*	Isla Monserato, Baja California
005	*dioica*	Agua Verde, Baja California
006	*dioica*	Mulege, Baja California
007	*neopalmeri*	Isla San Benito, Baja California
008	*pondii*	Isla Cedros, Baja California
011	*setispina*	San Borja, Baja California
014	*dioica*	San Borja, Baja California
017	*angelensis*	Isla San Lorenzo, Baja California
018	*angelensis*	Isla Angel de la Guardia, Baja California
020	*fraileana*	San Francisquito, Baja California
022	*insularis*	Isla Ventura, Baja California
023	*brandegei*	San Ignacio, Baja California
025	*maritima*	Santa Rosalilla, Baja California
027	*blossfeldiana*	Punta Prieta, Baja California
028	*glareosa*	Punta Prieta, Baja California
029	*brandegei (lewisiana)*	Mezquital, Baja California
030	*blossfeldiana*	Mezquital, Baja California
032	*goodridgei*	Isla Cedros, Baja California
033	*goodridgei (rectispina)*	Isla Cedros, Baja California
034	*albicans*	Isla San Dieguito, Baja California

035	*fraileana*	Isla Cerralbo, Baja California
036		San Evaristo, Baja California
037	*evermanniana*	Isla Cerralbo, Baja California
038	*slevinii*	Isla San Jose, Baja California
039	*cerralboa*	Isla Cerralbo, Baja California
040	*halei*	Isla Magdalena, Baja California
044	*dioica* form	Isla Magdalena, Baja California
045	*baxterana*	San Bartolo, Baja California
046	*peninsularis*	Cabo de San Lucas, Baja California
048	*schumannii*	San Jose del Cabo, Baja California
049	*baxterana*	Todos Santos, Baja California
051	*baxterana (gatesii)*	Cabo de San Lucas, Baja California
052	*petrophila*	Sierra de la Laguna, Baja California
053	*capensis*	Bahia de Los Muertos, Baja California
054	*phitauiana*	San Bartolo, Baja California
055	*armillata*	San Jose del Cabo, Baja California
058	*dioica*	Punta Blanca, Baja California
059	*dioica*	Mezquital, Baja California
060	*dixanthocentron*	Tomellin Canyon, Oaxaca
061	*supertexta*	Calapa, Oaxaca
062	*dixanthocentron*	Tomellin Canyon, Oaxaca
063	*dixanthocentron*	Tomellin Canyon, Oaxaca
064	*senilis*	La Ciudad, Durango
065	*crucigera*	Teotitlan de Camino, Oaxaca
066	*huitzilopochtli*	Tecomavaca, Oaxaca
066a	affinity *huitzilopochtli*	Cuicatlan, Oaxaca
067	*dixanthocentron*	Santa Barbara, Oaxaca
068		Calapa, Oaxaca
069	*haageana*	Zapotitlan, Puebla
070	*scrippsiana*	Ahuatitlan, Nayarit
076	*bocensis*	Topolobampo, Sinaloa
077	*mazatlanensis*	Topolobampo, Sinaloa
079	*sonorensis*	Guirocoba, Sonora
081	*gueldemanniana*	Guirocoba, Sonora
082		San Antonio, Sonora
083	*sonorensis*	Guirocoba, Sonora
085		San Antonio, Sonora
086	*hertrichiana/ standleyi*	Sierra Oscura, Sonora—Chihuahua
094	*hertrichiana*	Agua Blanca, Sonora
099	*multidigitata*	Isla San Pedro Nolasco, Sonora
601	*sheldonii*	Ensenada Chica, Sonora
602	*swinglei*	Arrieros, Sonora
606	*swinglei*	Bahia Kino, Sonora
611	*microcarpa*	Nacozari, Sonora
612	*miegeana*	Nacozari, Sonora
614	*goldii*	Nacozari, Sonora
616	*wrightii var. wilcoxii*	Nacozari, Sonora
617	*mainiae*	Soyopa, Sonora

618	*tesopacensis*	Tesopaca, Sonora
619	*hertrichiana*	Encinal, Sonora
621	*marksiana*	Rancho del Padre, Sinaloa
623	*beneckei*	El Marmol, Sinaloa
625	*mazatlanensis*	Cerro de la Cobriza, Sinaloa
626	*senilis*	Tepehuanes—Topia, Durango
628	*heyderi* var. *gummifera*	Santiago Papasquiaro, Durango
632	*orcuttii* (Hort, non Boedeker)	Alvarez, San Luis Potosi
633		San Luis Potosi
634	*erythrosperma*	Alvarez, San Luis Potosi
635	*marksiana*	Topia, Durango
639	*theresae*	Puerto Coneto, Durango
640	*guelzowiana*	San Francisco Asis, Durango
641	*longiflora*	Puerto Coneto, Durango
642		Santiago Papasquiaro
649	*barbata*	Cosihuariachic, Chihuahua
653	*egregia*	Jimenez-Parral
658	*microthele*	Sierra de la Paila, Coahuila
668	*rekoi*	Ixtlan de Juarez, Oaxaca
669	*deherdtiana* var. *dodsonii*	Sierra de San Felipe de Agua, Oaxaca
670	*rekoi*	Nejapa—Santa Maria, Oaxaca
671	*solisioides*	Petlalzingo, Puebla
672	*mystax*	Suchixtlahuaca
673	*rekoi*	Mitla, Oaxaca
674	*rekoi*	Nejapa, Oaxaca
676	*haageana*	Huahuapan—Mitla, Oaxaca
677	*haageana*	Tonala, Oaxaca
678	*pectinifera*	Tehuacan
679	*haageana* var. *schmollii*	San Antonio—Calapa
680	*muehlenpfordtii*	Teotitlan de Camino—Huautla
681	affinity *huitzilopochtli*	Teotitlan
686	*pygmaea*	Bernal—Toliman
692	*zacatecasensis*	Sombrerete, Zacatecas
694	*moellerana*	Sierra Madre, Zacatecas
696	*mercadensis*	Cerro del Mercado, Durango
698	*moellerana*	Nieves, Durango
700	*barbata (santaclarensis)*	Santa Clara Canyon, Chihuahua
701	*microcarpa* var. *grahamii*	Santa Maria, Chihuahua
707	*lasiacantha*	Ceballos
711	*herrerae*	Vista Hermosa, Queretaro
715	*perbella*	San Pablo, Queretaro
716	*painteri*	San Juan del Rio
717		Sierra Zamorano, Queretaro
722	*nejapensis*	Nejapa, Oaxaca
745	*glassii*	Nuevo Leon
753	*rhodantha*	Real del Monte, Hidalgo
760	*vetula*	Vizarron
761		Coalcoman, Michoacan
762	*mazatlanensis*	Manzanillo
763		Manzanillo

764	*beneckei*	Buenaventura, Colima
772	*bocensis (rubida)*	Cerro Culagua
773	*mazatlanensis*	Cerro Culagua
774	*tayloriorum*	Isla San Pedro Nolasco
775	*boolii*	Bahia San Pedro, Sonora
776		Agua Prieta, Sonora
777	*saboae* fa. *haudeana*	Yecora, Sonora
778	*wrightii* var. *wilcoxii*	Yecora, Sonora
781	*wrightii* var. *wilcoxii*	Yecora—El Trigo
782		Maycoba, Sonora
783	*saboae* fa. *saboae*	El Terrero, Chihuahua
787	*heyderi* var. *gummifera*	Julimes, Chihuahau
797	*lenta*	Viesca, Coahuila
1004	*winterae*	Nuevo Leon
1005	*mystax*	Tehuacan
1010	*densispina*	Sierra Zamorano
1011	*magnimamma*	Sierra Zamorano
	(vagaspina)	
1015	*haageana*	Acultzingo, Veracruz
1018	*haageana*	Chazumba, Oaxaca
1020		Rinconada
1021	*plumosa*	Rinconada
1025	*longicoma*	Huizache
1026	*albicoma*	Rancho Perdido
1028	*winterae*	Providencia
1029	*chionocephala*	Providencia
1033	*grusonii (mexicensis)*	Viesca
1034	*gaumeri*	Progreso, Yucatan
1037	*beneckei*	Apatzingan
1038	*napina*	Tehuacan
1041	*carnea*	Teotitlan
1042	*wrightii* fa. *wolfii*	Santa Clara, Chihuahua
1043	*deherdtiana*	Mitla
1044	*jaliscana*	Monte Escobedo, Zacatecas
1045	*pettersonii*	Monte Escobedo, Zacatecas
1046	*zephyranthoides*	Monte Escobedo, Zacatecas
1047	*densispina*	Monte Escobedo, Zacatecas
1048	*zacatecasensis*	Monte Escobedo, Zacatecas
1049	*zacatecasensis*	Mezquitic, Jalisco
1050	*densispina*	San Juan Capistrano—San Juan, Nayarit
1051	*densispina*	Huejuquilla, Jalisco
1052	*discolor*	Esperanza, Puebla
1053	*discolor*	Orizaba—Esperanza, Puebla
1055	*rekoi* var. *aureispina* n.n.	San Martin Buenavista, Oaxaca
1056		San Martin Buenavista, Oaxaca
1057	*rekoi*	Mitla, Oaxaca
1058	*rekoi*	Mitla, Oaxaca
1059	*dixanthocentron*	Tomellin Canyon
1060	*pilispina*	Providencia
1062	*gigantea*	San Luis de la Paz
1063	affinity *viereckii*	Aramberri, Nuevo Leon
1066	*klissingiana*	Palmillas
1069	*winterae*	Aramberri, Nuevo Leon
1073	*zeyerana*	Nazas
1074	*stella-de-tacubaya*	Nazas
1077	*barbata*	Chihuahua
1078	*barbata (garessii)*	Matachic, Chihuahua
1079		Yepachic, Chihuahua
1080	*yaquensis*	Fort Pitaya, Sonora
1083	*aureilanata*	Villar
1087	*dixanthocentron*	Tecomavaca—Cuicatlan, Oaxaca
1090	*candida*	Sandia
1091	*nana*	Lourdes, San Luis Potosi
1093	*haageana* var *schmollii*	San Antonio
1096	*guerreronis*	Mezcala
1097	*albilanata*	Mezcala
1098	*pringlei*	Tultenango, Mexico
1103	*carretii*	Icamol
1104	*eriacantha*	Jalapa, Veracruz
1106	*pilcayensis*	Pilcaya, Mexico
1107	*bella* or *nunezii*	Taxco, Guerrero
1108	*halbingeri?*	Ocotepec, Oaxaca
1109	*crucigera*	Tecomavaca, Carretara Pemex
1110	*schiedeana (dumetorum)*	Minas San Rafael, San Luis Potosi
1113	*sphacelata (viperina)*	Tecomavaca, Oaxaca
1114	*tonalensis*	Tonala, Mexico
1115	*zacatecasensis*	San Juan Capistrano, Zacatecas
1116		Road to Tres Picos near Cuicatlan, Oaxaca
1117	*scrippsiana*	Jesus Maria, Nayarit
1118	*gigantea*	Huejuquilla & San Juan Capistrano, Zacatecas
1119		Huejuquilla & San Juan Capistrano, Zacatecas
1120		Jerez, Zacatecas
1121	*nana (trichacantha)*	Salinas, San Luis Potosi
1124	*rekoi*	San Juan del Estado, Oaxaca
1125	*oteroi*	San Juan del Estado, Oaxaca
1126	*crucigera*	San Miguel Maninaltepec, Oaxaca
1128	*haageana*	Yolox & Quiotepec, Oaxaca
1129	*lanata?*	Mitla & Ayutla, Oaxaca
1130		Tlacotepec, Oaxaca
1131	*melaleuca*	Palmillas, Tamaulipas
1132	*haageana*	Tlacotepec, Oaxaca
1133	*aureilanata (f. alba)*	San Luis Potosi
1134	*lindsayi*	Barranca de Cobre, Chihuahua
1135	*lindsayi*	Barranca de Cobre, Chihuahua
1139	*baumii*	San Vicente, Tamaulipas
1140	*lindsayi*	Choix- San Vicente, Tamaulipas
1141	*mazatlanensis*	Las Bocas, Sonora & Topolobampo, Sinaloa
1144	*guillauminiana*	Mazatlan-Durango
1146	*candida*	Viesca, Coahuila
1148	*picta*	Palmillas, Tamaulipas
1149	*roseo-alba*	La Reja, La Reforma, Tamaulipas

1150	*magnimamma*	El Picacho, Sierra de Salamanca
1152	*compressa*	San Juan del Rio— Ixmiquilpan
1153	*viereckii*	Tula & Palmillas, Tamaulipas
1154	*heidiae*	El Papayo, Actopan, Puebla
1155	*xaltianguensis*	Aguililla, Michoacan
1156	*sphacelata*	Tres Picos, Cuicatlan, Oaxaca
1157	*sphacelata*	Tomellin, Oaxaca
1158	*supertexta*	Quiotepec, Oaxaca
1161	*obconella*	Barranca de Venados, Hidalgo
1163		Canoas, Zacatecas
1165	*leucantha*	Sierra San Miguel, San Luis Potosi
1166	*nana*	Salinas-Ojo Caliente, Zacatecas
1170	*roseoalba*	Ciudad Victoria, Tamaulipas
1171	*laui* fa. *laui*	Mina Asbestos, Ciudad Victoria, Tamaulipas
1173	*heyderi* var. *hemisphaerica*	Providencia, Nuevo Leon
1176	*stella-de-tacubaya*	Mapimi, Durango
1177	*pennispinosa* v. *nazasensis*	Mina Navidad
1182	*bocasana*	Sierra de las Bocas, San Luis Potosi
1186	*glassi* var.	Cerro del Viejo, Zaragoza, Nuevo Leon
1186a	*glassi* var.	Cerro del Viejo, Zaragoza, Nuevo Leon
1194	*magnifica*	Chalatzingo, Morelos
1195	*jaliscana*	Mezquitic-Huejuquilla, Jalisco
1196	*zephyranthoides*	San Juan del Rio- Ixmiquilpan
1199	*rubrograndis*	La Reforma, Tamaulipas
1201	*nunezii*	Iguala, Guerrero
1203	*bocensis (rubida)*	Bacuberito, Sinaloa
1210	*baxterana*	La Paz, Baja California
1211	*baxterana*	Pichilingue, Baja California
1212	*insularis*	Sierra Pintada, Lava, Baja California
1213	*louisiae*	Tortugas and Guerrero Negro
1215	*louisiae*	Socorra, Sand, Baja California
1218		Ciudad del Maiz, Tula, Tamaulipas and San Luis Potosi
1219	*laui* fa. *dasyacantha*	Mina Asbestos, Ciudad Victoria, Tamaulipas
1220	*rubrograndis*	Mina Asbestos, Ciudad Victoria, Tamaulipas
1222	*laui* fa. *subducta*	Mina Asbestos, Ciudad Victoria, Tamaulipas
1223	*carmenae*	La Reja, Tamaulipas
1224	*laui* fa. *laui*	Mina Asbestos, Ciudad Victoria, Tamaulipas
1225	*hutchisoniana*	Mulege-Comondu, Baja California
1226	*zuccariniana*	Acultzinga, Veracruz
1227		Ciudad Valles-Tampico, San Luis Potosi
1228	*hutchisoniana*	San Jose del Cabo, Baja California
1231	*camptotricha*	Rio Jalpan, Queretaro
1232	*hahniana*	Jalpan-Rio Verde, San Luis Potosi
1234	*canelensis*	Nacori Chico-Pinos
1241	*winterae*	Nuevo Leon
1245	affinity *zeilmanniana*	San Andres, Jalisco, 2200 m
1249		Agua Caliente, Pueblo Nuevo, Durango, 1500 m
1250	*longiflora* fa. *stampferi*	El Salto, Durango, 2700 m
1255		Las Animas, Sonora, 600 m
1256	*canelensis*	Sierra Canela, Chihuahua, 2000 m
1259	*wiesingeri*	Toluca
1269	*zephyranthoides*	Xochistlahuaca, Oaxaca, 1800 m
1270	*varieaculeata*	Coxcatlan, Puebla
1271	*haageana*	San Martin Peras-San Juan del Rio, Oaxaca
1272	*evermanniana*	Insel Cerralbo, Baja California
1273	*hertrichiana*	Maycoba, Sonora
1277	*sphaerica*	Ciudad Victoria, Tamaulipas, 800 m
1281	*canelensis*	Sierra Canelo, Chihuahua
1282	*weingartiana*	Ascension, Nuevo Leon
1283	*kraehenbuehlii*	Tamazulapan, Oaxaca
1293	*gueldemanniana* var. *guirocobensis?*	Sierra de Alamos, 1100 m
1296	*rubrograndis*	Dulces Nombres, Nuevo Leon, 2300 m
1297	*microthele*	La Hincada, San Luis Potosi, 1000 m
1298	*surculosa*	La Hincada, San Luis Potosi, 1000 m
1300	*pygmaea*	Vizarron, Queretaro, 1500 m
1302	*aurihamata*	Higuerillas, Queretaro, 2300 m
1303		Bernal-Higuerillas, 2200 m
1304		Higuerillas, Queretaro
1307	*zacatecasensis*	Zacatecas, Zacatecas, 2600 m
1308		Campos Mennonitas, Zacatecas, 2300 m
1309		Rayones, Nuevo Leon
1314	*rekoi*	Mitla-Camaron, Oaxaca
1321	*dixanthocentron*	west of Cuicatlan, Oaxaca
1322	*glassii* var.	Encantada-Siberia, 3100 m
1332		El Bernal, Gonzalez, Tamaulipas
1334	*moellerana*	Grenze Zacatecas, Durango

1335	*heyderi* var. *macdougalii*	Nogales, Sonora
1339	*glassi* var.	Jame, Coahuila, 3000 m
1340		Jame-Casillas, Coahuila, 2000 m
1344	*humboldtii*	Metztitlan-Ixmiquilpan, Hidalgo
1345	*longiflora*	Guanacevi, Durango
1346	*hertrichiana*	Maycoba, Sonora
1347	*camptotricha*	Higuerillas, Queretaro
1348	*egregia*	Nazas, Durango
1350	*pennispinosa*	Mapimi, Durango
1351	*pottsii*	Saltillo, Coahuila
1352	*beneckei*	
1353		south of San Miguel el Alto, Jalisco, 2000 m
1354	*scrippsiana*	north of Nochistlan, Zacatecas, 2200 m
1355	*jaliscana*	Metzquitie, Jalisco & Huejuquilla, 1800 m
1357	*petterssonii*	Metzquitie, Jalisco & Huejuquilla, 1800 m
1359	*zacatecasensis*	Fresnillo, Zacatecas, 2000 m
1360		Sierra Chapultepec, Zacatecas, 2300 m
1364	*bocensis*	south of Guamuchil, Sinaloa

The *Mammillaria* 'rockery' at Huntington Botanical Gardens, California. Species include mainly *M. compressa*, *M. geminispina* and *M. parkinsonii*.

COMMENTARY
ON
SPECIES

COMMENTARY ON SPECIES

The following commentary on species takes as its starting point Craig's *Mammillaria Handbook*, published in 1945, and embraces all the names published since that date, as well as those persistently appearing in various publications such as Backeberg's *Kakteen Lexicon*. It follows as a basis for acceptance of species names David Hunt's 'Review of Mammillaria Names in Common Usage', published in the journal of The Mammillaria Society over the years 1967 to 1975, as well as his further papers 'Schumann & Buxbaum Reconciled' and 'Schumann & Buxbaum Recompiled', published in the journal of the Cactus & Succulent Society of Great Britain.

Species accepted by the author will have below the name and literary references the appropriate subgenus or series it is allocated to. Where there is no such allocation it may be assumed that the species is not accepted by the author and the species to which it is referred will then be mentioned. Where some species are followed by the comment that Hunt allies the species with another, this reflects *possible* future reduction of status envisaged by Hunt, but at the time of going to print not yet implemented.

The photographs should be viewed with the variability of species firmly in mind, and should not be regarded as the blueprint, as it were, for the species. I have tried to bring out in the specimens pictured the essential character of the species, and this can often only be achieved by good, close-up treatment; the indications of size of plants should be taken rather from the description of the species than the individual photographed.

The descriptions are based as far as is possible or desirable on original descriptions of the species; the numbers of spines, for instance, should not be regarded as dogmatically the required number for a plant to be allocated to that species, and the same considerations apply to other features, within reason of course.

The brief references to the sources of literary mentions are those considered most important, and the abbreviations are amplified in the Bibliography (page 155); the main references to currently running journals are to those of The Mammillaria Society (*MSJ*), the Cactus & Succulent Society of America (*Cact. Amer.*), the Cactus & Succulent Society of Great Britain (*Cact.*

GB) and the West German Cactus and Succulent Society (*Kakt. u. a. Sukk.*), which are the main societies publishing useful information on *Mammillaria*. Subscription to all these societies is recommended for the serious student or for any collector wishing to keep up to date with naming and thinking on the genus, and to the recently formed West German specialist Mammillaria society, *Arbeitskreis für Mammillarien-Freunde, e.V.* For details see page 154

The subgenus, series and group references refer to the Classification chapter (page 13); if no subgenus is shown it means that the species falls under the subgenus *Mammillaria*.

Habitat details are those gleaned from original descriptions or subsequent reliable reported findings, but should not be taken to represent the full possible range for any species.

The name immediately following the species name is that of the original author. If an author's name appears in brackets this indicates that the present designation is a change in some way from that of the first description, e.g. *M. rekoi* (B. & R.) Vaupel, was originally described as *Neomammillaria rekoi* by Britton and Rose, and changed to *Mammillaria rekoi* by Vaupel.

M. acanthophlegma Lehm., *Del. Sem. Hort. Hamb.* 1832; *MSJ* **11**:56 (1971).
See under *M. haageana*

M. alamensis Craig, *Mamm. Handb.* 299 with fig. (1945); *MSJ* **7**:36 (1967) & **10**:34 (1970).
This elusive species, described by Craig in his handbook from a plant collected by Howard Gentry near Alamos in Sonora, Mexico, has been a source of confusion since it was described. Numerous plants seen under this name have almost invariably closely resembled *M. sheldonii*. The only apparent difference according to the descriptions is in the spine count, being for *M. alamensis* 9 radials and 1 central, and for *M. sheldonii* 11 to 18 radials and 1 to 4 centrals. Craig's photograph shows a plant with clear allegiance to *M. sheldonii*, and in view of the proximity of the reported localities it is here regarded as synonymous.
Reported from Sonora, near Alamos.

M. albescens Tiegel, *Deutsch. Gartenz.* **48**:260
(1933); *MSJ* **8**:44 (1968); *Cact. Amer.* **43**:45 (1971).
      See under *M. camptotricha*.

M. albiarmata Boed., *Jahrb. Deutsch. Kakt. Ges.*
1:67 (1935–1936); *MSJ* **7**:36 (1967).
Series **Macrothelae**   M. HEYDERI Group
      This species is sometimes regarded as merely a
white-flowered, more densely-spined form of *M.
coahuilensis*, as well as perhaps synonymous with the
briefly described, white flowered *Porfiria* (syn. *Mammillaria*) *coahuilensis* var. *albiflora*. Because of its
distinct appearance it is maintained separately here.
      It was described as simple and flattened-globular in
shape, to 4 cm wide and 1·5 cm high with thick, carrot-
like roots and axils naked or with a slight tuft of wool.
Radial spines 20 to 25, 2 to 5 mm long, the upper
shorter, straight, white or creamy-white, tipped
orange-pink, becoming 'horn' coloured. There are no
central spines. Flowers are 2 cm long and wide,
creamy-white with pale brownish-pink to pale pink
midstripe. Fruit is reddish-pink, seeds brown.
      Reported from Coahuila, near Saltillo.

M. albiarmata

M. albicans (B. & R.) Berger, *Kakteen* 308 (1929);
The Cact. **4**:138 with fig. (1923); *MSJ* **7**:36 (1967)
Series **Ancistracanthae**   M. DIOICA Group
      This is a rare and exceedingly attractive species. It is
columnar, to 20 cm tall and 6 cm wide, and clusters
from or near the base. Axils have dense wool. The
white radial spines number 14 to 21, 5 to 8 mm long,
almost obscuring the plant body. Central spines,
usually 4 to 8, are straight and white too, sometimes
with dark brown tips. The contrast of the white, pink-
striped, large flowers is breathtaking, and a good-sized
plant in flower is a wonderful sight. Fruit is orange to
red, seeds black.
      Craig equated *M. slevinii* with this species, the

difference being in its darker spines and less woolly
areoles, but see under that name.
      Plants labelled *M. albicans* have until recently
usually been a heavily clustering form of *M. albilanata*,
not *M. albicans* at all.
      Reported from Baja California, on Santa Cruz and
San Diego Islands. See colour plate.

M. albicans

M. albicoma Boed., *Monatsschr. Deutsch. Kakt. Ges.*
1:241 with fig. (1929); *MSJ* **7**:37 (1967)
Series **Proliferae**   M. PROLIFERA Group
      This delicately beautiful species is not common in
collections, although the 30 to 40 dense, white, hairlike
radial bristles, which completely obscure the plant
body, put it in appearance alongside such other
popular, white-spined species as *M. schwarzii*, *M.
plumosa* and *M. glassii*. Axils have dense, white wool
and fine, tortuous, hairlike bristles adding to the
density of the covering. The straight central spines,

M. albicoma

usually 3 or 4 (sometimes absent) are 4 to 5 mm long, white with reddish-brown tips, just protruding beyond the radials, which are about 10 mm long. They betray their presence by their stiffness and can be felt with a gentle fingertip. The small flowers are pale greenish-yellow to cream coloured, the fruit is red, seeds black. In time it will cluster to form a flat mound of many heads, each about 4 or 5 cm across.

Reported from Tamaulipas, near Jaumave.

M. albidula Backeb., *Die Cact.* **5**:3429 (1969); *MSJ* **7**:37 (1967) & **9**:8 (1969) & **11**:56 (1971)
    See under *M. haageana*.

M. albiflora (Werderm.) Backeb., *Blatt. f. Kakteenf.* pt. 2 (1937); *Notizbl. Bot. Gart. Mus. Berlin* **11**:277 (1931); *MSJ* **11**:8 (1971)
    See under *M. herrerae*.

M. albilanata Backeb., *Kakteenk.* 1939: **47** with fig. (1939); *Cact. Amer.* **43**:199–201 (1971); *MSJ* **9**:6–9 (1969)
Series **Supertextae** M. SUPERTEXTA Group
    This snow-white spined species is common in collections, although in less sunny situations it shows a reluctance to flower. Generally solitary until a good age, it makes a thick stem up to 8 cm wide and to 15 cm or more tall. The axils have persistent, white, very

M. albilanata

coarse, woolly hair, giving the top third of the plant a snow-covered appearance. Radial spines number 15 to 20, 2 to 4 mm long (the longer spines at the sides of the areoles), straight to slightly curved, stiff and chalky white. Central spines number 2 (sometimes to 4), 2 to 3 mm long, straight, stiff, white to cream coloured, brown at the very tip, stronger than the radials. Flowers are small, to about 7 mm long, deep carmine, standing out from the whiteness of the spines. Fruit is pink to red, seeds pale brown. Reported from

Guerrero, Iguala to Chilpancingo in the Zopilote Canyon.

Hunt refers to this species *M. fuauxiana*, which differs only in its longer central spines, described as 5 mm long; this is the form more commonly seen in collections.

M. albilanata (fuauxiana)

M. aljibensis Hort. (Schmoll catalogue name), *MSJ* **11**:56 (1971)
    See under *M. perbella*.

M. alpina Hort.
    See under *M. kraehenbuehlii*.

M. amoena Hopf. ex Salm-Dyck, *Cact. Hort. Dyck.* 1849; 99 (1850); *Cacti. Amer.* **43**: 75–76 with figs. (1971)
    See under *M. discolor*.

M. ancistroides Lehm., *Del. Sem. Hort. Hamb.* (1832); *MSJ* **11**:57 (1971)
    This is a dubious name linked with *M. glochidiata* or *M. jaliscana*.

M. ancistroides Lem., *Cact. Gen. Nov.* 38 (1839)
    An insufficiently described species, invalid in view of the earlier use of the name (see above), and as unidentifiable.

M. angelensis Craig, *Mamm. Handb.* 165 with fig. (1945); *MSJ* **14**:77 (1974)
Series **Ancistracanthae** M. DIOICA Group
    Hunt regards this species as perhaps an insular form of the widespread *M. dioica*.

    It makes a distinctive plant, whatever its affinities, with a stem about 6 cm wide and up to 15 cm tall. Although described by Craig as solitary it will cluster in time. Axils have thick white wool, especially in the growing area, and 15 or more stiff, twisting white bristles to 10 mm long. Radial spines number 16, 5 to

10 mm long (the lower the longer), straight, stiff, smooth and white, sometimes tan at the very tips. Central spines number 3 to 4, 8 to 14 mm long, the lower hooked, longer and more erect, smooth, dull purplish-brown, lighter to brownish-cream at the base; the straight spines are almost in the same plane as the radials. Flowers are up to 2 cm long, 3 cm wide, creamy to white with pinkish midstripe at the tips of the outer petals; petals often narrow and widely separated. Fruit is reddish, seeds black.

Reported from Angel de la Guardia Island, Los Angeles Bay, and on the nearby mainland of Baja California.

M. angelensis

M. angularis Link & Otto, Pfeiffer, *Enum. Cact.* 12 (1837); *MSJ* **11**:57 (1971)

A name long since referred to *M. compressa*, but it clings on.

M. applanata Engelm., *Mem. Tour. North Mex.*, Wislizenus, 105 (1848)

See under *M. heyderi*.

M. arida Rose, Monatsschr. Kakteenk. **23**: 181 (1913); *MSJ* **7**:41 (1967)

Referred to *M. baxterana*.

M. armatissima Craig, *Mamm. Handb.* 300 (1945); *MSJ* **10**:21 (1970); *Cact. Amer.* **43**:4 (1971)

Referred to *M. gigantea*.

M. armillata K. Brandegee, *Zoe* **5**:7 (1900); *MSJ* **7**:42 (1967)

Series **Ancistracanthae** M. DIOICA Group

This is a very distinctive species, slenderly columnar, 4 to 5 cm in diameter and up to 30 cm tall,

eventually clustering. Axils are bristly and a little woolly. Radial spines number 9 to 15, 7 to 12 mm long, straight. Central spines number 1 to 4, 1 or more hooked, 10 to 20 mm long. In habitat the spine colour varies from horn-yellow to almost black, the older spines darkening in bands and giving the plants a striped appearance 'like a racoon's tail' according to Brandegee. In cultivation this banding is not usually so apparent; plants seen have pale to dark brownish-yellow spines, tipped brown to dark brown, the centrals more heavily so.

Reported from the very tip of Baja California, at San Jose del Cabo.

M. armillata

M. ascensionis Reppenhagen, *Kakt. u. a. Sukk.* **30**:61 (1979); *Cact. Amer.* **51**:126 (1979) as *M. glassi* var. *ascensionis*

As indicated above this species was rapidly reduced to varietal level by Glass and Foster—see under *M. glassii*.

M. atroflorens Backeb., *Die Cact.* **6**:3892 (1962); *MSJ* **6**:40 (1966) & **7**:42 (1967)

Hunt refers this invalidly published name to *M. mystax*.

M. aureiceps Lemaire, *Cact. Aliq. Nov.* 8 (1838); *MSJ* **13**:79 (1973); *Cact. GB.* **39**:74 (1977); *Cact. y Suc. Mex.* **20**:89 (1975) & **21**:3 & 31 (1976)

Series **Heterochlorae** M. RHODANTHA Group

This species is maintained for the shorter yellow-spined plants found in association with *M. rhodantha*. Other species associated are *M. fera-rubra*, with orange-brown or gingery-red spines, *M. pringlei*, with long, curving yellow spines, and *M. fuscata* and *M.*

rhodantha var. *sulphurea*; these last two are referred to *M. aureiceps*. *M. aureiceps* makes an eventually tall (to 30 cm or more) thick columnar plant, usually dichotomously dividing before reaching this height, or leaning over under its own weight and becoming decumbent; the width of the stem is about 8 to 10 cm. Axils have white wool and bristles. Radial spines number 30 or more, golden-yellow and interwoven. Central spines number 6 to 8, sometimes 9, 15 to 20 mm long, curving back on the plant body. Flowers are deep purplish-pink, about 15 to 20 mm long, not often opening widely. Fruit is greenish to pinkish-purple, seeds are brown.

Reported from the mountains north of Mexico City, at 2,600 m altitude.

M. aureiceps

M. aureilanata Backeb., *Monatsschr. Kakteenk.* **24**:158 (1914); *Beitr. Sukk. u. Pflege* **13** (1938); *MSJ* **7**:42 (1967) & **19**:4 (1979)
Series **Lasiacanthae** M. LENTA Group

The earlier name of this very attractive, densely woolly species was *M. cephalophora*, which was invalid because Salm-Dyck had previously used the name for a species subsequently referred to *Coryphantha pycnacantha*. The 25 to 30 spines, all radial, are thin and wool-like, soft to the touch, translucently white in youth turning yellow—there is an entirely white-spined form, fa. *alba* (Backeb.) Krainz. Axils are naked. The flowers, white to yellowish-pink, are among the earliest to appear in the year, invariably the buds showing deep in the axils by Christmas time in England, and opening in March or earlier. The roots are thick and carrot-like, and if insufficient depth of pot is provided, are quite capable of pushing the plant out of the soil. The hemispherical top of the plant, showing above the surface, takes many years to make a solitary, billiard ball-sized plant, contracting each year to almost its previous year's size in the resting period. Fruit is pinkish-white, seeds black.

Reported from San Luis Potosi, in particular from Villar, south of Guadalcazar on the railroad from San Luis Potosi to Cerrito, and on to Tampico, and about 32 km north of San Luis Potosi on low, green hills.

M. aureilanata

M. aureoviridis Heinr., *Kakt. u. a. Sukk.* **4**:56 with figs. (1937); *MSJ* **7**:42 (1967)
Hunt refers this name to *M. aurihamata*.

M. auriareolis Tieg., *Deutsch. Gartenz.* **48**: 412 with fig. (1933); *MSJ* **7**:43 (1967)
Hunt refers this name to *M. parkinsonii*.

M. auricantha Craig, *Mamm. Handb.* 301 with fig. (1945); *MSJ* **14**:48 (1974)
Hunt refers this name to *M. canelensis*.

M. auricoma A. Dietr., *Allg. Gartenz.* **14**:308 (1846); *MSJ* **14**:37 (1974)
This is merely a white to yellowish-white spined form of *M. spinosissima*.

M. aurihamata Boed., *Zeitschr. Sukk.* **3**:340 with fig. (1928); *MSJ* **7**:43 (1967)
Series **Stylothelae** M. WILDII Group

This is the name preferred by Hunt for the species *M. aureoviridis* and *M. boedekerana*, the latter regarded as a dubious species.

It was described as simple and clustering from the body, globular to ovate, to 6 cm tall and 4 cm wide. Axils have no wool, but a few bristles, white and nearly the same length as the tubercles. Radial spines number 15 to 20, 8 mm long, smooth, yellowish-white, hairlike but stiffish. Central spines number 4, the upper 3 straight, 10 mm long, the lower longer and hooked, all yellowish-white in youth, becoming golden yellow to brownish yellow, giving a glowing aura to the plants. Flowers are 15 mm long, 12 mm wide, described as bright sulphur yellow, with bright olive green outer petals; flowers seen on cultivated plants have invariably been more creamy yellow with reddish-brown midstripe on the outer petals. Fruit is red, seeds dark brown to nearly black.

Reported from San Luis Potosi and central Mexico, by Craig from Guanajuato, Monte Gordo.

M. aurihamata

M. aurisaeta Backeb., *Die Cact.* **6**:3892 with fig. (1962)

Hunt refers this name to *M. picta*.

M. auritricha Craig, *Mamm. Handb.* 302 with fig. (1945); *MSJ* **14**:48 (1974)

Referred to *M. canelensis*.

M. avila-camachoi Backeb., *Die Cact.* **5**:3464 (1961); *MSJ* **11**:57 (1971)

Referred to *M. parkinsonii*.

M. aylostera Werderm., *Kakteenk.* **99**: 112 with fig (1938); *MSJ* **7**:76 (1967)

Referred to *M. beneckei*.

M. bachmannii Boed. ex Berger, *Kakteen* **323** (1929); *Mamm. Vergl. Schluss.* 59 (1933); *MSJ* **7**:60 (1967)

Classed as a dubious species by Hunt, there is no doubt that plants usually seen under this name owe more to *M. hahniana* or forms of it than to the original concept of this species name.

M. backebergiana Buchenau, *Nat. Cact.* **21**:47 & 90 (1966); *MSJ* **7**:60 (1967); *Int. Newer Mamm.* 3 with fig. (1973)

Series **Polyacanthae** M. SPINOSISSIMA Group

Usually a single stem about 5 or 6 cm in diameter and up to 30 cm tall, this species is one of the best in the series, with striking, yellowish-brown spines and the typical, generous rings of purplish-red flowers. The spines are fewer and more robust than in *M. spinosissima*, all straight, and reveal more readily the

lightish green plant body. Axils have a little wool at first. Radial spines number 10 to 12, occasionally as few as 8, 8 to 10 mm long, yellowish-white tipped brown, older spines brownish-grey. Central spines number 2 or 3, similar to the radials. Flowers are 10 to 13 mm wide, purplish-red. Fruit is whitish-green below, green above, the seeds brown.

No locality was given with the original description, but it has been reported since from an area in the conjunction of the states of Guerrero, Michoacan and Mexico.

The combination from former specific status of var. *ernestii* (Fittkau) Glass and Foster has recently been made (*Cact. Amer.* **51**:126. 1979). This variety has generally a darker green body than the type and only

M. backebergiana var. *backebergiana*

M. backebergiana var. *ernestii*

one central spine; the spines too are darker than the type. Reported from Tonatico in the state of Mexico.

M. balsasensis Boed., *Monatsschr. Deutsch. Kakt. Ges.* **3**:121 (1931); *MSJ* **7**:76 (1967); *Cact. Amer.* **43**:202 (1971)
   Referred to *M. beneckei*.

M. balsasoides Craig, *Mamm. Handb.* 158 (1945); *MSJ* **7**:76 (1967); *Cact. Amer.* **43**:202 (1971)
   Referred to *M. beneckei*.

M. barbata Engelm., *Mem. Tour. North Mex.* 105 (1848); *Rev. Gen. Pl.* **1**:260 (1891); *The Cact.* **4**:144 (1923); *Cactog.* 2 (1926); *Cact. Amer.* **49**:23 & 51 (1977); *MSJ* **7**:61 (1967) & **17**:36 (1977) & **18**:15 (1978)
Series **Ancistracanthae** M. BARBATA Group
   The Zimmermans' excellent work on the *M. wrightii*, *M. wilcoxii* and *M. viridiflora* complex (*Cact. Amer.* ref. above) did not extend to consideration of *M. barbata*, except to indicate that it is closely allied to *M. morricalii*, *M. santaclarensis* and *M. garessii*, and that in principle they agreed with Hunt's opinion that all these four species are probably synonymous. They reserved their position however, by saying that 'further field work in Chihuahua is desirable before these species are formally combined under the name *barbata*, which has priority over the others by many years.' Nevertheless they are all dealt with in this book under this species.
   An interesting account appeared in the *Mammillaria Society Journal* (last ref. above) by Steve Brack, who explored the type localities of these species in Chihuahua: *M. barbata*, examined at Cosihuiriachic in western Chihuahua, had plants in that locality of differing radial spine counts—in old, large plants the count was higher, up to 50 or more in 2 series (layers), but in smaller plants there were normally 22 to 30

M. barbata

radials. A large plant collected with a high radial spine count subsequently produced only about 25 radials in only 1 series when in cultivation. Plants of this species were often found growing in thick moss and lichen on cliff faces, some under overhangs where they would 'almost never get direct sunshine.'
   Expanding the original description of *M. barbata* in the light of these findings, we have a globose stemmed plant, often clustering densely, stems individually 3 to 4 cm in diameter, axils naked. Radial spines 22 to 30 (to 60 in older plants), white, sometimes brown tipped. Central spines several, 1 or 2 hooked, brown. Flowers 15 mm long, light straw coloured or greenish, petals fringed. Fruit is pinkish-purple, spherical, seeds brown.
   M. garessii was difficult to find in any quantity according to Steve Brack, and was growing in pockets of moss with just the top sticking out. The plants found were small, only 3 cm in diameter and 2·5 cm tall. Cowper in his original description of the species said it grew in cracks in large boulders in semi-shaded situations, and was not uncommon at the type locality, 'a bushy, rocky hill about 8 to 9 km south-west of Matachic, Chihuahua.' Whether Steve Brack was unlucky in his searching or whether the plants have been collected to near extinction is a matter for conjecture. Certainly this species has been available in recent years on the seed lists, and seedlings grow strongly given an open compost and a careful hand with watering. Cowper described the species as clustering, with heads 4 to 8 cm tall, 2·5 to 5 cm wide, with 16 to 22 radial spines, translucent white or pale pink flecked with fine black specks to give plants an off-white appearance except at the apex, where the strongly coloured centrals, 4 to 15 mm long, may be tipped pink or orange; central spines 1, very occasionally 2, stronger than the radials, hooked strongly (Brack says one may be straight), light reddish-brown to dark red, the growing point appearing bright red from this colouring; flowers 25 mm long, 15 mm wide, white or pink, greenish outside, petals fringed; fruit greenish-purple to red, skin somewhat transparent with the seeds visible; seeds reddish-brown, darker when dry.
   M. morricalii occurs 200 km north-east of Cosi in the Cumbres de Majalca in a similar ecological area with canyons and steep cliffs covered with moss, where this species grows, usually 'on north-facing slopes, in deep shade.' Described as solitary or with 2 to 5 heads, each 5 to 13 cm tall and 1·5 to 8 cm wide, with very short wool in the axils, this species has 20 to 25 radial spines, 5 to 8 mm long, light straw to yellow giving an overall yellow cast to the plants. There is 1 hooked central spine, yellow at base and orange above, 7 to 13 mm long. Flowers are 20 mm wide, salmon-pink to orange or yellowish-orange, sometimes with darker mid-stripe, outer petals fringed. Fruit is green to purplish-red, somewhat transparent, seeds dark reddish-brown. Cowper described the occurrence as scarce: 'two days

crawling on hands and knees seldom produces more than two or three plants.'

M. santaclarensis was named from a similar ecological area again, the Santa Clara canyon, 24 to 28 km west of the Ciudad Juarez to Chihuahua highway at Km. 1757. It grows 'in deep shade in bright green moss on large boulders, often in vertical or almost vertical situations.' Described by Cowper as simple, 2 to 16 cm long, 2 to 5 cm wide, with naked axils; radial spines 30 or more in mature plants, 16 to 25 in younger plants, stiff, straight, 5 to 12 mm long, white or straw coloured, 8 to 10 may be brown or brown-tipped, longer and stronger than the others; central spines 1 to 4, the higher number in older plants, stiff, strongly hooked, 5 to 18 mm long, sometimes 1 longer than the others, reddish-brown to dark brown, yellow at base; occasionally there are 1 or more sub-centrals, similar to the centrals but a little shorter, more slender and straight; flowers 2 cm long, 1·5 cm wide when fully open, not recurved, pink or pale pink with darker midstripe, outer petals greenish and fringed; fruit is green to purplish-red, seeds dark reddish-brown.

With such a coincidence of characters it is most probable that as anticipated by Hunt and the Zimmermans we have here one, variable species, which, when the proper field studies are carried out (or possibly before) will be reduced to one species under the name having priority, *M. barbata*. Certainly the photograph of *M. morricalii*, *M. garessii* and *M. santaclarensis* together confirms their similarity; without the advantage of discernible spine colour anyone would be hard put to distinguish them.

M. santaclarensis (top left), *M. morricalii* (top right) and *M. garessii* (below)

M. barkeri Schmoll ex Backeb., *Die Cact.* **5**:3464 (1961); *MSJ* **4**:26 (1964) & **7**:77 (1967); *Cact. Amer.* **43**:202 with figs. (1971)

This sparsely described species is referred to *M. beneckei*.

M. baumii Boed., *Zeitschr. Sukk.* **2**:238 with figs. (1926); *MSJ* **7**:61 (1967); *Cact. Amer.* **40**:20 (1968)

Subgenus **Dolichothele**

A densely white-spined species, clustering to form large clumps, which produce a large number of scented, yellow flowers in May and June in England. Axils have a little wool. Central spines are whitish-yellow, 5 to 6 in number, up to 18 mm long; the 30 to 35 radial spines are very thin and white, up to 15 mm long, interlacing to obscure the body of the plant. The flowers, clear yellow, are 25 mm long, 28 mm broad, stigma-lobes yellowish-green. Fruit is wide and ovoid in shape, greyish-green, the seeds dark brown. Reported from Tamaulipas, near San Vicente, usually found under bushes.

There seem to be in cultivation two types of growth for this species, one forming comparatively large heads, 3 to 5 cm in diameter, slow to cluster, but eventually doing so, and another which clusters early in life to form clumps of heads each about 2 to 3 cm across. Large clumps, more than about 10 cm, are not common, as this species seems a little sensitive to over exposure to sun or to long periods of dryness at the root, when either cause will result in parts of the plant drying up.

M. radiaissima has long been dismissed as a redescription of this species.

M. baumii

M. baxterana (Gates) Boed., *Kaktus ABC*, 398 (1935); *Cact. Amer.* **6**:3 (1934); *MSJ* **7**:74(1967)
Series **Macrothelae**   M. PETROPHILA Group

Hunt now prefers this name to that of *M. arida* and reduces to synonymy here *M. marshalliana* and *M. pacifica*. Plants have been available under all three names in recent years, and certainly the seedlings closely resemble each other. They are simple, occasionally clustering or branching dichotomously, flattened globular, to 15 cm wide and tall, although plants in cultivation mostly have a good way to go before reaching anything like these dimensions. Axils have slight wool, but no bristles. Radial spines number 7 to 13, 10 to 15 mm long, the lower longer, all straight, stiff, smooth and white sometimes brown-tipped in youth. Only 1 central spine, 10 to 20 mm long, stouter than radials, straight, stiff, smooth and white with brown tip. All spines are somewhat brittle. Flowers are 15 mm long, 20 mm wide, greenish yellow with pinkish-purple midstripe. Fruit is bright red, seeds brown.

Reported from the cape area of Baja California.

M. gatesii is referred here too.

M. baxterana

M. x beaujardii Bertrand, Cactus (Paris), **no.12**: 11 (1947); *MSJ* **2**:73 (1962)

A name given to hybrids between *M. camptotricha* and *M. decipiens*.

M. beiselii Diers, *Kakt. u. a. Sukk.* **30**:57 (1979)

Series **Polyedrae** M. KARWINSKIANA Group

This recently described species was found by Karl-Werner Beisel, for whom the plant was named. It is described as columnar to club-shaped, often offsetting and dichotomously dividing, with stems up to 40 cm tall, and up to 12 cm across. Axils have persistent white wool and longer hairlike bristles. Radial spines number 5 to 8, up to 25 mm long, straight to slightly curved, needle-shaped to coarser, white to grey, sometimes yellow, the younger spines sometimes tipped reddish-brown. One central spine, up to 55 mm long, thicker than the radials, nearly straight, sometimes a little bent, white to yellowish, tipped reddish-brown on the new growth, later white to light greyish. Flowers are funnel- to bell-shaped, about 16 to 19 mm long, 9 to 12 mm wide, cream-coloured with variably wide reddish-brown mid-stripe. Fruit is red, turning to whitish-brownish, seed yellowish-brown to reddish-brown.

Reported from near the coast in Colima-Michoacan, growing in humus in rock crevices and under rocks, mainly in open ground, but also in woodlands in partial shade.

Affinities are suggested by the author of the description to *M. nejapensis*, *M. collinsii* and *M. confusa*—also to *M. knippeliana* and to a lesser extent to *M. scrippsiana* from Jalisco—'the species is an intermediate between groups in the southern Pacific ocean part of Mexico and those in the north around Nayarit and Sinaloa'. It remains to be seen whether it is a distinct species.

M. beiselii

M. bella Backeb., *Rep. Spec. Nov.* **51**:63 (1942); *Cact. GB.* **10**:92 (1948); *MSJ* **7**:75 (1967); *Cact. Amer.* **43**:198 (1971)

Series **Polyacanthae** M. NUNEZII Group

This species is closely related to *M. spinosissima*. Described as solitary, ultimately clustering, I have not seen it in cultivation other than as a slow-growing, solitary plant, although in time it will no doubt oblige by clumping. There are bristles in the axils adding to the dense spination. Radial spines are barely distinguishable from the centrals, about 20 in number. Centrals are longer, 4 to 6, with an occasional hooked spine; the lower part of the centrals and most of the radials are glossy white, the upper part varyingly red

M. bella

tipped. The flowers, in several rings, are bright carmine, 20 mm long, 18 mm broad. Fruit is greenish to purplish-pink, seeds reddish-brown. *M. deliusiana* is referred to synonymy with this species.

Reported from Guerrero, near Taxco. Hunt allies this species to *M. nunezii*.

M. bellacantha Craig, *Mamm. Handb.* 303 with fig. (1945); *MSJ* **7**:75 (1967) & **14**:48 (1974)

Hunt refers this incompletely described species to *M. canelensis*.

M. bellisiana Craig, *Mamm. Handb.* 304 with fig. (1945); *MSJ* **7**:76 (1967)

This species, practically unknown in collections today is equated with *M. sonorensis* or *M. tesopacensis*.

M. beneckei Ehrenb., *Allg. Gartenz.* **12**:401 (1844); *Linnaea* **19**:347 (1847); *MSJ* **7**:76 (1967); *Cact. Amer.* **43**:202 with figs. (1971)

(syn. *M. balsasensis*, *M. balsasoides*, *M. nelsonii*, *M. aylostera*, *M. barkeri*, *M. colonensis* and *M. guiengolensis*)

Subgenus **Oehmea**

This species has of late been more commonly seen in collections, and seems to prefer a minimum temperature of 8°C (50°F) to ensure its continued appearance, as it is inclined to rot off without much encouragement and shows a marked reluctance to flower in England. Care with watering is necessary. It clusters readily after a few years and will make a fair sized clump with luck. The body-colour will turn a handsome brown,

M. beneckei

tinged with purple in good light conditions and set off well the deep yellow flowers, if it obliges you with blooms. In passing it should be mentioned that flowers seen by the author have been a rich, deep yellow, by no means orange, as has been indicated sometimes in the past, although the richness of colour would allow perhaps such poetic licence. The individual heads are usually globular to short-cylindrical, clustering

haphazardly at all levels. Axils have a little wool but no bristles. Radial spines number 12 to 15, and are 6 to 8 mm long, whitish or yellowish tipped brown. Central spines 2 to 6, 8 to 12 mm long, with one or two longer and hooked, coloured brown or nearly black. The deep yellow flowers are large, up to 30 mm in diameter with dark orange stigma-lobes. Fruit is red and slender, the seeds very distinctively large for *Mammillaria*, 2·5 mm long, dark brown and rough.

Reported variously from the State of Michoacan on cliffs at La Salada (*M. nelsonii*); Guerrero, near Balsas (*M. balsasensis*); Guerrero along the lower Rio Balsas (*M. aylostera*); Guerrero between Taxco and Acapulco 'in the shade of trees on the mountain sides' along the highway between Rio Balsas and Chilpancingo (*M. balsasoides*); in the same area as the last mentioned near Colonia (*M. colonensis*); near the Rio Elota in Sinaloa (*M. barkeri*).

M. bergii (Miq.) Walp., *Comm. Phyt.* 103 (1838); *MSJ* **11**:57 (1971)

An undetermined species name which Craig and Hunt ascribe tentatively to *M. ortegae*, itself dubiously identifiable.

M. bicolor Lehm., *Del. Sem. Hort. Hamb.* 1830. 7 (1830); *MSJ* **11**:57 (1971)

Long since referred to *M. geminispina*.

M. bicornuta Tiegel, *Cacti and other Succ.* 83 (1935); *MSJ* **8**:13 (1968)

Hunt indicates that this name is a synonym for *M. bucareliensis*, which he relegates to subspecific status beneath *M. magnimamma*.

M. 'Birmandreis' Bertrand, *Cactus (France)* no. **33**: 94 (1952); *MSJ* **2**:73 (1962)

This cultivar name is said to apply to a hybrid between *M. hahniana* and *M. bosshardtii*, the latter itself said to be a hybrid between *M. crucigera* and *M. sempervivi*, which is confusing for its genes let alone collectors!

M. blossfeldiana Boed., *Monatsschr. Deutsch. Kakt. Ges.* **3**:209 (1931); *MSJ* **8**:13 (1968)

Series **Ancistracanthae** M. MICROCARPA Group

This species is a gem, and is less difficult in cultivation than many of its fellows in the series, growing readily from seed to make a flowering plant in two or three years, and clumping readily thereafter. Its main attraction lies in the wonderful flowers, which are large, freely produced, with whitish petals and a striking pyjama stripe in the centre of each of rose-carmine. In cultivation it is not 'mainly simple' as originally described, clustering after a short while. The heads are about 3 or 4 cm in diameter and to 5 cm or more tall. Axils have a little wool, but no bristles. Central spines are 4 in number, the upper 3 straight and similar to the radials, the lower 1 longer (10 mm) and hooked, dark brown to black. Radial spines 15 to 20, 5 to 7 mm long, yellowish tipped darker, giving the plants a yellow cast. Flowers are about 2 to 4 cm in diameter, coloured as described above. Fruit is orange-red, seeds black.

Reported from Baja California at Punta Prieta (28.5°N) in hot, dry desert, in granite and gravelly soil, often scarcely showing above the surface.

Two varietal names have appeared: var. *grandiflora* Hort.—flowers in this species as indicated vary in size, and this invalid name was given to a form with larger flowers; var. *shurlyana* Gates, (*Cact. Amer.* **13**:78 with fig. 1941) was described as differing from the type in having a more cylindrical habit of growth, fibrous rather than thick roots, usually pinker (meaning a wider stripe?) and from an inland rather than a coastal

M. blossfeldiana

M. blossfeldiana (low-growing form)

habit. This is clearly merely an ecological variant, the most interesting aspect of which is the precise locality given for it: Baja California, in a small range of granite hills 9 km west of Mesquital Ranch, 28°30′N, 113°55′W, altitude about 150 m. Further references give localities in the Isla Guadalupe. A more distinct form is often seen, however, with about 14 chalky-white radials and 1–2 black-brown centrals, and altogether a more squat habit. This seems to be intermediate between this species and *M. goodridgii*, and may indicate that the two should be merged under the latter name, which has priority. They are certainly close enough in their occurrence in habitat for this to be so.

M. bocasana Poselger, *Allg. Gartenz.* **21**:94 (1853); *MSJ* **5**:61 (1965) & **8**:13 (1968); *Cact. Amer.* **42**:175 with fig. (1970)
Series **Stylothelae** M. WILDII Group

To say that this name covers a wide range of plants in cultivation is an understatement. There are many variations in collections: on the amount of wool, or rather hairlike bristles, varying from comparatively sparse (*M. longicoma* and perhaps *M. hirsuta*) to very dense (so called var. *splendens* or var. *multilanata*), and in the flower colour, from white to pale yellow to deep pink. The original description therefore deserves close examination and in view of the undoubted wide propagation from cultivated plants, habitat seed should be sought if 'true' plants are required. Poselger described his plant from San Luis Potosi, Sierra de Bocas, between stones, as clustering, axils naked, central spines only 1, 5 to 6 mm long and hooked, brownish tipped; radials very numerous, hairlike, 8 to 10 mm long, pure white. Most plants in cultivation under this name differ in having more and longer central spines, long axillary wool and longer radial spines (to 20 mm), but few *Mammillaria* enthusiasts would hesitate in identifying these densely hairy plants as *M. bocasana*! More doubts arise with other names which attach themselves to plants of this ilk, especially those more sparsely hairy. Of these the favourite is perhaps *M. longicoma*. The description of this species coincides more with the more sparsely hairy *M. bocasana* plants, in that the plant has long white hairs in the axils and 4 central spines, 10 to 12 mm long, 1 or 2 hooked, and in the flower description: outer perianth segments pinkish, darker along the centre, inner perianth segments lanceolate, acute, nearly white or sometimes tinged with rose. Glass and Foster reported finding plants of this description 19 km north-west of the town of San Luis Potosi, the area cited by Poselger for his *M. bocasana*! Whether it is correct to retain the first name of *M. bocasana*, and adapt the original rather inadequate description to apply to these plants, or whether it is more correct to discard the old name in favour of the more identifiable later name of *M. longicoma* is arguable. But if the name *M. bocasana* is discarded it will be many years, if ever, before it ceases to appear on labels in collections.

Other names muddled here are *M. kunzeana*, which will not do at all, as the description calls for bristle-like straight radials; the name *M. schelhasii* is also often found on plants of this species, but they usually have far shorter centrals than depicted in Craig's illustration and called for in Pfeiffer's description—12 to 18 mm.

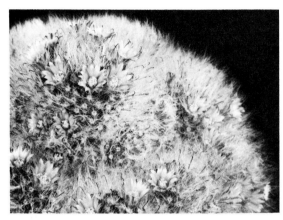

M. bocasana

M. bocensis Craig, *Mamm. Handb.* 56 with fig. (1945); *MSJ* **8**:14 (1968)
Series **Macrothelae**   M. SONORENSIS Group

This is not a very well-known species in collections. The plant body is usually simple, but it will cluster in time, with individual stems flat-globular, about 8 or 9 cm in diameter. Axils have a little wool but no bristles. Radial spines number 6 to 8, 5 to 14 mm long, straight, chalk-white to reddish with brown or black tip, quite strong. There is 1 central spine, stronger and usually longer (8 to 15 mm long), straight to a little

curved, reddish-brown with darker brown or black tip; the flowers are 15 to 20 mm long, pale pinkish or greenish with brownish midstripe, fruit reddish, seeds light brown.

Reported from Sonora, Las Bocas, found 'in salty flats of the coastal plain, deep-seated under bushes and adjacent to the beach'.

Names associated here are *M. neoschwarzeana* and *M. rubida*, more often seen, as seedlings under these names have appeared in recent years.

M. boedekerana Quehl, *Monatsschr. Kakteenk.* **20**:108 with fig. (1910); *MSJ* **8**:14 (1968)

A dubious species according to Hunt. Plants seen under this name are usually referrable to *M. aurihamata*.

M. bogotensis Werderm., *Neue Kakt.* 98 (1931)
A synonym of *M. columbiana*.

M. bombycina Quehl., *Monatsschr. Kakteenk.* **20**:149 with fig. (1910); *MSJ* **8**:27 (1968)
Series **Stylothelae**   M. BOMBYCINA Group

This species has been the doyen of the show benches when it comes to classes for large *Mammillaria* for many years, since it makes an exceedingly handsome large clump, with attractive colour-contrasting spination and wool. The individual heads are usually about 7 to 8 cm tall (not counting the lower part of large clumping specimens) and about 5 or 6 cm in diameter not including the spines. One of the features of this species is the dense white wool in the axils between the tubercles. The 30 to 40 stiff, radial spines are thin and needle-like, 8 mm long, glassy white, and they help together with the wool to set off the 4 centrals, coloured yellow or reddish-brown; the lower central is longer, 20 mm, and hooked, the other 3 are straight, 11 mm long. The flowers are 15 mm long and wide, and are cited in Craig's handbook as bright carmine-red, but Britton and Rose report them, (as in Quehl's original description) as light purple, which is the colour of all

M. bocensis

M. bombycina

the cultivated plants I have seen or heard of. Fruit is whitish, seeds black.

Reported by Craig from the states of Coahuila and San Luis Potosi (Santa Maria).

M. bonavitii Schmoll ex Backeb., *Die Cact.* **5**:3466 with fig. (1966); *MSJ* **9**:39 (1969)

A catalogue name by Schmoll for a form of *M. rhodantha*.

M. boolii Lindsay, *Cact. Amer.* **25**:48 with fig. (1953); *MSJ* **8**:14 & 27 (1968); *Int. Newer Mamm.* 4 with fig. (1973)
Series **Ancistracanthae** M. MICROCARPA Group

Although it has been suggested that this may merely be a variant of *M. insularis*, it has not as yet been combined, and is unlikely to be until a thorough examination of the occurrence of both species in the wild is achieved. It was described as globose, with stems about 3·5 cm tall and 3 cm wide, taller in cultivation. Axils are woolly at first, later naked. Radial spines number about 20, white, needle-like, 15 mm long. Central spine solitary, 1·5 to 2 cm long, yellowish with darker tip, but not the almost black tip of the centrals of *M. insularis*. Flowers are large, to 3 cm long and wide, lavender-pink with paler margins.

Reported from Sonora, San Pedro Bay, and abundantly in the nearby San Carlos Bay area.

M. boolii

M. x bosshardtii Maire, *Cactus (France)* **no. 24**:53 (1950); *MSJ* **8**:27 (1968)

A name given to hybrids between *M. crucigera* and *M. sempervivi*.

M. brandegei (Coulter) Brandegee, *Erythea* **5**:116 (1897); *Contr. US Nat. Herb.* **3**:96 (1894); *MSJ* **8**:27 (1968)
Series **Macrothelae** M. BRANDEGEI Group

This species was described in 1894. Craig reduced the former *M. gabbii* to varietal status under *M.*

brandegei after Britton and Rose's reduction to synonymy. Hunt reduces both this and 'probably' *M. lewisiana* to synonymy.

M. brandegei var. *magdalensis* Schwarz is an invalid name for a variant with less central spines (1 or 2), which are also slightly longer—not here upheld.

The type was described as globose to cylindric (most seen in cultivation are flat-globose), flattened at the crown, solitary or clustering, with heads to 9 cm in diameter. The axils are woolly. Radial spines number 9 to 16, 8 to 10 mm long, whitish to yellowish-brown with dark tips. Central spines number 1 to 6, reddish-brown tipped dark brown, longer and stronger than the radials (much longer sometimes—see below). Flowers are 15 mm long, greenish-yellow. Fruit is pinkish to red, seeds brown. See colour plate.

Reported from Baja California, at San Ignacio and as far as the Mission San Fernando, among rocks.

M. lewisiana, although regarded as conspecific with

M. brandegei

M. brandegei (lewisiana)

M. brandegei, is worth seeking out, as it is a distinctive form with long central spines curling over the top of the plant in a most appealing way. It is found in the northern part of the Vizcaino desert.

M. brauneana Boed., *Kakteenk.* **1**:113 with fig. (1933); *MSJ* **8**:28 (1968)
Series **Leucocephalae**

Described as usually solitary, 8 cm in diameter, becoming thickly columnar in time, this is not such a commonly seen plant in collections at present as it used to be some 20 years ago. Radial spines number 25 to 30, to 5 mm long, white and very thin; centrals 2 to 4, 5 to 7 mm long, stiff and much thicker than radials, reddish or yellowish-brown with black tips. Flowers are up to 13 mm wide, red-violet (or deep pink), fruit carmine, seeds dark brown.

Reported from Tamaulipas, near Jaumave.
Hunt allies this species to *M. klissingiana*.

M. brauneana

M. bravoae Craig, *Mamm. Handb.* 112 with fig. (1945); *MSJ* **8**:28 (1968)
Referred to *M. hahniana*.

M. braynii Hort.
A catalogue name of the firm of H. E. Born of West Germany, unidentified.

M. bucareliensis Craig, *Mamm. Handb.* 61 (1945); *MSJ* **8**:28 (1968) & **12**:40 (1972)
Referred to *M. magnimamma*.

M. buchenaui Backeb., *Descr. Cact. Nov.* **3**:8 (1963); *MSJ* **8**:29 & 83 (1968) & **11**:58 (1971)
Referred to *M. crucigera*.

M. bullardiana (Gates) Boed., *Cact. Succ. Journ.* **6**:4 (1934); *Kaktus ABC* 387 (1935)
Generally accepted, though not by some diehard nurserymen, as a synonym of *M. hutchisoniana*.

M. busonii Bachel, *Kakt. u. a. Sukk.* **22**:78 (1971)
A good joke appropriate to the genus, worth the trouble of seeking out the journal to appreciate fully— prudes should not bother.

M. buxbaumiana Hort.
A catalogue name for *M. boolii*.

M. cadereytana Hort., *Das Kakteenlex.* 231 (1966)
Referred to *M. pygmaea*.

M. cadereytensis Craig, *Mamm. Handb.* 305 (1945); *MSJ* **8**:43 (1968); *Cact. GB*. **39**:100 (1977)
Hunt now ascribes this name to synonymy with *M. perbella*. Plants seen under the name *M. cadereytensis*, however, differ considerably from this species, and I quite accepted Hunt's former opinion that it equated to *M. parkinsonii*. But even with this species there are differences which would ensure that fellow collectors would dispose of their plant under this name. It has altogether shorter spines than most *M. parkinsonii*, and the flowers—not readily produced in England—are again a fair step away from *M. parkinsonii* in colour, with none of their creamy-yellow colouring; they are pinkish maroon with darker midstripes to the inner petals, and deep brown stripes on the outer petals.

Reported from Queretaro, in Angostura de Charcos.

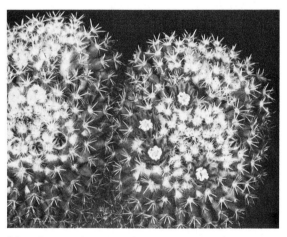

M. cadereytensis

M. caerulea Craig, *Mamm. Handb.* 306 with fig. (1945); *MSJ* **8**:43 (1968)
Hunt refers this name to *M. chionocephala*.

M. calacantha Tiegel, *Kakteenk.* 1933. 232 with fig. (1933); *MSJ* **8**:43 (1968)
Series **Heterochlorae** M. RHODANTHA Group

This species is very close to *M. rhodantha*. The main apparent differences are in the way the spines lie closer to the body of the plant, and in the number of spines. Axils are woolly at first, later naked. Radial spines number 25 to 35, 5 to 7 mm long, straight, pale yellow becoming greyish. Central spines number 2 to 4, 10 to 15 mm long, straight or slightly curved, stronger than the radials, light reddish-tan with brown tips. Flowers are typical of the group with short tubes so that they barely protrude beyond the spines, 8 mm long and 12 to 14 mm wide, carmine-pink with deeper midstripe. Fruit is pink, light green at base, seeds light yellowish-brown.

Reported from Queretaro, in Angostura de Charcos. Craig also reported it from Guanajuato.

M. calacantha

M. calleana Backeb., *Cactus (Paris)* **no. 7**:30. 130 (1951); *Die Cact.* **5**:3448 with fig. (1961); *MSJ* **8**:44 (1968)

This species makes flattish clusters of small heads, each about 3 cm in diameter, with wool in the axils in youth. There is 1 honey-coloured, hooked central spine up to 10 mm long; radial spines number 22, light

M. calleana?

yellow, to 6 mm long. Flowers are white, about 10 mm long and wide. Fruit is red, seeds black.

Reported from Hidalgo, in humus under bushes, in half shade. Plants under this name are inseparable from *M. wildii*, or do not conform to the description.

M. camptotricha Dams, *Gartenwelt* **10**:14 (1905); *MSJ* **8**:44 (1968); *Cact. Amer.* **43**:5 (1971)

Series **Decipientes** M. DECIPIENS Group

This distinctive and very well-known species would hardly need describing were it not for the closely related *M. albescens*, now generally regarded as a variety of this species, with which it merges by transitional forms. The type was described in 1905 as having no central spines and 6 to 8 radials up to 27 mm long, bristle-like, yellowish, twisting and curving; var. *albescens* is similar, but with whitish, shorter spines, more or less straight, 1 often central. Other than these differences, they are the same, with bristles in the axils, white, smallish flowers produced sporadically throughout the year, about 17 mm long, not usually

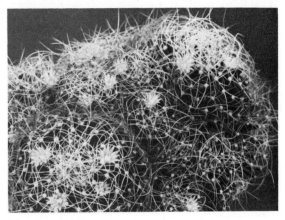

M. camptotricha

M. camptotricha (albescens)

opening widely, and not protruding beyond the spines; fruits are green to pale pink, seeds light brown. Intermediate forms occur with varying lengths of spines, coloured from white through yellow to brownish.

Reported from the eastern part of the state of Queretaro between Higuerillas and San Pablo.

Hunt allies this species to *M. decipiens*.

M. candida Scheidw., *Bull. Acad. Sci. Brux.* **5**:496 (1838); *MSJ* **8**:45 (1968); *Cact. Amer.* **42**:281 (1970) & **47**:195 (1975)

Subgenus **Mammilloydia**

This popular, slow-growing species is likely to occur in collections three or even four-fold. Firstly the type, which has bristles in the axils; 8 to 12 central spines, 5 to 9 mm long, pure white or pink to brown at the tips; about 50 radial spines, a little weaker than the centrals, white; the flowers are rose-pink, 2 cm long, the fruit red (see below) and seeds shiny black. Secondly there is *M. candida* var. *rosea* (Salm-Dyck) Schum., really a form with longer central spines, pinkish-brown at the tips in youth but otherwise the same. Thirdly there is *M. ortiz-rubiona* (Bravo) Werderm., with reportedly fewer spines (25 to 30 radials and 4 to 6 centrals), fewer and larger tubercles, long axillary hairs and paler flowers. And last-named is *M. candida* var. *caespitosa* Voss, described in 1970 as a heavily clustering form, although in time all the above will form beautiful clusters like small piles of snowballs. Hunt equates plants grown as *M. ortiz-rubiona* to *M. candida*, as they invariably have many more than the requisite number of spines (see above) and likewise var. *rosea* and var. *caespitosa* are not upheld on such minor variations. In cultivation two forms are usually seen: one is white spined (sometimes pink-tipped) with projecting central spines and eventually a heavily clustering habit; the other has an altogether smoother, less tousled spine appearance, through more adpressed spines, which are more strikingly pink or brownish than the other form. The last described makes large individual stems to 20 cm tall, but about the same width (9 to 10 cm), clustering much more slowly and later in life, and has a less depressed or flat top than the more commonly seen form. Reported from San Luis Potosi, in particular from between Huizache and Ciudad del Maiz, and from the borders of Guanajuato and Queretaro (*M. ortiz-rubiona*).

The seed character, which points towards divergence from perhaps *Neolloydia* stock separately from all other *Mammillaria* induced Buxbaum to create the new genus *Mammilloydia*. Moran, supported subsequently by Hunt, expressed the opinion that at most this should be regarded as a subgenus. Certainly the name has not been generally taken up and the species to all intents has been retained in *Mammillaria*. Fruit as observed on cultivated plants is never red as described. It is pink, pale greenish below, and airship shaped in the manner of *M. glassii*. See colour plate.

M. candida

M. canelensis Craig, *Mamm. Handb.* 307 with fig. (1945); *MSJ* **8**:38 & 57 (1968) & **14**:48 (1974)

Series **Macrothelae** M. STANDLEYI Group

Hunt ascribes various names to this species, which have never been serious contenders for specific recognition: *M. floresii*, *M. laneusumma*, *M. bellacantha*, *M. auritricha* and *M. auricantha*, while Craig allied *M. canelensis* to the earlier described *M. standleyi*. Of all these names *M. standleyi* and *M. canelensis* have become widely used and continued to be accepted as separate species, while the remainder have fallen by the wayside, with the possible exception of *M. floresii*, which has hung on over the years, but with no real justification—plants labelled *M. floresii* have sometimes been misidentified plants of *M. scrippsiana*. Plants in cultivation under the name *M. canelensis* usually have pink flowers, about 15 mm long and wide, although sometimes the yellow-flowered

M. canelensis

form is seen. They make large solitary plants to about 11 cm wide and 15 cm or more tall, eventually offsetting. The axils have dense wool and bristles and this abundance is a strong feature of the species. The radial spines vary from 8 to 25, 5 to 15 mm long, very fine and white, and almost hidden in the thick wool in the axils. Central spines number usually 4, sometimes 2 to 10 are seen, fairly constantly orange-yellow to red-brown, 6 to 30 mm long, mostly 10 to 15 mm, usually curved. Flowers are freely produced, as described above. Fruit is purplish-red, seeds brown.

Reported from south-west Chihuahua and south-east Sonora.

M. capensis (Gates) Craig, *Mamm. Handb.* 156 with fig. (1945); *Cact. Amer.* **4**:372 (1933) & **41**:166 (1969); *MSJ* **8**:57 (1968)
Series **Ancistracanthae** M. DIOICA Group

This is a species rare in collections, from near the southern tip of the Baja California peninsula. The death rate in seedlings indicates that it is likely to be difficult in cultivation in common with some others of this group. It was described as clustering, with cylindrical stems, axils naked or with 1 to 3 short bristles. Radial spines number 13, 8 to 15 mm long, needle-like, white at base shading through red-brown to black at the tip; the 1 strongly hooked central spine is similarly coloured, 15 to 20 mm long. Flowers are pink or whitish, 20 mm long and wide. Fruit is orange-scarlet, seeds black. It grows nearby geographically to *M. armillata*, and the description could well be encompassed by this species, with allowance for the different flower, but specimens seen are immediately distinguishable, and until further field work proves otherwise they are maintained herein separately. The name is often misapplied.

Reported from Puerto de Bahia de los Muertos, Baja California, and from Todos Santos with white flowers and straight spines.

M. capensis

M. caput-medusae Otto ex Pfeiffer, *Enum. Cact.* 22 (1837)

Referred to *M. sempervivi*, but some plants received under this name are referrable to what is commonly grown as *M. lloydii*.

M. carmenae M. Castaneda, *An. Inst. Biol. Mex.* **24**:233 with figs. (1953); *MSJ* **8**:58 (1968) & **19**:78 with fig. (1979); *Kakt. u. a. Sukk.* **28**:280 (1977); *Cact. Amer.* **50**:180 (1978); *Cact. GB.* **41**:100 with fig. (1979)
Series **Lasiacanthae** M. SCHIEDEANA Group

For a long time this species has merely been a name in the list of unobtainable *Mammillaria* species, to the extent that one would doubt its existence were it not for the photographs accompanying the original description and in Backeberg's *'Die Cactaceae'* from which one can deduce that here is a very fine, individual species. As the photograph shows, the fugitive has been sought out and is alive and well, recently discovered by Alfred Lau, with the exploration well related in the German Society's journal. It has proved to be a vigorous grower, and in a year or two it is expected that it will be as common in collections as *M. saboae* and *M. theresae* now are. It clusters, making globular or ovoid bodies 3 or 4 cm in diameter and a little taller. The axils have wool and bristles. Radial spines number more than 100, to 5 mm long, white or pale yellow and pubescent; there are no central spines. Flowers are white tinged pink, 11 mm long and wide, with 4 or 5 yellow stigma-lobes. The fruit is greenish, seeds black.

Reported from Tamaulipas, in the 'municipio' of Jaumave, on the ranch 'La Reja', in crevices of rocks on north-facing landslips. See colour plate.

M. carmenae

M. carnea Zucc. ex Pfeiffer, *Enum. Cact.* 19 (1837); *MSJ* **8**:58 (1968)
Series **Polyedrae** M. POLYEDRA Group

This is a well-known, widely and easily grown species, solitary or clustering with age, with angled tubercles and usually 4 spines in an upright cross formation, the upper and lower longer—upper 8 to 12 mm long, lower 10 to 20 mm long—the 2 lateral spines only about 6 mm, all pinkish-brown tipped black, straight or a little curving, especially the longer spines; all are sub-central. Flowers are pale pink with a slightly darker midstripe, 15 to 20 mm long, 12 to 15 mm wide, with green stigma-lobes. Fruit is red, seeds brown.

Although reported originally from Hidalgo, between Ixmiquilpan and Zimapan, Craig doubted this as all subsequent collections have been from further south: from Puebla (Tehuacan), Guerrero (Taxco), Oaxaca and the state of Mexico.

Named varieties *robustispina*, *aeruginosa*, *cirrosa* and *subtetragona* are discounted as minor variants.

M. carnea

M. carretii Rebut ex Schum., *Gesamt. Kakt.* 542 (1898); *MSJ* **8**:58 (1968)
Subgenus **Dolichothele**

The plant commonly seen under this label clusters to form a small group of flat-globular heads, and this conflicts with Rebut's description of a solitary species. But the spines fit the description, i.e. 1 central, 14 to 16 mm long, hooked, chestnut-brown, radials about 14, up to 13 mm long, somewhat curved and yellow. Flowers are white, with a rosy midstripe on the inner petals, 2·5 cm long, with greenish stigma-lobes. Fruit is slender and green, seeds dark brown. Craig described the seeds as black, regarding *M. unihamata* as synonymous, but this is not now upheld, and the differing seed colour ratifies the distinction of the two.

Reported by Boedeker from Nuevo Leon.

Although slow growing the cultivation of this species presents no real problems. It needs little root-depth, being shallow rooting, as is the way with many hooked-spine species. Perhaps this feeble hold on the soil together with the hooked spines is to facilitate distribution, as the spines can catch on to passing animals; they will certainly catch on to the human species if placed too near the front of the staging.

The colouring of the spines and the long, hooked centrals are the main features of this species, which takes some time to fill an 18 cm (7 inch) pan with its flat cluster of heads protected by the upstanding array of hooked centrals.

M. saffordii is referred to this species.

M. carretii

M. casoi H. Bravo, *An Inst. Biol. Mex.* **25**:537 with figs. (1954); *MSJ* **8**:59 (1968)
See under *M. mystax*.

M. celsiana Lem., *Cact. Gen. Nov. Sp.* **41**:98 (1839); *MSJ* **8**:76 (1968); *Cact. Amer.* **42**:267 (1970)
See under *M. muehlenpfordtii*.

M. centraliplumosa Fittkau, *Cact. y Suc. Mex.* **16**:39 (1971); *MSJ* **15**:27 (1975); *Cact. GB.* **39**:74 (1977)

Seedlings raised under this name in the last few years have produced distinct, dark red-spined plants obviously allied to *M. spinosissima*, with slightly

M. centraliplumosa

narrower columns than normally seen in that species. They also appear to be identical to some seedlings raised some years ago as *M. neocoronaria*. But you will look in vain for the plumose central spines indicated in the name, unless you use a strong glass, and even then it seems not to be a consistent character. Hunt dismisses the name as merely a slender stemmed form of *M. spinosissima*.

M. centricirrha Lem., *Cact. Gen. Nov. Sp.* **42** (1839); *MSJ* **12**:39 (1972)
  See under *M. magnimamma*.

M. cerralboa (B. & R.) Orcutt, *Cactog.* 7 (1926); *The Cact.* **4**:116 with fig. (1923); *MSJ* **8**:76 (1968)
Series **Ancistracanthae**   M. DIOICA Group
  This is a lovely yellow-spined member of this group, unknown for many years, but recently seed has been available and several nurseries have had seedlings for sale. Britton and Rose mention hooked spine plants collected at the same time as the described type plant with straight spines, and subsequent authors have attested to the plants found on Cerralbo Island having one or more hooked spines. The species was described as solitary (it clusters in time in cultivation), cylindric, 10 to 15 cm tall, tubercles yellowish, spines all yellow, very much alike, about 11 in number, 1 usually more central, the longer ones nearly 2 cm long. Flowers are small, 1.5 cm long or less, greenish-cream and not opening very widely. The fruit colour is unrecorded, but the seeds are black.

M. cerralboa

Reported from Cerralbo Island off the east coast of the lower end of Baja California.
  Hunt allies this species to *M. armillata*.

M. 'Cerroprieto' Hort.
  A catalogue name for plants which seem referrable to *M. magnimamma*.

M. chavezei Cowper, *Nat. Cact. Journ.* **18**:8 (1963)
  Referred to *M. viridiflora*.

M. chionocephala J.A. Purpus, *Monatsschr. Kakteenk.* **16**:41 with fig. (1916); *MSJ* **8**:77 (1968)
Series **Leucocephalae**   M. SEMPERVIVI Group
  This species is not as often seen in collections as one might suppose from its attractive, white, woolly appearance. It is usually solitary, but will make large clusters late in life. The individual heads are short, thick-cylindric, about 9 or 10 cm wide and up to 15 or 20 cm tall, with a great deal of wool and many 2 cm long bristles in the axils, giving rise to the specific name, which means white-headed. Radial spines number 22 to 24, up to 8 mm long, white and bristle-like. Central spines number 2 to 4, rarely 5 or 6, 4 to 6 mm long, white sometimes tipped brown. Flowers are rose-pink or white or shades between, about 1 cm wide. Fruit is carmine, seeds brown. *M. ritterana* is referred here.
  Reported from Coahuila, Sierra de Parras and elsewhere in Coahuila and Durango.

M. chionocephala

M. cinobiltinei Hort., *MSJ* **8**:77 (1968)
  An unidentified catalogue name of many years ago.

M. coahuilensis Moran, *Zeitschr. Sukk.* **2 pt. 13**:210 (1926) & **3**:39 (1927); *Gentes Herbarum* **8**:324 (1953); *MSJ* **8**:77 (1968) & **14**:52 and 56 (1974); *Cact. Amer.* **42**:229 with fig. (1970)
Series **Macrothelae**   M. HEYDERI Group
  This species was known for many years as *Porfiria schwartzii* (Fric.) Boed. (not to be confused with *M. schwarzii* Shurly, a completely different species—see under that name), but it seems to have gained acceptance now as a good *Mammillaria* species. The name *schwartzii* could not be used on its transfer to *Mammillaria* as it was so similar to the afore-mentioned

M. schwarzii—a view not shared by Haage in the English edition of Backeberg's *Cactus Lexicon*. The species forms thick carrot-like roots and is almost invariably solitary, with a very flattened hemisphere of tubercles above ground. The tubercles are 3-sided, the axils a little woolly. The 1 central spine is 6 mm long, straight, needle-like, grey-white, with brownish tip. The radial spines, about 16, are a little weaker than the central, grey-white, the lower a little longer, to 6 mm long. All the spines are finely pubescent, but this is observable only with a glass. The flowers are outstandingly large for the size of the body, being about 3 cm in diameter. The colour of the petals within is white with pink midstripe, the outside pink with brownish stripe. Fruit is red, seeds dark brown. The type was described from Coahuila, near San Pedro, at the Laguna de Viesca in cracks in the dry lake.

A variety—var. *albiflora*—was described briefly in 1926, with, as the name indicates, white flowers; this may equate to *M. albiarmata*—see under that name, which is maintained separately herein.

parts under *M. collinsii*, being I suppose the more familiar name. The three are maintained separately here. *M. collinsii* has stems about 4 or 5 cm in diameter, and forms a large clump; body colour in full light is bronze to purplish, though not so brightly purple as *M. voburnensis*. Axils have wool and bristles. Radial spines number usually 7, 5 to 7 mm long, pale yellowish below with dark brown, nearly black tips. Central spine usually solitary, longer and darker than radials, but not very distinguishable. Flowers are more readily produced than in the other two species mentioned, and are about 15 mm long and wide, pale yellow with reddish midstripe, more prominent on the outer petals. Fruit is deep red, seeds brown.

Reported from Oaxaca, near Tehuantepec, San Geronimo. A distinctive form with yellow wool is seen labelled *M. collinsii* from Chiapas, which closely resembles *M. eichlamii*. Other forms under place names are sometimes seen: from Salina Cruz, Tehuantepec and Veracruz. The three species mentioned intermingle in the wild, and their separate specific identification is doubtful.

M. coahuilensis

M. collinsii

M. collina Purpus, *Monatsschr. Kakteenk.* **22**:162 (1912) and **23**:99 with fig. (1913); *Cact. Amer.* **44**:171 with fig. (1972)

Referred to *M. haageana*.

M. collinsii (B. & R.) Orcutt, *Cactog.* 7 (1926); *The Cact.* **4**:101 with figs. (1923); *MSJ* **8**:78 (1968); *Cact. GB.* **39**:100 (1977)

Series **Polyedrae** M. KARWINSKIANA Group

In spite of suggestions that this and *M. eichlamii* should be reduced beneath the prior name *M. voburnensis*, they have maintained their separate identity, with the merest doffing of caps to the idea by some nurseries in listing (incorrectly) the constituent

M. collinsii (from Chiapas)

M. colonensis Craig, *Mamm. Handb.* 219 with fig. (1945); *MSJ* **8**:79 (1968);

This name is referred to *M. beneckei*.

M. columbiana Salm-Dyck, *Cact. Hort. Dyck.* 1849. 99 (1850); *MSJ* **8**:79 (1968
Series **Supertextae**   M. SUPERTEXTA Group

This species, from 200 km north-east of Bogota 'on slaty hillsides' according to Werdermann (who described it as the synonymous *M. bogotensis*) is well-known in cultivation, and small seedlings commonly marketed about 10 years ago have become narrowly columnar to 15 cm or more tall, with offsets just beginning to appear around the base. The short, golden-yellow, central spines are 6 to 8 mm long, usually 4 or 5 in number, and give the whole plant a characteristic yellow cast. The 18 to 20 bristle-like radial spines are small, 4 to 6 mm long, and white. The small pink flowers barely protrude from the thick wool in the axils. Cultivation presents no problems unless it is in the tendency for the lower part of the stem to become discoloured from the prolific fruit produced; this can be alleviated to a certain extent by early removal of the fruit, as the discolouring is caused by the formation of sooty mould on the decaying fruits. The fruit is small, about 1·5 cm, and coloured orange; the seed is brown. This is a widespread species in the wild, the locality given above by Werdermann for '*M. bogotensis*' reaffirming its South American distribution, as implied by the name *M. columbiana*. A white-spined form—var. *albescens* Haage & Backeb.—has been described from Capitanejo, 300 km north-west of Bogota at 1200 m altitude, and a form has also been found on Jamaica on 'inaccessible' limestone cliffs. It is also known from Peru and Venezuela.

M. columbiana

M. compressa DC, *Mem. Mus. Nat. Hist. Paris* **17**:112 (1828); *MSJ* **8**:80 (1968)
Series **Macrothelae**   M. COMPRESSA Group

This is a heavily clustering species making huge mounds in time. These are the stuff of the 'big *Mammillaria*' classes often seen in shows in pans 60 cm across, competing with *M. magnimamma* and *M. bombycina* for size. The angled tubercles gave rise to the name *M. angularis*, and plants of this species are still sometimes seen under this synonym. The spines are variable in length and colour, and plants in cultivation fall broadly into two types: firstly larger individual heads clustering openly with long, upstanding spines to 7 cm or longer, red-brown for a third of their length (often labelled var. *longiseta* or var. *rosea*), the other commonly seen has smaller heads, clusters more compactly and has more prominently white spines, red-brown only at the tips, and lying closer to the plant body. Both types have 4 to sometimes 6 spines, unequal in length, the lower much longer; in addition there are occasionally 1 to 3 short additional spines in a radial plane low down on the areole. The flowers, not always freely produced in cultivation, are bright purplish-pink and not very large (to 1·5 cm in diameter). Fruit is red, seeds brown.

M. compressa

M. compressa. A large clump

Reported from Hidalgo, San Luis Potosi; abundant in all its forms near Ixmiquilpan and Tasquillo, Hidalgo.

M. confusa (B. & R.) Orcutt, *Cactog.* 7 (1926); *The Cact.* **4**:102 with figs. (1923); *MSJ* **8**:81 (1968); *Cact. Amer.* **44**:97 (1972)
See under *M. karwinskiana.*

M. conspicua Purpus, *Monatsschr. Kakteenk.* **22**:163 (1912) & **24**:37 (1914); *An. Inst. Biol. Mex.* 122 (1930); *MSJ* **9**:8 (1969); *Cact. GB.* **39**:98–99 (1977)
See under *M. haageana.*

M. conzattii (B. & R.) Orcutt, *Cactog.* 7 (1926); *The Cact.* **4**:103 (1923)
See under *M. karwinskiana.*

M. coronaria Haw., *Rev. Pl. Succ.* 69 (1821)
A name probably erroneously applied to this genus in the first place (the plant described was 1·5 m tall), but which has persisted as a misnomer for *M. neocoronaria*, itself a dubious name referred to *M. spinosissima.*

M. cowperae Shurly, *Cact. GB.* **21**:58 with fig. (1959)
See *M. moellerana.*

M. craigii Lindsay, *Cact. Amer.* **14**:107 with fig. (1942); *MSJ* **8**:82 (1968)
This is a flattened-ball shaped species getting to about 10 cm in diameter in cultivation. The axils are very woolly, especially at the top of the plant, and the smallish, deep purplish-pink flowers push through the wool. There are 1 to 3 (usually 2) central spines, up to 3 cm long, golden coloured with brown tips, and 8 similar radial spines up to 2·5 cm long. Fruit is red, seeds brown.
Reported from south-west Chihuahua, Sierra Tarahumara, a few kilometres from Choro, Barranca del Rio Urinque, at about 1800 m altitude, in crevices with leafmould. It is either not in cultivation or is confused with another species nowadays.

M. criniformis DC, *Mem. Cact.* 8 with fig. (1834); *MSJ* **8**:82 (1968)
A dubious species, which various authors have ascribed usually to synonymy with *M. glochidiata* (Hunt to *M. wildii*), but with no certainty as to its identification. Plants seen in cultivation under this name are usually readily referred elsewhere, and it is a name best discarded completely.
Reported from Hidalgo, near Zimapan.

M. crinita DC, 'Rev. Fam. Cact.' in *Mem. Mus. Nat. Hist. Paris* **17**:112 (1828); *Mem. Cact.* 7 with fig. (1834); *MSJ* **8**:82 (1968)
Series **Stylothelae**   M. WILDII Group

Unlike the preceding name this one is firmly becoming attached to a pale yellow-spined plant in cultivation, which accords with the brief description: simple and clustering, 4 cm in diameter (a little more in cultivation), axils naked, radial spines 15 to 20, 16 to 18 mm long, white straight, pubescent, central spines 4 or 5, 12 to 15 mm long, all yellow, very slender, needle-like, slightly thicker than the radials, pubescent, one or more hooked, flowers 16 mm long, whitish to yellowish or pinkish-cream with pink midstripe, fruit reddish, seeds black.
Reported from Hidalgo, at Zimapan and Rancho de San Antonio.
Hunt ascribes the name to *M. wildii*, but the plants seen at present pretending to this name are readily distinguishable from that species with more resemblance to *M. sinistrohamata.*

M. crinita

M. crispiseta Craig, *Mamm. Handb.* 308 with fig. (1945); *MSJ* **8**:82 (1968)
Hunt ascribes this name to synonymy with *M. mystax.*

M. crocidata Lemaire, *Cact. Aliq. Nov.* 9 (1838); *MSJ* **8**:82 (1968)
This is a dubious species, with inadequate description and no locality cited. Plants under this name usually turn out to be *M. obconella.*

M. crucigera Mart., *Nov. Act. Nat. Cur.* **16**:340 with fig. (1832); *MSJ* **8**:82 (1968)
Series **Supertextae**   M. SUPERTEXTA Group
The very closely set, small spines of this species make it a collectors' piece, but it is not very commonly seen in collections, being very slow-growing and not easy to raise from seed. Plants from the wild are sometimes seen in captivity, and are often large, woody clumps with many heads and a little battered from rough handling in transit. A photograph of a clump in the wild squeezing out of a rock crevice appeared on the front cover of the American Society's journal in

1974, the January-February issue, and later (could it be the same clump?) in a bonsai pan in the November-December 1975 issue of the same journal. The individual heads are about 4 cm across. The axils have a small amount of white wool, particularly in youth. Radial spines number 24 or more, tiny, at 2 mm long, white and slender. Central spines number 4, occasionally there are 5, only 2 mm long again, but stronger than the radials, waxy yellow or brownish, forming tiny, separated crosses on the plant, hence the name. Flowers are deep pinkish-purple, small, with 4 or 5 purple stigma-lobes. Fruit is red, the seeds yellowish to dark brown. There has been some confusion as to the identification of this species in the past, which now seems to be resolved. The original description gave no

M. crucigera

M. crucigera (a large cluster)

locality data, but the species has been reported by Craig from the state of Oaxaca, and by Krainz from Puebla, Oaxaca, and in error from Hidalgo and San Luis Potosi. The plant pictured on the cover of the American Society's journal, mentioned above, was from near Tilapa on the border between Oaxaca and Puebla, where it grows in nearly pure gypsum, often at the very edge of cliffs.

M. dawsonii (Houghton) Criag, *Mamm. Handb.* 67 (1945); *Cact. Amer.* **7**:88 (1935)

Hunt reduces this name to synonymy with *M. glareosa*.

M. dealbata Dietr., *Allg. Gartenz.* **14**:309 (1846); *MSJ* **9**:8 (1969)

See under *M. haageana*.

M. decipiens Scheidw., *Bull. Acad. Sci. Brux.* **5**:496 (1838); *MSJ* **8**:92 (1968)

Series **Decipientes** M. DECIPIENS Group

A well-known, clustering species, closely related to *M. camptotricha*, similar to var. *albescens* of that species, this one differs in having the addition of 1 or 2 yellowish, central spines tipped brown, as well as the usually 7, yellowish-white, straight radials. The flowers too are similar to *M. camptotricha*, white and rarely opening wide, as well as having a distinct fragrance. Fruits are green with a reddish tinge, the seeds brown. It likewise presents no difficulty in cultivation.

Locality for the type was not recorded, but it has been reported from east of the city of San Luis Potosi in the state of that name. A form with no central spines occurs in the Valley of Lourdes.

M. decipiens

M. deherdtiana Farwig, *Cact. Amer.* **41**:27 with figs. (1969) & **51**:125 (1979); *MSJ* **11**:59 (1971); *Kakt. u. a. Sukk.* **27**:241 (1976)

Series **Longiflorae** M. NAPINA Group

One of the stunningly beautiful, large-flowered

species which has recently been discovered, this species was named in recognition of Cyriel de Herdt, the Belgian cactus nurseryman, for his efforts in saving and propagating the plants of this species collected by its discoverer Fritz Schwarz. It has proved to be slow-growing, and sometimes difficult to establish or to flower, but worth the extra effort or skill for the attractive spination and the large, deep pink flowers. It was described as solitary, flat-globose, 2·5 cm tall, 4·5 cm wide, with slightly woolly or bare axils. Radial spines number 33 to 36, 3 to 6 mm long, light yellow at first, becoming white, sometimes slightly reddish-brown at the tips. Central spines number 1 to 6, but are sometimes absent, especially in youth, 3 to 5 mm long, occasionally to 7 mm, pale to dark reddish-brown. Flowers are large, up to 5 cm wide, tube up to 2 cm long (20 cm in error in the original description), bright rose-violet with darker midstripe and tip to the petals, stigma-lobes white, numbering 4. Fruit remains half-embedded in the stem, 3 to 4 mm wide, pale green where exposed, seeds dark brownish-black.

Reported from the road between Oaxaca and Tehuantepac, between the villages of Nejapa, Juquila Mixes and Lachiguiri in the state of Oaxaca. Some doubt has been expressed as to the separate standing of the three members of the *M. napina* group, viz. *M. napina*, *M. deherdtiana* and *M. dodsonii*, in particular the separation of *M. dodsonii* from this species, and Glass and Foster recently proposed the latter's reduction to varietal level beneath this species, a position already being referred to by collectors and nurserymen.

The differences as enunciated by Glass and Foster for var. *dodsonii* are in the lower tubercle spiral count (5 and 8 compared with 8 and 13 in var. *deherdtiana*, as the type must now be called); less and longer radial spines: 20 or 21, 10 to 18 mm long; 3 to 5 longer central spines, 10 to 20 mm long; and a tendency to cluster more readily than the type.

M. deliusiana Shurly, *Cact. GB.* **10**:92 with fig. (1948)

Acknowledged by Shurly to be a synonym for *M. bella*.

M. densispina (Coulter) Orcutt, *Cactog.* 7 (1926); *Contr. US. Nat. Herb.* **3**:96 (1894); *Monatsschr. Kakteenk.* **30**:55 (1920); *MSJ* **8**:92 (1968)

Series **Leptocladodae**   M. ELONGATA Group

Usually seen as solitary, densely-spined golden balls this species is deservedly popular in collections, especially as young seedlings are most attractive in appearance.

There seem to be two quite distinct forms in cultivation, with red central spines, or with all yellow spines—the latter often labelled *M. esaussieri*, an unpublished name.

M. deherdtiana var. *deherdtiana*

M. deherdtiana var. *dodsonii*

M. densispina

While occasionally offsetting, this species is usually solitary and globular, and plants I have grown have remained solitary for many years. Central spines were reported as numbering 6, 10 to 12 mm long, straight, more rigid than the radials and darker yellow, black tipped—most seen in cultivation have dark red-brown tipped centrals—about 25 radials were described as 8 to 10 mm long, unequal, yellow and slender. Flowers are not large (15 to 20 mm in diameter, 10 mm long), barely protruding beyond the dense spines, yellow, with a hint of a reddish midstripe. Fruit was described as red, although in cultivation it is more often greenish-pink, seeds reddish-brown.

Reported from San Luis Potosi, and by Craig from Queretaro and Guanajuato.

Hunt places *M. mieheana* beneath this species, but plants seen under this name have more in common with *M. elongata*, being heavily clustering with slightly thicker stems than most forms of *M. elongata*, with pale yellow, almost white spines and very felty areoles. It flowers too at the same time as *M. elongata* and produces fruits too contemporarily with that species. It is herein treated separately.

M. denudata (Engelm.) Berger, *Kakteen* 288 (1929); *Cact. Mex. Bound.* **2 pt. 1**:5 (1859)
See under *M. lasiacantha*.

M. diacentra Jacobi, *Allg. Gartenz.* **24**:91 (1856)
Unidentified for 120 years, this should now be laid to rest as an unknown warrior.

M. diguetii (Weber) D. R. Hunt, *Bull. Mus. Hist. Nat. Paris* **10**:383 (1904); *The Cact.* **4**:20 (1923); *MSJ* **14**:25 (1974) & **19**:7 (1979); *Cact. GB.* **39**:39 (1977)
This species after all these years is unknown in collections. Rumours of its collection occasionally circulate—but never the plants! It is said to differ from *M. senilis* in its more rigid, dark straw-coloured spines and shorter-tubed (3 cm) flowers. There remains the anomaly of the flower colour, which for *M. senilis* was described as orange-yellow, and for *M. diguetii* as deep red. All plants and photographs I have seen of *M. senilis* have had red flowers of the length required for that species. I know of no photograph of *M. diguetii* nor of any reference in books or journals since the original description, based on direct knowledge of plants of *M. diguetii*. Its existence separate from *M. senilis* is doubted.

Reported from the mountains of Jalisco.

M. dioica K. Brandegee, *Erythea* **5**:115 (1897); *Cact. Amer.* **24**:76 (1952); *MSJ* **8**:93 (1968)
Series **Ancistracanthae** M. DIOICA Group
This is one of the most widespread species in the wild, variable in habit from long-columnar stems with robust spines to squat-columnar or globose with much finer spines. The flower distinguishes it from close relatives (*M. microcarpa, sheldonii* etc.) being white

with a yellowish or yellow-green tinge, usually with a suggestion of a reddish midstripe, but smaller, less spreading or reflexing than others in the group—wide funnelform. Stigma-lobes are prominent, about 8 mm long, yellow to brownish-green, usually greenish-yellow. Fruit is bright scarlet, seeds black. Axils have wool and bristles. Radial spines number 11 to 22, 5 to 7 mm long, white tipped, brownish to black or pinkish throughout. Centrals 3 or 4, brownish or blackish, the lower longer and hooked. It occurs from a little northward of San Diego (a friend collected that illustrated in the back 'garden' of a hotel in San Diego)

M. dioica

M. dioica

down into Baja California and nearby islands. See colour plate.

M. discolor Haw., *Syn. Pl. Succ.* 177 (1812); *Cact. Amer.* **43**:75 with figs. (1971); *MSJ* **8**:93 (1968)
Series **Heterochlorae** M. DISCOLOR Group

Named for its contrasting radial and central spines this is a well-known attractively fine-spined species. It forms a ball of dense spines, about 8 cm or more across, with the plant body barely distinguishable through the spines. Axils are naked. The 16 to 20 radials are about 10 mm long, slender and coloured white to pale yellow to brown. Centrals number 6 to 8, amber yellow or darker to almost black, thin, needle-like, about the same length but slightly thicker than the radials. The flowers are up to 20 mm long, yellow or whitish, with a reddish midstripe on the outer petals, varying to deep pink overall with darker midstripe. Fruit is red, seeds brown. The locality of Haworth's type plant is unknown, being described from a plant in 'Mr Vere's collection'. It is reported from Puebla, which is also the locality for *M. esperanzaensis*, usually regarded as a variety at most of *M. discolor*, differing only in having fewer central spines (4 to 7). *M. ochoterenae* from Oaxaca is also regarded as conspecific, as too is *M. pachyrhiza.* The name *M. amoena* has also been misapplied to *M. discolor*.

M. discolor

M. dixanthocentron Backeb., *Descr. Cact. Nov.* **3**:8 (1963); *MSJ* **9**:8 (1969); *Kakt. u. a. Sukk.* **32**:21 (1971)
Series **Supertextae** M. SUPERTEXTA Group

This is a very distinctive looking species with its neat array of prominent central spines, worth a place in any collection. It was described as solitary, to 20 cm tall and about 7 to 8 cm wide, with woolly axils, about 20 radial spines, thin and white, 2 to 4 mm long. The central spines are the outstanding feature, numbering 2, or sometimes 4, the upper 5 mm long, the lower to about 15 mm long, yellow, later brownish or whitish

with brown tips. Flowers were described as red, but invariably on plants in cultivation they are yellowish-pink with deeper midstripe. Fruit is yellow below to orange above, seeds brown.

Reported from Arroyo Verde, near Tecomavaca, Oaxaca.

M. dixanthocentron

M. dodsonii Bravo, *Cact. Suc. Mex.* **15**:3 (1970); *MSJ* **11**:59 (1971); *Kakt. u. a. Sukk.* **27**:241 (1976)
Referred to *M. deherdtiana*.

M. dolichocentra Lemaire, *Cact. Nov. Hort. Monv.* **3** (1838); *Cact. Amer.* **43**:121 (1971)
Referred to *M. obconella*.

M. donatii Berg. ex K. Schum., *Gesamt. Kakt. Nachtrag.* 135 (1903); *MSJ* **9**;8 (1969)
Referred to *M. haageana*.

M. droegeana (Rebut ex K. Schum.) Borg, *Cacti* 332 (1937); *Gesamt. Kakt.* 438 (1898)
Referred to *M. microhelia*.

M. dumetorum J. A. Purpus, *Monatsschr. Kakteenk.* **22**:149 (1912) & **23**:89 (1913)
Referred to *M. schiedeana*.

M. duoformis Craig & Dawson, *Allan Hancock Found. Occ. Papers* 1–2:59 (1948); *MSJ* **8**:94 (1968); *Int. Newer Mamm.* 5 (1973)
Series **Polyacanthae** M. NUNEZII Group

This specific name is at present upheld by Hunt to embrace a variable species, which has given rise to several conspecific names, including *M. hamata*, a poorly described earlier name, but rejected because of the uncertainty of identity, *M. heeriana* nom.nud. (the most popular trade name), *M. erythrocalix* and *M. rossiana*.

It is generally a clustering species with cylindric

stems about 3 or 4 cm in diameter, forming large clumps in time. There are bristles in the axils. Radial spines number about 18 to 20, 5 to 7 mm long, slender, needle-like, straight, orange-tan at base, chalky-white to pale yellow above. Central spines number 4, stronger than radials, 10 to 12 mm long, pinkish-tan below, blackish-brown above, the upper three straight, the lowermost longer and hooked. Flowers are 15 mm long, 12 mm wide, bright crimson with brownish outer petals. Fruit is brownish-pink, seeds brown.

Reported from Puebla on the Puebla to Oaxaca highway near Tehuitzingo, on dry lava slopes facing south, and Guerrero, on the Acapulco highway to Mexico City just west of Tierra Colorado. This form was later described as *M. xaltianguensis*.

M. duoformis

M. durispina Boed., *Zeitschr. Sukk.* **3**:342 with fig. (1928); *MSJ* **8**:95 (1968)
Series **Heterochlorae**   M. POLYTHELE Group
   This is a strong spined, columnar species, described originally as solitary, although in time it will offset from the base; the stems are usually about 5 or 6 cm in diameter. The axils are woolly but have no bristles.

M. durispina

The 6 to 8 radial spines—there are no centrals—vary from about 7 mm long for the lower and lateral spines to a long upper spine, to 15 mm long. They are straight and quite thick, greyish-white, tipped dark red-brown to almost black. Flowers are typical of the group, smallish, to 15 mm long, carmine and appearing in the latter part of the summer. Fruit is greenish-red, seeds pale yellowish-brown.

Reported by Boedeker from the state of Guanajuato and by Craig from the state of Queretaro.

This is a well-known species, presenting no problems in cultivation, best grown in strong light to encourage strong development of the spines, which are its best feature.

Hunt equates *M. kellerana* here.

M. dyckiana Zucc., *Pl. Nov. Monac.* 705 (1837); *MSJ* **9**:8 (1969)
   See under *M. haageana*.

M. ebenacantha Schmoll ex Backeb. (not Shurly), *Die Cact.* **5**:3469 (1961) & **6**:3890 with fig. (1962)
   An invalidly published name, in any case a synonym for *M. karwinskiana*.

M. echinaria DC, *Mem. Mus. Nat. Hist. Paris* **17**:110 (1828); *Cact. Amer.* **43**:5 (1971); *MSJ* **9**:9 (1969)
   The standing of this species has been in doubt for some time, due to its closeness to *M. elongata*. Hunt is of the opinion that because of its distinct appearance, with thicker stems, central spines, and its distribution and ecology, in the open rather than in ravines, where the less strongly spined and generally narrower stemmed *M. elongata* grows, it warrants varietal recognition under *M. elongata*.

M. egregia Backeb., *Die Cact.* **5**:3261 with figs. (1961); *MSJ* **9**:5 (1969); *Int. Newer Mamm.* 6 with fig. (1973)
Series **Lasiacanthae**   M. LASIACANTHA Group
   A beautiful and comparatively rare member of this close-spined series, this species is close in appearance to *M. lasiacantha* and *M. magallanii*. The original description by Backeberg is of a simple plant, to 5 cm tall and wide, with woolly axils, no central spines, radials 50 or more in several series or layers, white tipped pink when young, flower 11 mm long, 8 to 9 mm wide, outer petals white striped pink, inner brownish-olive-greenish white, striped darker in the middle. Fruit and seed were not described.

   The locality was not cited, but this group comes from eastern and north-eastern Mexico, extending into New Mexico in the USA. This is an extremely slow-growing species, most easily distinguishable from others resembling it by the brownish flowers. It will eventually become columnar in cultivation, but for years will be no intrusion on bench-space; a plant of about golf ball size is already at least 7 or 8 years old.

   Hunt allies this species to *M. lasiacantha*.

M. egregia

M. eichlamii Quehl., *Monatsschr. Kakteenk.* **18**:65 (1908); *MSJ* **9**:5 (1969); *Cact. GB.* **39**:100 (1977)
Series **Polyedrae** M. KARWINSKIANA Group

Hunt has suggested that this species, with *M. collinsii*, should be reduced to varietal level within the prior name *M. voburnensis*, but the combination has not yet been made, and it is happily maintained here as it is a distinctive addition to any collection, very easily separated from its companions by the yellow axillary wool, which is its strong feature, as well as its persistent green body colouring, compared with purplish in *M. voburnensis* and copper-brown in *M. collinsii*.

It is heavily clustering, though slower growing than the other two, forming a tallish mound in time with the distinct impression that it might be grafted; individual heads are about 4 or 5 cm across. Axils have white

M. eichlamii

bristles as well as the dense yellow wool already mentioned. There are 7 or 8 radial spines, whitish with brown tips (sometimes brown only at the very tips), 3 to 5 mm long, the lower longer. Central spines occasionally 2, but mostly only 1, reddish-brown for most of their length, darker at the tips, 4 to 5 mm long. The areoles are also prominently woolly with the same yellow wool, especially in youth. Flowers are cream coloured with a dark red stripe down the outer petals, only about 12 mm across. Fruit is red, seeds brown.

Reported from Guatemala, near Sabanetas.

M. ekmanii Werderm., *Repert Spec. Nov.* **29**:242 (1931); *MSJ* **3**:51 (1963)

An unidentified species from Haiti, Ile la Navasse, unknown in cultivation at present.

M. elegans DC, *Rev. Fam. Cact. in Mem. Mus. Hist. Nat. Paris* **17**:111 (1828); *MSJ* **9**:6 (1969); *Cact. GB.* **39**:97 (1977)

The rejection of this well known name is probably the bitterest pill to swallow in David Hunt's recent revision of the genus, but the application of the name has for some time been a source of doubts and confusion, and arguments for its retention are scantily based, prompted more by conservatism than logic. See now under *M. haageana*.

M. elongata DC, 'Rev. Fam. Cact.' in *Mem. Mus. Hist. Nat. Paris* **17**:109 (1828); *MSJ* **9**:9 (1969)
Series **Leptocladodae** M. ELONGATA Group

This species is so variable that collectors have been known to concentrate on getting together various forms of it to the extent of 50 or more different, or nearly different, plants. The thickness of stem is one variable in this species, which forms clusters of finger-like stems, ranging from barely 1 cm across to a thickness of 3 cm or more including the spines. But it is the spine colour which leads to the most variation, varying from almost white, through pale yellow, golden yellow to yellow tipped red-brown, or dark chocolate brown, with every conceivable colour between, and variation too in the number of radial and central spines. The radial spines, usually 15 to 20 in number vary in their placing, sometimes radiating evenly and recurved on to the plant body, sometimes erect and forming a very bristly stem. There are occasionally plants with one or more spines more centrally placed. These thicker stemmed, more spiny plants with one or more central spines are generally allocated to the species *M. echinaria*, which is here regarded as a variety at most of *M. elongata*. Hunt's view is that this is justified, even in such a variable species, because of the distinctly larger growth with more central spines, and more importantly because of its separate distribution and ecology, in open ground rather than in ravines, where the type tends to grow. The flowers vary too with the different forms, but are generally pale yellow to deeper yellow occasionally striped slightly pink, about 1 cm long and wide. Fruit is red, pink at first, seeds light brown.

Reported from a wide area in Hidalgo and Queretaro. See colour plate.

A similar species maintained separately, but tenuously, is *M. mieheana*, although with the acceptance of *M. echinaria* under *M. elongata* there is little reason for maintaining it, except for the reason that it would inevitably disappear completely in view of the variation of *M. elongata*. It may well be the link between *M. elongata* and *M. densispina*, having characteristics of both.

The species *M. sphacelata* (includes *M. viperina*), although superficially similar, is not to be confused here, and can readily be distinguished by its chalk-whitish, brown tipped spines and purple flowers (or its reluctance to flower).

M. elongata

M. elongata (echinaria)

M. erectacantha Foerster, *Allg. Gartenz.* **15**:50 (1847); *Cact. Suc. Mex.* **13**:20 with fig. (1968); *MSJ* **9**:9 (1969)
Series **Heterochlorae** M. DISCOLOR Group

Although this species was described a long time ago

it has been little known in collections, although recently it has become available again. Seed sold in the last few years as *M. kellerana* var. *schmuckeri* has turned out to be this species.

It is described as simple, depressed to globose (becoming shortly columnar in cultivation) with thick, fleshy roots and white, woolly areoles in youth. There is 1 central spine, for which the species is named, erect, 6 to 8 mm long, brownish with dark brown tip, radials vary from 9 to 15 in number, usually 10 or 11, 2 to 6 mm long, white, brown tipped, longer at either side, the upper and lower shorter. Flowers are about 15 mm wide, bright red, contrasting well with the white wool in the growing area. Fruit is red, seed light brown.

Reported by Father Fittkau in the Sierra de Guadalupe and by Sr. Felipe Otero at Tlalnepantla in Hidalgo, both north-east of Mexico City.

Hunt allies this species to *M. wiesingeri*.

M. erectacantha

M. erectohamata Boed., *Monatsschr. Deutsch. Kakt. Gès.* **2**:189 with fig. (1930); *MSJ* **9**:24 (1969)

Hunt equates this species name from the original description with *M. aurihamata*. Plants sometimes seen with this name in the trade are something akin to *M. bocasana* with sparser wool.

M. eriacantha Link & Otto ex Pfeiffer, *Enum. Cact.* 2 (1837); *Beschr. und Synon.* 30 (1837); *Pl. Nov. Monac.* 704 (1837); *MSJ* **9**:24 (1969)
Series **Polyacanthae** M. ERIACANTHA Group

This is a very distinctively spined species which has been distributed widely in the last few years. It is slimly columnar, usually solitary, although it will produce offsets after reaching about 12 cm in height. The spines mark it out from its fellows in the series, being an attractive greenish-yellow and distinctly pubescent. There are 2 straight central spines, pointing up and down, 8 to 10 mm long and a little thicker than the radials, which number 20 to 24 and are pale yellow, about 6 mm long. The flowers are not freely produced and are very small, greenish-yellow, barely protruding beyond the spines. Fruit is reddish-purple, seeds pale brown.

Reported from several localities in the state of Veracruz.

M. eriacantha

M. ernestii Fittkau, *Cact. Suc. Mex.* **16**:36 (1971); *Cact. Amer.* **43**:200 (1971); *MSJ* **15**:38 (1975); *Cact. Amer.* **39**:74 (1977); *Cact. GB.* **39**:74 (1977)

There seems little doubt that this is merely a darker bodied and darker spined form of *M. backebergiana*, and Glass & Foster have recently made the combination—see under that name.

M. erythrocalix Buchenau, *Cact. Suc. Mex.* **11**:17 with fig. (1966); *MSJ* **9**:24 (1969)

Referred to *M. duoformis*.

M. erythrosperma Boed., *Monatsschr. Kakteenk.* **28**:101 with fig. (1918); *MSJ* **9**:25 (1969)
Series **Stylothelae** M. WILDII Group

This is a well-known member of the series, making large clusters of heads each about 4 or 5 cm in diameter and the same in height, and just as rapidly unmaking them with its tendency, reported by several collectors, to disintegrate into mush. The axils have long, hair-like, white bristles, which combine with the 15 to 20 radial spines, similarly white, 8 to 10 mm long, to give the whole plant the appearance of a thinly woolled *M. bocasana*. The central spines number 1 to 3, occasion-

ally 4, reddish-brown in the upper parts with a yellowish base, 1, the lowest, being hooked. Flowers are red to deep dusky pink, 15 mm long and wide, fruit long and pinkish-red, seeds dark reddish-brown.

Reported from San Luis Potosi by Boedeker and by Craig from Alvarez in that state. See colour plate.

M. erythrosperma

M. esaussieri Fric, nom.nud.

A Schmoll catalogue name for plants of *M. densispina* from Queretaro. It is generally applied to forms of this species with all yellow spines.

M. eschanzieri (Coulter) Craig, *Mamm. Handb.* 329 (1945); *Contr. US. Nat. Herb.* **3**:104 (1894) & **3**:1678 (1926); *MSJ* **9**:25 (1969)

After a few years' flirtation with this name Hunt has now discarded it in favour of *M. nana*—see under that name.

M. esperanzaensis Boed., *Mamm. Vergl. Schluss.* 40 (1933); *Cact. Amer.* **43**:75 with figs (1971)

This name is referred to *M. discolor*.

M. esserana Boed., *Zeitschr. Sukk.* **3**:289 with fig. (1928); *MSJ* **9**:26 (1969)

Referred to *M. karwinskiana*.

M. estanzuelensis Moeller ex Berger, *Kakteen* 287 (1929); illus. only *Deutsch. Gartenz.* **51**:218 (1926); *MSJ* **9**:26 (1969)

Referred to *M. candida*.

M. estebanensis Lindsay, *Cact. Amer.* **39**:31 with fig. (1967); *MSJ* **9**:26 (1969)
Series **Ancistracanthae** M. DIOICA Group

This may be just an island form of the ubiquitous *M. dioica* according to Hunt, but it is easily distinguishable with its denser spination. Stems are cylindrical, about 3·5 cm in diameter in cultivation, clustering, axils with wool and bristles. Radial spines number 15 to 22, straight, to 10 mm long, chestnut or gold fading to white. There is 1 central spine, straight or hooked (sometimes both on the same plant), 4 to 15 mm long, chestnut with chocolate coloured tip. Flowers are about 20 mm wide, white, with 5 to 6 light green stigma-lobes. Fruit is 15 to 20 mm long, red, seeds black.

Reported from Baja California, on the island of San Esteban.

Hunt allies this species to *M. dioica*.

M. estebanensis

M. euthele Backeb., *Die Cact.* **5**:3167 (1961)
An invalidly published name, synonymous with *M. melanocentra*.

M. evermanniana (B. & R.) Orcutt, *Cactog.* 7 (1926); *The Cact.* **4**:97 with fig. (1923); *Cact. Amer.* **47**:173 (1975); *MSJ* **9**:26 (1969)
Series **Macrothelae**   M. PETROPHILA Group

M. evermanniana

There has been confusion of this species in the past with the more recently described *M. tayloriorum*, not helped at all by the unfortunate transposition of the captions to the photographs of the two in question when the latter was described in the American journal.

The stem is usually solitary, globose to short thick-columnar, with white wool and bristles in the axils. Radial spines 12 to 15, 8 to 10 mm long, thin, needle-like, chalky white, brown tipped; central spines usually 3, 10 mm long, a little stouter than the radials, similarly coloured. Flowers are yellow, about 1 cm long and wide; fruit is red, seeds brown.

Reported from Cerralbo Island in the Gulf of California.

M. falsicrucigera Backeb., *Die Cact.* **6**:3895 (1962)
A provisional name for what subsequently turned out to be the true *M. crucigera*.

M. fasciculata Engelm. in Emory, *Notes Mil. Reconn.* 156 with fig. (1848); *MSJ* **9**:38 (1969)
A history of confusion with a species, possibly of the genus *Echinocereus* leaves this name in doubt, and the more identifiable name *M. thornberi* seems to have been widely accepted.

M. fera-rubra Schmoll in Craig, *Mamm. Handb.* 309 (1945); *Cact. GB* **39**:74 (1977); *Cact. Suc. Mex.* **21**:36 (1976)
Series **Heterochlorae**   M. RHODANTHA Group
This species is maintained for orange-brown or gingery-red spined plants found in association with *M. rhodantha*. Other species associated are *M. aureiceps* and *M. pringlei*, both with yellow spines. *M. fera-rubra* is generally smaller in height than the others, except perhaps for *M. pringlei*, about 10 cm tall or more, 9 cm wide. Axils have short wool. Radial spines number 12 to 18, 3 to 7 mm long, the upper shorter, straight and white. Central spines number 6, occasionally 7, straight or slightly recurving, orange-brown or

M. fera-rubra

gingery-red, 12 mm long. Flowers are deep purplish-red, about 15 mm long and wide. Fruit is purplish-pink, seeds brown.

Reported from the west side of the valley of Mexico in Queretaro, and in particular from San Lazaro near Acambay in the state of Mexico, Toluca and in Michoacan near Morelia, and from further west near Ciudad Guzman and Tapalpa.

M. fertilis Hildm. ex K. Schum., *Gesamt. Kakt. Nachtrag.* 530 (1898); *MSJ* **9**:39 (1969)

If applied to anything in cultivation today this name is usually found on plants of *M. backebergiana*, which do not accord at all with the plant described as *M. fertilis*. Its application is now indeterminate.

M. fischeri Pfeiff., *Allg. Gartenz.* **4**:257 (1836); *MSJ* **11**:36 (1971)

A synonym of *M. karwinskiana*.

M. fittkaui Glass & Foster, *Cact. Amer.* **43**:115 with figs. (1971); *MSJ* **11**:60 (1971) & **15**:27 (1975); *Cact. GB.* **41**:98 (1979)
Series **Stylothelae**   M. BOMBYCINA Group

A recent species discovered by and named for Father Fittkau. It will undoubtedly pervade collections rapidly as it clusters freely, flowers prolifically and survives rough treatment. The stems are about 5 cm in diameter, offsetting from both the base and the body. The axils have no wool or bristles. Radial spines number 7 to 9, 6 or 7 mm long, fine, white, sometimes barely tipped dark brown. Centrals number 4, the upper 3 lying close to the radials, but thicker, a little longer (to 8 mm) and more brown in the upper part, white to pale yellowish below, the fourth 8 to 10 mm

long, strongly hooked, dark brown except at the very base. Flowers are 1 cm wide, 1·5 cm long, white to pale pink with slightly darker midstripe, especially at the tips of the segments, stigma lobes white. Fruit is small, pale tan, remaining down between the tubercles, seeds are large, very dark brown. It was found on rocks on the north shores of Lake Chapala near Guadalajara in Jalisco, and in the barranca of Guadalajara.

M. flavescens (DC) Haw., *Suppl. Pl. Succ.* 71 (1819); *Cat. Pl. Hort. Monsp.* 83 (1813); *MSJ* **9**:39 (1969)

An insufficiently described species which Hunt equates 'probably' to *M. nivosa*, but which is too indeterminate to take its place as a prior name.

M. flavicentra Backeb., *Descr. Cact. Nov.* **3**:8 (1963); *Kakteenlex.* 238 with fig. (1966); *MSJ* **9**:39 (1969); *Kakt. u. a. Sukk.* **22**:41 (1971)

Dismissed by Hunt as of uncertain status. Backeberg's illustration in the lexicon looks like a juvenile *M. muehlenpfordtii*.

M. flavihamata Backeb., *Die Cact.* **6**:3895 with fig. (1962); *MSJ* **9**:40 (1969)

Hunt refers this name to *M. gilensis*, although the yellow spines suggest *M. sinistrohamata* affinity.

M. flavovirens Salm-Dyck, *Cact. Hort. Dyck.* 1849. 117 (1850); *MSJ* **9**:40 (1969)

One of the many forms of *M. magnimamma*.

M. floresii Backeb., *Blatt. Sukk.* **1**:5 (1949); *Cactus (Paris)* **no. 33**:13 (1952); *MSJ* **8**:57 (1968)

See under *M. canelensis*.

M. formosa Galeotti ex Scheidw., *Bull. Acad. Sci. Brux.* **5**:497 (1838); *MSJ* **9**:81 (1969)
Series **Leucocephalae**   M. SEMPERVIVI Group

Stem is simple, short-cylindrical, axils woolly. Radial spines number 20 to 22 (or a few more), 3 to 6 mm long, thin and white. Central spines number 6,

M. fittkaui

M. formosa

sometimes 4 or 7, to 8 mm long, needle-like, pinkish with black tip, later grey, thicker than radials. Flowers are pale pink with pinkish-purple midstripe, stigmas greenish-yellow. Fruit is red, seeds light brown.

Reported from the state of Guanajuato: San Felipe, also reported from San Luis Potosi and Hidalgo from between Zimapan and Jacala.

M. fragilis Salm-Dyck, *Cact. Hort. Dyck* 1849. 103 (1850); *MSJ* **5**:45 (1965)
Referred to *M. gracilis.*

M. fraileana (B. & R.) Boed., *The Cact.* **4**:157 (1923); *Mamm. Vergl. Schluss.* 30 (1933); *MSJ* **9**:81 (1969).
Series **Ancistracanthae** M. MICROCARPA Group

This species is not well represented in collections, perhaps because it resists attempts to raise it from seed: like some others in this series it damps off easily or succumbs at any time to excess watering. But once the grower accepts that this species will not be hurried without hazard it will make slow, narrowly columnar stems, clustering from the base and sides. Radial spines usually number 11 or 12, 8 to 10 mm long, thin, needle-like and white. Central spines number 3 or 4, 10 mm long, dark brown with one hooked. Flowers are fairly large, to 2·5 cm long and wide, pink with a deeper midstripe, stigma-lobes pink, long and slender. Fruit is lilac-pink, seeds black.

Reported from Baja California, Pichilingue Island, Cerralboa Island, Monserato Island and Catalina Island, and from near La Paz on the mainland opposite Pichilingue Island.

M. fraileana

M. fuauxiana Backeb., *Herb. Bull.* **1**:53 (1950)
A variant of *M. albilanata* with longer central spines.

M. fuliginosa Salm-Dyck, *Cact. Hort. Dyck.* 1849. 93 (1850); *Mamm. Handb.* 257 with fig. (1945); *MSJ* **9**:81 (1969)

Plants seen under this name usually resolve as *M. obconella.*

M. fuscata Link & Otto ex Pfeiff., *Enum. Cact.* 28 (1837); *MSJ* **13**:79 (1973)
See under *M. aureiceps*

M. fuscohamata Backeb., *Die Cact.* **6**:3897 with fig. (1962); *MSJ* **9**:81 (1969); *Int. Newer Mamm.* 7 with fig. (1973)
Hunt equates this invalidly published name with *M. jaliscana.*

M. garessii Cowper, *Cact. Amer.* **42**:14 (1970) & **42**:93 (1970); *MSJ* **15**:21 (1975)
See under *M. barbata.*

M. gasserana Boed., *Zeitschr. Sukk.* **3**:75 with fig. (1927); *MSJ* **10**:17 (1970)
Hunt equates this name with the prior but awkwardly named *M. stella-de-tacubaya*, giving adequate reasons for this, although the rarity of this species in cultivation makes the point a little academic.

M. gasterantha Reppenhagen, *Kakt. u. a. Sukk.* **31**:138 (1980)
Series **Polyacanthae** M. NUNEZII Group

This recently described species is named a little unfortunately for its pot-bellied flower-shape, not unknown in this series already. It was described as simple at first, later offsetting from the base and sides. Globose at first, later short-columnar, with dense wool and spines at the growing tip, and dull green body-colour, and bare axils. Radial spines number 13 to 16, 2 to 6 mm long, fine, straight, the upper the shortest, white. Central spines are 2 to 4 in number, usually 2, 5 to 10 mm long, needle-like, straight, the upper shorter, the lower sometimes hooked, brown with lighter base. Flowers only partly opening, with the petals fused together, 14 to 18 mm long, 7 to 10 mm wide at the opening, shining carmine. Fruit is red-brown, self-fertile, seeds brown.

Reported from west of Iguala in northern Guerrero at 1,600 m altitude on south-east facing slopes with some shrubby vegetation, in humus where there is some shade for part of the day. Reppenhagen's field number 934 is this species.

M. gatesii M. E. Jones, *Cact. Amer.* **8**:99 with fig. (1937); *MSJ* **10**:19 (1970)
Hunt places this species under *M. baxterana* from which it differs in clustering more readily and in having less radial spines (6 to 8) and centrals (only 1), the latter longer, up to 3 cm long.

M. gaumeri (B. & R.) Orcutt, *The Cact.* **4**:72 with figs. (1923); *Cactog.* 7 (1926); *MSJ* **10**:19 (1970)
Series **Macrothelae** M. HEYDERI Group
This is not a very well-known species in collections,

but has been available recently from nurseries. Stem is flattened-globose to short-cylindric, with naked axils. Radial spines number 10 to 12, sometimes up to 20, 5 to 7 mm long, white with brown tips, or the lower darker. One central spine to 10 mm long, usually brown. Flowers are creamy white to pinkish-white, 10 to 14 mm long. Fruit is crimson, seeds brown.

Reported from Yucatan, Progreso in rocky scrubland and open places, sometimes growing half-buried in sand in dunes on the seashore, from between Merida and Progreso.

Hunt allies this species to *M. heyderi* var. *meiacantha*.

M. gaumeri

M. geminispina Haw., *Phil. Mag.* **63**:42 (1824); *MSJ* **10**:20 (1970)
Series **Leucocephalae** M. GEMINISPINA Group

This well-known, lovely white-spined species typifies the variability of species in this genus, as regards the spine length in particular; the forms with longer central spines tend to be the more sought after. It will form massive clumps eventually, as seen in the Huntington Botanical Gardens. The stems are short-columnar, about 8 cm in diameter and up to 18 cm tall, with woolly axils. Radial spines number about 16 to 20, chalky white, 5 to 7 mm long, interlacing to give the whole plant a white appearance, from a distance looking like clusters of paradoxical snow in the desert. The 2 central spines are more robust and usually much longer, up to 4 cm or more, standing out strongly from the plant body, white tipped dark brown. Flowers, which are sometimes reluctant to oblige in England, are deep pink with darker midstripe, about 15 mm long and wide. Fruit is red, seeds brown.

Reported from Ixmiquilpan, Zimapan, Venados and Mineral del Monte, in Hidalgo and Tampico, Veracruz. But most plants in cultivation under this name are from the Barranca of Metztitlan. (See colour plate.)

M. geminispina

M. gigantea Hildm., *Gesamt. Kakt.* 578 (1898); *MSJ* **10**:20 (1970)
Series **Macrothelae** M. PETTERSSONII Group

This well named species has solitary heads which attain the size of half a football, and a good sized specimen is an impressive sight among its smaller brethren. I have never seen a clustering plant, although the original description allowed for this. Axils are woolly. Radial spines number about 12, to 3 mm long and white. Central spines are strong, 4 to 6 in number, the lower longest, to 2 cm long, dark yellowish to reddish purple with dark brown to black tip, later greyish. Flowers are greenish, creamy yellow with dark red midstripes to the petals, 15 mm long and wide. Fruit is purplish-pink, seeds brown.

Reported from Guanajuato between Queretaro and San Luis Potosi, on rocky hillsides. Hunt equates *M. armatissima* and *M. hastifera* to this species.

M. gigantea

M. gilensis Boed. in Backeb. & Knuth, *Kaktus ABC*, 385 (1935); *Jahrb. Deutsch. Kakt. Ges.* **1**:60 with fig. (1936); *MSJ* **10**:21 (1970); *Cact. GB.* **39**:71 (1977)

The plant originally described under this name bears little resemblance to those generally grown as the species today. As expounded by Hunt (last reference above) Boedeker's original illustrations of *M. gilensis*, *M. posseltiana* and *M. rettigiana* show probably one and the same species, which by priority would take the name of *M. rettigiana*. Certainly the illustration accompanying this article, reproduced from Boedeker's original, of *M. gilensis* shows much more than the description that plants more usually under this name are wrongly identified.

M. glareosa Boed., *Mamm. Vergl. Schluss.* **59** (1933); *Cact. Amer.* **7**:88 (1935); *MSJ* **10**:30 (1970)
Series **Macrothelae**   M. BRANDEGEI Group

Above ground this species makes a flat ball-shaped plant, with thick, fleshy roots below ground. The tubercles are distinctly 4-angled, the axils woolly. Radial spines are about 9 or 10 up to 6 mm long, the upper 2 or 3 thin and whitish, the lower thicker and brown. There is 1 central spine, 6 mm long, brown. Flowers are 12 mm long, pale greenish-yellow with reddish-brown midstripe on the outer petals. Fruit is light pink, white below, seeds reddish-brown. *M. dawsonii* is referred here by Hunt.

Reported from Baja California near the coast at around latitude 28°50′ south-west of Punta Prieta and at Punta Blanca, at Santa Rosalillita Bay, deep-seated in silty flats.

Hunt allies this species to *M. brandegei*.

M. glareosa

M. glassii Foster, *Cact. Amer.* **40**:132 with fig. (1968); *MSJ* **10**:30 (1970)
Series **Stylothelae**   M. GLASSII Group

This heavily clustering, small-headed species has rapidly invaded collections since its introduction,

because of its ease of propagation from the numerous offsets produced and its self fertility. Its dense white spination and characteristic small globular heads, only about 2 cm in diameter, make it unmistakable, but for the record the detail is as follows: axils with 20 or 30 white, hairlike, fine bristles; radial spines 50 to 60, 10 to 15 mm long, white, hairlike and interlacing; 6 to 8 subcentral spines hardly distinguishable from the radials, 4 to 5 mm long, pale golden amber, the 1 central spine similar; flowers to 14 mm long and 3 to 5 mm wide, pale pink and freely produced, followed by unusually shaped fruits, evenly tapered at both ends, fusiform, purple-pink; seeds black.

Reported from Nuevo Leon, near the town of Dieciocho de Marzo, 'near the rim of a deep canyon in full shade with good drainage'. In cultivation it certainly seems to prefer a position out of the worst excesses of the sun, although our poor English sun is rarely a danger, and some hours of sunshine a day may be allowed without real risk. The recent description of *M. ascensionis* by Reppenhagen was rapidly reduced by Glass and Foster to varietal level beneath *M. glassii*, although perhaps *forma* would have been more appropriate. It differs only in fewer axillary hairs, a more rounded apex to the stems, slightly woolly areoles, longer central spines and most noticeably larger flowers, 18 to 27 mm wide.

The plant with Lau's collection number 1186 is a worthy variation to this species, yet to be described, with well coloured, mid-pink large flowers and other forms have recently been found. (See colour plate.)

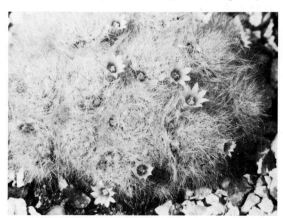

M. glassii

M. glochidiata Mart., *Nov. Act. Nat. Cur.* **16**:337 plate 23 (1832); *MSJ* **10**:31 (1970)
Series **Stylothalae**   M. WILDII Group

Hunt expresses doubts on whether the plants grown today under this name correspond with the original description, since there is a discrepancy, mainly in the flower, described originally as having greenish-reddish or yellowish outer petals, the inner petals white. Cultivated plants have invariably light pink flowers, about 12 mm across. In other respects plants in collections seem to accord with the original description—densely clustering to make a tallish mound with characteristically weak spines, axils with bristles, radial spines 12 to 15, about 12 mm long, white, bristle-like, thin, central spines minutely pubescent, similar to the radials but a little longer, 3 or 4 in number, 1 standing more upright and hooked, the other spreading, brownish. Flowers as above; fruit is deep red, seeds black. Not surprisingly the locality for this species is also confused, being reported shortly after its description by Zuccarini from the state of Oaxaca, near San Pedro Nolasco, but later it was said to come from Hidalgo.

M. glochidiata

M. glomerata (Lam.) DC, _Encycl._ **1**:537 (1783); _Prodr._ **3**:459 (1828); _MSJ_ **10**:31 (1970)

Hunt refers this name to _M. ekmanii_, itself a dubiously determinable species.

M. goldii Glass & Foster, _Cact. Amer._ **40**:151 (1968) & **51**:123 (1979); _MSJ_ **10**:31 (1970) & **19**:18 (1979); _Cact. GB._ **41**:97 (1979)

Series **Longiflorae** M. SABOAE Group

The reduction of this name to varietal level by Rowley and form level by Glass and Foster under _M. saboae_, has been declared invalid by Hunt referring to Article 33.2 of the _International Code of Botanical Nomenclature_. It is therefore maintained here, for the present at least, as a good species. This is yet another of the marvellous discoveries made in the last ten years or so, of large-flowered, tiny-spined _Mammillaria_ species, and this at a time when many collectors probably considered that there could be nothing new of interest to be found. It is a real miniature, with reluctantly clustering stems only about 3 cm in diameter and barely as tall, with thick carrot-like roots and naked axils. There are no central spines, and the 35 to 45 radials are tiny, 2 to 3 mm long, glassy white, radiating evenly around prominent areoles coloured golden-yellow. The flowers are out of all proportion to

the tiny plant, being about 3.5 cm long and broad, set up well above the body on a slender tube and coloured lilac-pink, with whitish stigma-lobes. The fruit remains embedded in the stem, with quite large, black seeds.

This wonderful addition to the genus was rediscovered by Dudley Gold, who led Charles Glass to the spot where he recalled seeing the plants some 50 years before, in Sonora, a few miles north of Nacozari on the road to Agua Prieta, in volcanic tuff, fully exposed to the sun, but nearly covered with pebbles of tuff. When in flower in habitat the impression is of crocus flowers pushing up through the ground, so abundantly do the flowers appear from the almost submerged plants.

It is a more demanding plant to grow well than _M. saboae_ and var. _haudeana_, much more leisurely in its growth, and liable to go off its roots if excessive watering in an attempt to hasten it is applied. It is a plant where the insurance of a plant on a graft in addition to one on its own roots is advisable.

M. goldii

M. goodridgii Scheer emend Salm-Dyck, _Cact. Hort. Dyck_ 1849:91 (1850) (as _M. goodrichii_); _Bot. Voy. Herald_, 286 (1856); _Cact. Amer._ **24**:78, 80 (1952); _MSJ_ **10**:32 (1970)

Series **Ancistracanthae** M. MICROCARPA Group

This name tends to be somewhat random in its application in collections, and the plant pictured is only one of two I have seen which conform to the description. There is too a straight-spined form, named as var. _rectispina_ Dawson. Plants under this name in cultivation often seem to be _M. sheldonii_ or similar. It is not an easy plant to grow to any size, as the roots are sparse, like many in the series, and susceptible to too much water. Stems are about 3 or 4 cm in diameter and a little taller, with coarsely woolly axils, and clustering readily from the base. Radial spines number 11 to 15, 4 to 7 mm long, chalky white, tipped dark brown, straight. Central spines number 4, to 10 mm long; one, the longest, is hooked (sometimes straight—var. *rectispina*), white, brownish-black in the upper part. Flowers, to about 2·5 cm across, are white with a wide, indistinct, purple-pink stripe, and are freely produced. Fruit is scarlet or orange, seeds black.

There is a low growing form of *M. blossfeldiana* (see photograph) which differs in habit, colour of spines and number of spines, owing more to *M. goodridgii* than *M. blossfeldiana* except in the flowers, which are large and sumptuous in the manner of the latter. This may represent a transition between the two, which occur on the same latitude, with *M. blossfeldiana* on the coast of Baja California at Punta Prieta, and *M. goodridgii* on islands just off the coast—Cedros and Guadalupe. There is a suggestion too in this species of *M. louisiae*, but until recollection takes place extensively in the area in Baja California, including the islands, the position of these species one with another will remain in doubt.

Reported from Baja California, on the islands of Cedros and Guadalupe.

M. goodridgii

M. gracilis Pfeiff., *Allg. Gartenz.* **6**:275 (1838); *Linnaea* **19**:351 (1846); *MSJ* **5**:65 (1965) & **10**:71 (1970)
Series **Proliferae** M. GRACILIS Group

This charming, diminutive-headed species is probably the most widely grown *Mammillaria* in collections, and probably the most neglected. Like *M. prolifera* and *M. yaquensis* it is almost impossible to re-pot without finishing the operation with half the plant in separate pieces, and the consequent distribution is inevitably very widespread, since cactus collectors tend to be soft-hearted and reluctant to dispose too cruelly of surplus plants. The species is divided into two varieties, within which there is some minor variation: var. *gracilis*, the type, which is the chalky-white-spined variety with larger heads than the other, rarely more than 2 to 2·5 cm in diameter, but reaching up to 13 cm in height, though this is not apparent from

the dense clustering habit. Radial spines are about 6 mm long, chalk-white, about 16 in number, centrals up to 5, but only on mature growth, tipped dark brown, and about 10 mm long. Flowers generally do not appear before there are central spines present, and are small, cream-coloured with a brownish midstripe. Fruit is whitish, showing the black seeds through the almost transparent walls of the berries.

Reported from Hidalgo, Puente de Dios, at Metztitlan and Zimapan, and later from Ixmiquilpan and Tolantonga in Queretaro.

M. gracilis var. *gracilis*

Var. *pulchella* Salm-Dyck, *Cact. Hort. Dyck.* 1849. 103 (1850), has a more slender habit, with stems up to 2 cm in diameter and up to 5 cm tall. There are no central spines, and 11 to 16 radials, white, but not chalky-white, the upper 2 or 3 brownish. Flowers, fruit and seed are similar to the type. There are in addition two interesting forms of this species: a cristate and a sort of monstrose form with, it appears, double the ration of spines on each areole.

M. gracilis var. *pulchella*

M. graessnerana Boed., *Monatsschr. Kakt.* **30**:84 with fig. (1920); *MSJ* **10**:72 (1970)
Series **Supertextae** M. SUPERTEXTA Group

This is not a common species in collections, and is prone to rot off in the first few years from seed. It is however immediately recognizable with its clustering habit and woolly appearance, with the yellow to red-brown central spines giving it an overall attractive colouring. The wool is predominant and is present in both areoles and axils, especially in the younger growth. Radial spines number 18 to 20, 6 to 8 mm long, the lateral spines being longer, needle-like and glassy white. Central spines number 2, occasionally 4, thicker than the radials, 8 mm long, dark red-brown, paler at the base. Flowers are small, purplish-pink. Fruit is small and red, seeds brown. Hunt expresses some doubt as to the separate standing of this name, as its locality or even its occurrence in the wild is unproven.

Hunt allies this species to *M. columbiana*.

M. graessnerana

M. grahamii Engelm., *Proc. Amer. Acad.* **3**:262 (1857); *Cact. Bound.* 7. pl 6 with figs. (1858)
Referred to *M. microcarpa*.

M. grusonii Runge, *Gartenflora* **38**:105 with fig. (1889); *MSJ* **4**:37 (1964) & **10**:72 (1970)
Series **Macrothelae** M. HEYDERI Group

This usually solitary stemmed species can get very large for this genus, reaching 25 cm in diameter, and for many years staying globular, eventually becoming thick-columnar. The light green tubercles are 4-angled, and axils woolly at first, later naked. Radial spines number about 14, straight, 6 to 8 mm long, the upper shorter, reddish becoming white in age. Central spines number 2, occasionally 3, 4 to 6 mm long similar

to the radials but stronger, projecting upwards and downwards. Flowers are light yellow, 2·5 cm long and wide, open bell-shaped. Fruit is scarlet, seeds brown.

Reported from Coahuila, Sierra Bola.

Hunt refers to this species the names *M. mexicensis* and 'probably' *M. pachycylindrica*.

M. grusonii

M. gueldemanniana Backeb., *Beitr. Sukk.* **1**:57 (1941)

Although this name is seen fairly frequently in collections, it is very often applied to plants of *M. sheldonii*. The description was of a clustering species with narrow stems about 5 cm in diameter and up to 10 cm tall, with naked axils. Radial spines number 20 or 21, whitish, about 6 mm long. Central spine only 1, short, about 2 mm long, dark brown to blackish. Flowers white, with light pink edges to the petals and a carmine-pink throat. Fruit scarlet, seeds black. Var.

M. gueldemanniana?

guirocobensis (Craig) Backeb. differs in having 1 to 3 central spines, 1 hooked, reddish-brown, and flowers 2 cm long, more widely bell-shaped.

The identity of either is uncertain.

Reported from Sonora, near Alamos, north-east Sinaloa and south-west Chihuahua.

Hunt allies the species to *M. sheldonii*.

M. guelzowiana Werderm., *Zeitschr. Sukk.* **3**:356 with fig. (1928); *MSJ* **7**:10 (1967) & **10**:72 (1970); *Kakt. u. a. Sukk.* **22**:1 (1971)
Series **Ancistracanthae** M. GUELZOWIANA Group

The large, brilliantly coloured flowers of this species make it among the most sought after species in the genus, and, as is the way of things, its propensity to collapse if overwatered leads to very few mature, large specimens being seen. It is perhaps a good idea to have an additional seedling plant a few years younger than the main representative in a collection, as a re-placement; if the larger should happen to survive for a long time it is in any case a very acceptable species to have two of.

Stems slowly cluster from the base, and are flat-globular with naked axils. Radial spines are numerous, 60 to 80, white and hairlike, up to 1·5 cm long, giving the plants a characteristic fluffy appearance, very similar to more densely spined forms of *M. bocasana*. Central spines vary from 1 to 3, 4 to 11 mm long, one or more hooked and longer, 11 to 16 mm, reddish or yellowish (usually called var. *splendens*), and smooth,

M. guelzowiana

the straight spines coloured only at the tip. The flowers are the largest in the genus, nearly 5 cm long and 6 cm wide, intensely bright purplish-red, a little lighter coloured in yellow-spined plants. The fruit is small, almost globose, remaining close set between the tubercles, pinkish-red in red-spined and yellowish in yellow-spined plants, with black seed.

Reported from Durango, 'on grassy mountain tops' along the Rio Nazas valley west of highway 45.

The name var. *splendens* has no significance, other than as a means of differentiating between red and yellow central spined forms. (See colour plate.)

M. guerreronis (Bravo) Boed., *An. Inst. Biol. Mex.* **3**:395 with figs. (1932); *Cact. Amer.* **42**:128 (1970) & **43**:201 with fig. (1971); *MSJ* **10**:73 (1970)
Series **Polyacanthae** M. NUNEZII Group

This is a species commonly seen as a small plant in English collections, but rarely as a large one, as it shows its dislike of our winters firstly by marking badly with 'cold spots', orange-brown marks, and often secondly by collapsing altogether, unless a temperature of 10°C (50°F) can be maintained as a minimum. Even when grown successfully it shows a marked reluctance to flower here too, and the specimen pictured is the only one that I am aware has flowered in England. It makes cylindrical stems in clusters, each to 6 cm in diameter and up to 60 cm long in habitat. It grows in the state of Guerrero, in the Canon del Zopilote (Buzzard Canyon), where it is sometimes found hanging from the steep sides of the canyon with the weight of the stem pulling the base downwards and only the growing tip looping upwards, but it is generally an unusually erect species for the series.

M. guerreronis

There are 15 to 20 bristles in the axils, radial spines number 20 to 30, 5 to 10 mm long, white and bristle-like, and 4 central spines longer and stouter than the radials, white or slightly pinkish, tipped pale brown, up to 1·5 cm long, 1 sometimes more or less strongly hooked, but often all straight. Flowers are red or a 'lively tannish-pink' in the style of close relatives of *M. spinosissima*. Fruit is greenish-white, becoming pink, seeds brown.

Reported by Hunt from personal investigation that straight and hooked spine plants freely intermingle in the canyon, and on this basis he rejects Craig's varieties *recta* and *subhamatam*. On the same grounds the names '*zapilotensis*' or '*zopilotensis*' have no relevance.

M. guiengolensis Bravo (ex MacDougall), *An. Inst. Biol. Mex.* **32**:187 with figs. (1962); *Cact. Amer.* **38**:24 with fig. (1966) & **43**:202 with figs. (1971); *MSJ* **10**:73 (1970)

This name is referred to *M. beneckei*.

M. guillauminiana Backeb. (not *M. guillaumeniana* Lem., which is a synonym of *M. decipiens*), *Cactus (Paris)* **no. 33** suppl. 2:81 (1952); *Die Cact.* **5**:3450 with fig. (1961); *MSJ* **10**:74 (1970)
Series **Stylothelae**   M. BOMBYCINA Group

Hunt expresses the opinion that this species in this muddled group may be referrable to synonymy with *M. mercadensis* along with *M. sinistrohamata*.

M. guillauminiana

Although described as solitary, this is, like all this group, a clustering species forming low mounds of flattened heads about 3 to 5 cm in diameter. The axils are naked. Radial spines about 30 to 32, white, bristle-like, 6 to 7 mm long, centrals 4 or 5, up to 6 mm long, lowermost hooked with brownish tip, paler at base. Flower is 1 cm long, 8 to 10 mm wide, petals white with pale olive-green midstripe on the outer petals and a prominent rose midstripe on the inner petals giving an overall pink flower when open. Fruit is red, seeds black.

Reported from Durango, 60 km east (or west?) of Durango itself, in humus amongst rocks in the shade; also reported from El Salto, by Schwarz. (See colour plate.)

M. guirocobensis Craig, *Mamm. Handb.* 220 with fig. (1945)
Referred to *M. gueldemanniana*.

M. gummifera Engelm, Wislizenus *Mem. Tour. North Mex.* 105 (1848); *MSJ* **11**:8 (1971)
Referred to *M. heyderi*.

M. haageana Pfeiff., *Allg. Gartenz.* **4**:257 (1836); *MSJ* **9**:8 (1969)
Series **Supertextae**   M. SUPERTEXTA Group

There is little doubt that this is the name we should apply to plants hitherto labelled as *M. elegans*. This latter name has been discarded by Hunt as confused. The well known and well documented variability of '*M. elegans*' more than allows for the submergence of the other names ascribed by Hunt to this species under *M. haageana*, viz. *M. acanthophlegma*, *M. albidula*, *M. collina*, *M. conspicua*, *M. dealbata*, *M. donatii*, *M. dyckiana*, *M. meissneri* and *M. elegans* var. *schmollii*. It is often a solitary stemmed plant in cultivation, occasionally clustering in age, from 5 to 10 cm wide and up to 15 cm tall in the broader stemmed types. The axils are woolly, especially in youth and sometimes have bristles. Radial spines number 18 to 30, smooth and white, 3 to 6 mm long, shining. Central spines vary in colour from black through brown to red-brown, usually 2 in number, but varying from 1 to 4, straight to a little recurved, 6 to 10 mm long or more. The flowers are small, deep purplish-pink, about 10 mm long and wide. Fruit is red, seeds light brown.

M. haageana

As to be expected the species is reported from a wide area in Puebla and Oaxaca, particularly from Tehuacan, Puebla. It seems sensible in such a widely variable species to retain the more distinctive forms for the benefit of collectors, and by the time this book is published this is likely to have been done by Hunt in a revised species list at present in preparation.

M. haageana (conspicua)

Likely candidates for retention are *M. haageana* var. *schmollii*, already retained by Hunt for narrow-stemmed, clustering plants with red-brown to almost black central spines, formerly known as either *M. meissneri* or *M. elegans* var. *schmollii*; and the thick columnar plants with brown to orange-brown centrals under the name *conspicua* at either variety or form level, former names associated here would be *M. conspicua*, of course, and the plant often labelled *M. vaupelii* (but nothing like this doubtful species'

M. haageana var. *schmollii*

description) with strikingly orange-brown spines in youth, becoming yellowish-brown. The type of *M. haageana* is the plant we have known for years as *M. elegans*, with reddish-brown to black central spines.

M. haehneliana Boed., *Kakteenk.* 27 with fig. (1934); *Cact. Amer.* **42**:267 with fig. (1970); *MSJ* **10**:88 (1970)

Hunt equates this name possibly to *M. nana*, which although a later name is more positively identifiable.

M. hahniana Werderm., *Monatsschr. Deutsch. Kakt. Ges.* **1**:77 with fig. (1929); *Cact. Amer.* **1**:127 (1930); *MSJ* **10**:88 (1970)

Series **Leucocephalae** M. GEMINISPINA Group

Most collectors come across this species early in their collecting, and have a clear idea of what is to be expected from plants bearing this name: a globular, densely hairy, usually solitary plant, which will cluster if you are lucky, bearing deep purplish-red contrasting flowers freely.

Conversely it was described as mostly caespitose, although in England this tends to be the rarer form, most staying solitary for many years. The body size was described as individually to 9 cm tall, 10 cm wide; again those which stay solitary make far bigger individual stems, to 20 cm or more tall and about 12 cm wide. Axils have white wool and 20 or more bristles to 4 cm long. Radial spines number 20 to 30, 5 to 15 mm long, white, fine and hair-like, mingling with the axillary bristles to form a dense covering. Central spines number 1 to 5, 4 to 8 mm long, easily falling when older, white tipped reddish-brown, straight, thicker than the radials; flowers to 2 cm wide, purplish-red, with transparent margins to the petals. Fruit is reddish-purple, seed brown.

Reported from Guanajuato and Queretaro, from the Sierra de Jalapa and Ocotitlan.

Hunt takes the view that the species includes several others: *M. bravoae*, *M. mendeliana* and *M. woodsii* as well as *M. hahniana* vars. *giseliana* and *werdermanniana*. Whatever happens taxonomically collectors are unlikely to accept complete dismissal of some of these names, since there is considerable difference between some of them, and it would indeed be a dissatisfied customer who ordered from a nursery *M. hahniana* because of its long-haired beauty, and who received the considerably shorter tonsured *M. woodsii* or almost hairless *M. mendeliana*. *M. woodsii* is probably the best candidate for retention of these hangers-on; it is often encountered in collections and it is an exceedingly handsome and popular species.

It was described as simple, occasionally offsetting late in life, flattened globular to thick-columnar, 8 cm wide or wider in good growing conditions, axils with dense white wool, especially in the growing area, and numerous white, hair-like bristles up to 25 mm long. Radial spines 25 to 30, 4 to 8 mm long, fine, hair-like, white and somewhat twisting. Central spines are mostly 2, occasionally 3 or 4, the lower to 16 mm long, upper 4 to 5 mm long, slender, needle-like, straight or with slight recurve, chalky, purplish-pink with black

M. hahniana

tip. Flowers are 10 to 12 mm long, 12 to 15 mm wide, inner petals with dark pink midstripe and pink margins, outer petals brownish, with dark pink midstripe and paler margins. Fruit is deep pink, seeds brown.

Reported from Guanajuato, Hacienda de Tarajeas (also the locality for *M. mendeliana*). (See colour plate.)

M. hahniana (woodsii)

M. halbingeri Boed., *Kakteenk.* **9** (1933); *MSJ* **9**:8 (1969)

Hunt discards this species as of uncertain status.

Plants raised from seed under this name have not hitherto had the required yellow flowers.

M. halei T. S. Brandegee, *Proc. Calif. Acad.* **2**:161 (1889); *Cact. Journ.* **2**:50 (1899); B. & R., *The Cact.* **4**:22 (1923); *MSJ* **13**:60 (1973)

Subgenus **Cochemiea**

Splitters may object to the inclusion of species of the genus *Cochemiea*, but it should be borne in mind that more than one of them started life as a *Mammillaria*, and Hunt gives good reasons for their inclusion as a subgenus following Mrs K. Brandegee's placing at this level. They will, whatever happens in the future, remain closely linked to *Mammillaria*, and it is appropriate to include them in this book—there is unlikely to be a book on *Cochemiea*!

This species makes clusters of stems each up to 50 cm tall and to 7·5 cm wide—clusters 1 or 2 m wide appear in the wild. The axils are very woolly. Radial spines have been recorded numbering from 10 to 21, 12 mm long, coloured light brown to pinkish-grey. Central spines number 3 or 4, 25 mm long and straight, similar to but stronger than the radials; this is the only *Cochemiea* with consistently straight centrals. Flowers are 2·5 to 5 cm long, stamens exserted, all parts scarlet, the petals forming a long tube before rolling back at the tips in characteristic fashion for the subgenus. Fruit is red, seeds black.

M. halei

Reported from Magdalena Island off the west coast of Baja California in sandy flats and on rocky hillsides in full sun.

M. hamata Lehm., *Enum. Cact.* 34 (1837); *MSJ* **8**:94 (1968)

Hunt rejects this poorly described species as of uncertain identity.

M. hamiltonhoytea (Bravo) Werderm., *Neue Kakt.* 99 (1931); *An. Inst. Biol. Mex.* **2**:130 with figs. (1931); *MSJ* **10**:89 (1970)

Hunt equates this species with *M. petterssonii*, although in his discussion in the *Mammillaria Society Journal* he compares it with *M. gigantea*. This indicates no inconsistency, however, as both these recognized species have close affinities with each other, and the margins between them become blurred. It was compared by Dra. Bravo, for good measure, with *M. johnstonii*. Plants from seed under this name are inseparable from *M. gigantea*.

M. hastifera Krainz & Keller, Schweiz, *Gart.* 11 with fig. (1946); *MSJ* **10**:90 (1970)

See under *M. gigantea*.

M. haudeana Lau & Wagner, *Kakt. u. a. Sukk.* **29**:250 (1978); *MSJ* **19**:21 (1979)

See under *M. saboae*.

M. heidiae Krainz, *Kakt. u. a. Sukk.* **26**:217 with fig. (1975); *Cact. Amer.* **48**:232 (1976); *Cact. GB* **41**:97 (1979)

Subgenus **Dolichothele**

This recently described species shares with only *M. carretii* and *M. surculosa* in this subgenus hooked central spines. It makes clusters of flat, globular heads, each about 5·5 cm wide and 3 cm tall. Axils have 1 to 5 thin, white bristles, up to 10 mm long. Radial spines number 16 to 24, straight but flexuous, to 11 mm long, glassy white, thin. There is usually only 1 central spine, rarely 2, about 12 mm long, hooked, yellow at base to brown at the tip, a little stronger than the

radials, but still flexuous, flowers to 3 cm long and 2·5 cm wide, yellow-green with prominent green stigma-lobes. Fruit is greenish, later brownish, seeds black.

Reported from an area north of the village of Acatlan in Puebla, at 1,300 m altitude.

Although it has not as yet been readily available its affinities suggest this will not long be the case. I am indebted for the photograph of this species to Helmut Broogh.

M. hemisphaerica Engelm., *Boston Journ. Nat. Hist.* **6**:198 (1850); *MSJ* **11**:7 (1971)

Referred to *M. heyderi* as a variety.

M. hennissii Boed., *Monatsschr. Deutsch. Kakt. Ges.* **4**:7 with fig. (1932); *MSJ* **8**:79 (1968)

Referred to *M. columbiana*.

M. herrerae Werderm., *Notizbl. Bot. Gart. Mus. Berlin* **11**:276 (1931); *Monatsschr. Deutsch Kakt. Ges.* **3**:247 with fig. (1931); *MSJ* **5**:18 (1965) & **11**:8 (1971) & **19**:4 (1979); *Kakt. u. a. Sukk.* **21**:221 (1970)

Series **Lasiacanthae** M. LENTA Group

This has remained since its discovery one of the choicest and most beautiful species of *Mammillaria* to grow. As is the way of things it is also difficult to grow well for any length of time, and reluctant to flower in this country, except where there are very sunny conditions. It makes ball-shaped stems, 2 to 3 cm wide, eventually clustering from the base, with many small tubercles completely hidden by the dense covering of snow-white spines. These are all radial and number 100 or more, unequal in length, about 1·5 mm long and bristle-like. Axils are naked. Flowers are large and showy when produced, to about 2·5 cm long and wide, clear pink, with green stigma-lobes. Fruit is described as whitish, seeds black.

The variety—var. *albiflora* Werderm.—differs in a more columnar habit, narrower stems, clustering randomly from the base and body, and with 60 to 80

M. heidiae

M. herrerae

white spines in the same habit (lying flat to the plant body), and of course white flowers, with a brown midstripe on the outer petals (See colour plate). Seeds of either are rarely offered, most plants in collections being imports from the wild. If difficulty in establishing this species on its own roots is met, grafting may be resorted to with advantage, and with careful watering and an open compost the character can be maintained.

Reported from Queretaro, near Cadereyta, and San Luis Potosi.

M. hertrichiana Craig, *Mamm. Handb.* 92 with figs. (1945); *MSJ* **14**:48 (1974); *Cact. GB* **33**:68 (1971)
Series **Macrothelae** M. STANDLEYI Group

Hunt refers this species to *M. standleyi* in his 'Review of Mammillaria Names in Common Usage' in the *Mammillaria Society Journal*, but maintains it in his paper 'Schumann & Buxbaum Reconciled'.

It is a clustering species after a few years, with individual heads about 6 or 7 cm across, flattened globular with slightly sunken apex. The axils have white wool, more plentiful in the growing area and an occasional bristle. Radial spines number 12 to 15, 3 to 10 mm long, the upper shorter, all slender, needle-like, white to pale tan with brown tip. Central spines are 4 or 5, uppers 5 to 10 mm long, lower to 25 mm long and heavier, chestnut brown. Flowers are 18 mm wide, 10 mm long, deep pink to purplish-pink, vividly coloured. Fruit is scarlet, seeds light brown. Plants distributed recently under the number *Lau 086* equate here.

Reported from Sonora, the Rancho el Agriminsor, east of Tesopaco.

M. hertrichiana

M. heyderi Muehlenpf., *Allg. Gartenz.* **16**:20 (1848); *MSJ* **11**:8 (1971); Weniger, *Cacti of the South-West* 152 (1972)
Series **Macrothelae** M. HEYDERI Group

Hunt disputes Benson's placing of the species associated here under *M. gummifera*, and maintains the name *M. heyderi* as the specific epithet to embrace those listed below. Benson subsequently retracted his suggestion. One wonders how much more rationalization of this sort could be done with extensive fieldwork on this genus, so full of specific names.

The species resolves as follows: *M. heyderi* var. *heyderi*—(syn. *M. applanata*): globose or somewhat flattened, axils with wool in youth. Radial spines 15 to 22, white with brown tips, bristle-like, the lower stouter and longer, 1 central spine, light yellowish-grey to brown at base and tip, about 6 mm long. Flowers cream with brownish-pink or greenish midstripe. Fruit is red, seeds reddish-brown.

M. heyderi var. *heyderi*

Reported from Texas and New Mexico in the USA, and Tamaulipas, Nuevo Leon and Chihuahua in Mexico, in particular from San Antonio and New Braunfels, west to El Paso in Texas, north to Carlsbad in New Mexico, south to Monterrey, Nuevo Leon, east to Matamores, Tamaulipas.

var. *gummifera* (Engelm.) Benson (syn. *M. gummifera*

M. heyderi var. *gummifera*

Engelm. in Wislizenus, *Mem. Tour North Mex.* 105. 1848)

Stem flattened-globose, 8 to 12 cm in diameter, axils white woolly in youth. Radial spines 10 to 12, white with brownish or blackish tips, the lower stouter and longer, often to 2·5 cm long and a little recurved, central spines 1 or 2, sometimes 4, brown with black tips. Flowers 3 cm long, 12 to 25 mm wide when fully open, brownish-red outside, inner petals reddish-white with dark red midstripe. Fruit is scarlet, seeds dark brown.

Reported from Cosihuiriachi in Chihuahua.

var. *hemisphaerica* Engelm. (syn. *M. hemisphaerica* in Wislizenus, *Mem. Tour North Mex.* 105. 1848)

Stem very flattened-globular, almost flush with the soil when resting, 8 to 12 cm broad, axils nearly naked. Radial spines 9 to 13, needle-like, the upper more delicate, 2 to 8 mm long, brownish or smoky-grey, often with black tips. One central spine, brown with black tip, 3 to 4 mm, or up to 8 mm long. Flowers cream coloured to dusky pink, 1 to 1·5 cm long, stigma-lobes 6 to 10, greenish-yellow. Fruit is red, seeds reddish-brown.

Reported from below Matamoros on the Rio Grande and near Brownsville, Texas, just across the river from Matamoros, Monterrey in Nuevo Leon and with long central spines from between Naco and Cananca in Sonora, Mexico.

M. heyderi var. *hemisphaerica*

var. *macdougalii* (Rose)Benson (syn. *M. macdougalii* Rose in Bailey, *Stand. Cycl. Hort.* **4**. 1982. 1916)

Stem flattened-globular, but in time nearly globular, up to 12 to 15 cm in diameter, axils often with long white wool. Radial spines 10 to 12, white or a little yellowish, the lower a little stronger, brown or black at the tips or throughout, to 20 mm long. Central spines 1 or 2, stout, yellowish, brown-tipped, similar to the radials, to 10 mm long. Flowers 3·5 cm long, cream coloured or pale yellow with faint tan midstripe. Fruit is red, seeds dark brown.

Reported from near Nogales in Arizona, USA and

from northern Sonora in Mexico; type locality is near Tucson, Arizona.

M. heyderi var. *macdougalii*

var. *meiacantha* (Engelm.) Benson (syn. *M. meiacantha* Engelm., *Pro. Amer. Acad.* **3**:263. 1856); *MSJ* **15**:17 (1975)

This variety is distinguished by having fewer, stronger spines than the others, and larger, more compressed tubercles. Stems are up to 12 cm across or more, axils woolly at first, later naked. Radial spines 5 to 9, needle-like, 6 to 10 mm long, the lower stronger and longer, pale pinkish, brown tipped. The central spine, sometimes not present, is 3 to 7 mm long, the same colour as the radials but darker tipped and stronger. Flowers are pink or whitish with pink midstripe, about 2·5 cm long. Fruit is scarlet, seeds brown.

Reported from south-east Arizona through New Mexico to Texas and in Mexico southwards to

M. heyderi var. *meiacantha*

Zacatecas at 1,200 to 1,600 m altitude, in gravel and rock, usually limestone, in the desert and in grassland.

var. *bullingtoniana* Castetter, Pierce & Schwerin, *Cact. Amer.* **48**:138 with figs. (1976)

Recently described as a new variety, the detailed description did not, unfortunately, give any clear indication of its differentiating characters from other varieties, and without good photographs of the plants in flower it is difficult to decide just what they are; the only outstandingly different character is in the flowers, which are considerably smaller than in other varieties.

Usually solitary, 6·4 to 15 cm tall and 10 to 12·5 cm wide. Axils woolly in youth, later naked. Radial spines number 10 to 14, occasionally 8, rarely more, needle-like, straight, 3 to 11 or 15 mm long, white to straw to reddish-brown, sometimes with reddish-brown tips, uppers shorter, lighter coloured and more slender, the lower stouter, longer and darker. Flowers are only 1 to 1·5 cm wide, 1·5 to 3 cm long—small for the species—white to cream to pink, midstripe on inside petals cream to yellow to pink often with greenish tint, outer stripe brownish-green. Fruit is red, seeds reddish-brown.

Reported from Cliff in New Mexico, USA, also known from extreme south-eastern Arizona, southern New Mexico and Texas, and in Mexico in northern Sonora and Chihuahua. In view of its lack of proper identification it is regarded as doubtfully distinct.

M. hidalgensis Purpus, *Monatsschr. Kakt.* **17**:118 with fig. (1907); *Cact. GB* **39**:74 (1977)

Referred to *M. polythele.*

M. hirsuta Boed., *Monatsschr. Kakt.* **29**:130 with fig. (1919); *MSJ* **11**:9 (1971)

A dubious species, which seems from the illustration and description to be something akin to *M. bocasana.*

M. hoffmanniana (Tiegel) Bravo, *Las Cact. Mex.* 687 (1937); *MSJ* **11**:10 (1971)

Referred to *M. obconella.*

M. huajuapensis Bravo, *An. Inst. Biol. Mex.* **25**:535 with fig. (1954); *MSJ* **11**:34 (1971)

Referred to *M. mystax.*

M. huitzilopochtli D. R. Hunt, *Cact. GB* **41**:106 (1979); *MSJ* **19**:79 (1979)

Series **Supertextae** M. SUPERTEXTA Group

For some time after its discovery this species was known by the number 'Lau 066', and equated at first tentatively to *M. crucigera*. Even on describing it David Hunt postulated that it could possibly turn out to be a natural hybrid between *M. crucigera* and *M. dixanthocentron*, its closest neighbours, but adds that wild collected seed appears to breed true. This would indicate that it is a good species, as it would throw back to its purported parents if it were a hybrid between

them, and produce seedlings varying from each other and between those 2 species, according to Mendelian principles.

It is a solitary plant at first, branching dichotomously after reaching about 5 cm or more tall (much later than *M. crucigera*, which branches also from the sides at an early age). Eventually individual stems get to about 13 cm or more tall and 8 to 9 cm wide. The axils are densely filled with whitish wool, but later become naked. The tubercles are very small and close together. Radial spines number about 15 to 30, 2·5 mm to 3·5 mm long, glassy white, straight to a little recurving. The central spines are at first not present, or are usually solitary (rarely there are 2), small (4 mm long), fine, dark brown and erect, projecting from the top edge of the areoles. Later an additional central spine often develops, standing out straight from the centre of the areole. This very prominent and unusual looking spine is much stronger, dark brown to black and 1·5 to 2 cm long (to 5 cm according to Lau). The flowers are small, 12 to 15 mm long, 7 mm wide, not expanding widely and carmine coloured. The fruit is red, seeds very small, brown.

Reported from Oaxaca in the Tomellin valley gorge, near the confluence of the Rio Salado and Rio Quiotepec, on red, conglomerate rocks.

Other collections from nearby may also be referrable to this species: *Lau 066a* and *Hunt 8841* from above Cuicatlan, with more central spines (2 to 9 are reported), fine and barely distinguishable from the radials; *Lau 681*, with 14 to 17 radial spines and 1 short central spine so far reported.

M. huitzilopochtli

M. humboldtii Ehrenb., *Linnaea* **14**:378 (1840); *MSJ* **11**:10 (1971)

Series **Lasiacanthae** M. HUMBOLDTII Group

This is a much sought-after species by collectors, being absolutely covered in snow-white spines, which completely hide the plant body. As with many species in the more desirable bracket, it presents some difficulties in cultivation, but providing watering is not overdone it should survive and will make a clump of glistening white heads in time. A very open compost seems desirable for this species, adapted as it appears to be to high amounts of sunlight and the consequent dry soil conditions. It makes more or less globular stems up to about 5 cm in diameter and in height, clustering from the base or a little way up the stem. As indicated above the spines mask the plant body, but the tubercles are small and closely set beneath them. Axils have bristles and wool. Radial spines number about 80, 4 to 6 mm long, unequal, straight, white, more or less at right angles from the areole to make smooth, golf-ball like heads. There are no central spines. Flowers are small (to 15 mm long and wide) and bright purplish-red, pushing open the tubercles to make their way between the spines and contrasting markedly with the overall whiteness of the plant. Fruit is red, seeds black.

Reported from Hidalgo in limestone hills between Ixmiquilpan and Meztitlan. (See colour plate.)

M. humboldtii

M. hutchisoniana (Gates) Boed., *Cact. Amer.* **6**:4 with fig. (1934) & **24**:80 with fig. (1952); *Kaktus ABC* 387 (1935); *MSJ* **11**:10 (1971)
Series **Ancistracanthae** M. MICROCARPA Group

This beautiful species has become available more widely in recent years, but is liable to remain a fairly uncommon plant in collections because of its facility for dying suddenly. It is often seen labelled *M. bullardiana*, which Craig regarded as conspecific, and with which opinion most authorities concur. The persistence of the latter name is possibly due to the continued listing of seed under that name by seed purveyors.

If it survives for you in cultivation it will quickly make a clump of elongated stems, 4 to 6 cm in diameter and up to 15 cm tall. The axils are slightly woolly or sometimes naked. Radial spines number 10 to 20,

straight, 7 to 10 mm long, light tan, purple-tipped. Centrals number 4, similar to the radials but a little stronger, the lowermost and sometimes one or two of the others hooked. Flowers are quite large, 2·5 to 3 cm broad, opening wide, cream-coloured, the outer petals striped maroon. Fruit is scarlet, seeds black.

Reported from Baja California, 14 km west of Calmalli in 'silty bottom land', from Isla Natividad and from elsewhere in central and southern Baja California—'*M. bullardiana*' was reported from La Paz in Baja California.

M. hutchisoniana

M. icamolensis Boed., *Kakteenk.* 168 with fig. (1933); *MSJ* **11**:18 (1971)
Hunt rejects this name as dubious.

M. inaiae Craig, *Cact. Amer.* **10**:111 (1939); *MSJ* **7**:3 (1967)
Hunt concurs with Foster's opinion that this is a straight-spined form of *M. sheldonii*.

M. infernillensis Craig, *Mamm. Handb.* 123 with fig. (1945); *MSJ* **11**:18 (1971)
Referred to *M. parkinsonii*.

M. ingens Backeb., *Repert. Spec. Nov.* **51**:63 (1942); *Stacht. Wildnis* 347 (1942); *Cact. Amer.* **43**: 121 (1971); *MSJ* **13**:23 (1973)
Referred to *M. obconella*.

M. insularis Gates, *Cact. Amer.* **10**:25 with fig. (1938); *MSJ* **11**:19 (1971)
Series **Ancistracanthae** M. MICROCARPA Group

This is another gem in this wonderfully flowered group, with particularly attractive contrasting spines. It has the disadvantage for collectors of a tendency to rot off if watering is overdone. It was described as clustering (Foster doubts this to be typical, and in cultivation it does tend to be seen as solitary), with thick, heavy roots and flattened-globular stems (shortly columnar in cultivation), axils a little woolly or naked. Radial spines number 20 to 30, 15 mm long (not 5 mm, a mistake in the original description), white, needle-like. One central spine, 1 cm long, needle-like, hooked, black tipped, a little stronger than the radials. The flowers are large, to 2·5 cm long and wide, light pink with white margins, outer petals light green. Fruit is orange-red, seeds dull black.

M. insularis

Reported from Baja California on the outermost islet in the Smith Island Group, Los Angeles Bay (Isle of Ventana), and from the nearby mainland a few miles south of Bahia de los Angeles. The black or very dark brown of the centrals contrasts wonderfully with the whiteness of the radials and the areoles, and the crowning glory of the large flowers make this a species well worth growing, although it is not often offered.

M. iwerseniana Hort.—a catalogue name for plants referrable to *M. parkinsonii*.

M. jaliscana (B. & R.) Boed., *The Cact.* **4**:160 (1923); *Mamm. Vergl. Schluss.* 35 (1933); *MSJ* **11**:19 (1971)
Series **Ancistracanthae** M. BOMBYCINA Group
This is another uncommon species, which in recent years has become available again, with attractive spines and flowers. It is more or less globular to short-columnar, clustering, with individual heads about 5 or 6 cm in diameter. The axils are naked. Radial spines number 30 or more, fine needle-like, white, to 8 mm long. Central spines vary from 4 to 6, sometimes 8, 7 to 9 mm long, straight except for the lowest one, which is longer (12 mm) and hooked, all reddish-brown, darker at the tips. The flowers are pink to purplish, 1 cm in diameter, delicately scented. Fruit is white to pink, seeds black.
Reported from Jalisco Rio Blanco near Guadalajara. Hunt allies this species to *M. mercadensis*.

M. jaliscana

M. johnstonii B. & R., *The Cact.* **4**:80 with fig. (1923); *MSJ* **11**:19 (1971)
Series **Macrothelae** M. PETROPHILA Group
Usually solitary, this species is common in collections in its various forms. It eventually achieves a good-sized globular to short-columnar plant about 15 to 20 cm tall and about 10 cm across. Axils are naked, radial spines 10 to 14, sometimes to 18 (see below), 6 to 9 mm long, stout, needle-like, whitish with brown tips, central spines 2, sometimes 4 or 6 (see below), much stronger and longer (10 to 25 mm) than the radials, purplish-brown to black. Flowers are quite large and wide, 2 cm long and wide, white, outer petals greenish-white to pale yellow with reddish-brown midstripe, stigma-lobes green. Fruit is large, widening consider-

M. johnstonii

ably towards the tip, scarlet, remaining swollen for a long time, often still present with the following year's flowers, seeds brown.

Reported from Sonora, San Carlos Bay on tufa ledges 'rising abruptly from the water's edge'.

Two varietal names are commonly seen, which Foster (*MSJ* **7**:3. 1967) discounts on the variability of the species and intermingling of the 'varieties'; the variability of the species was a point made by Craig too. Var. *sancarlensis* Craig was described as having 2 tortuous central spines, 15 to 18 radial spines and obtuse (rather than acute as in the type) inner petals. Var. *guaymensis* Craig has 4 to 6 straight centrals and 18 radials.

M. johnstonii (guaymensis)

M. johnstonii (sancarlensis)

M. joossensiana Quehl., *Monatsschr. Kakt.* **18**:95 (1908); *MSJ* **11**:20 (1971)

Synonymous with *M. bella*.

M. jozef-bergeri Wojnowski & Prajer, *Swiat Kakt.* 84 (1969); *MSJ* **11**:61 (1971)

Hunt states that this is a redescription of *M. collinsii*.

M. karwinskiana Mart., *Nov. Act. Nat. Cur.* **16(1)**:335 with fig. (1832); *MSJ* **11**:34 (1971)

Series **Polyedrae** M. KARWINSKIANA Group

This name covers a multitude of taxonomic sins, including *M. confusa*, *M. conzattii*, *M. ebenacantha*, *M. fischeri*, *M. multiseta* and *M. neomystax* (which Hunt relegates to synonymy); *M. polygona*, *M. praelii*, *M. subpolyedra* and *M. villifera* Hunt dismisses as 'ghosts from the past'; finally *M. pyrrhocephala* connected here is discounted as a dubious species.

M. karwinskiana is readily recognized and well-known in collections as a plant which tends to branch dichotomously, as well as clustering from the base and body, globular becoming a little elongated with age, with angular tubercles, wool and bristles in the axils. There are a variable number of spines, from 4 to 7, often 6, 1 occasionally central, longer (to 25 mm) and stronger than the others, which are sub-central (not radiating at near right-angles from the central spine and at the edge of the areole, but standing out from near the centre at an angle of about 45°); the spines are all dark brownish-red in youth fading to greyish-white tipped red-brown later. Flowers are white to pale yellow with a broad maroon midstripe, greenish at the base, 20 to 25 mm long, stigma-lobes 5 to 6, yellow. Fruit is bright red, seeds brown.

M. karwinskiana

Reported from around the city of Oaxaca. This is an easy species to grow and will readily make a clump to fill a 20 cm pan in a few years. The striping of the flowers is very prominent and attractive, and the flowers are freely produced. Hunt reports that *M. nejapensis* occurs between this species and *M. collinsii*, and is the 'connecting link' between these two similar species. It follows that these three may well resolve as one species, but this can be determined only in the field.

M. kellerana Schmoll in Craig, *Mamm. Handb.* 231 with fig. (1945); *MFJ* **11**:36 (1971)

Hunt equates this name with *M. durispina*. Plants

grown in recent years from seed sold as *M. kellerana* var. *schmuckeri* have turned out to be *M. erectacantha*.

M. kewensis Salm-Dyck, *Cact. Hort. Dyck* 112 (1849); *MSJ* **11**:36 (1971)
Series **Heterochlorae** M. POLYTHELE Group

This is a common plant in cultivation, making a thick, solitary column eventually up to 40 cm or more tall, at which stage it tends to collapse under its own weight and become decumbent. The axils in the growing part of the crown are woolly. The 6 spines are all in one plane, sub-central, standing out and recurving somewhat from near the centre of the areole, the upper and lower spines longer (10 mm) the others 6 mm, stiff, purplish brown (polished mahogany colour). The flowers are deep pink, the 5 stigma-lobes pale pink. The fruit is greenish to purplish-pink, seeds brown.

Reported from Hidalgo near Ixmiquilpan by Craig.

It has affinites with the nearby *M. polythele*, *M. durispina* and *M. obconella*, from which it is distinguished by the more numerous, less strong spines in the case of the first two, and by its deeper coloured spines for the last mentioned.

M. kewensis

M. kladiwae Hort.

Plants in circulation under this name resemble *M. nunezii*.

M. klissingiana Boed., *Zeitschr. Sukk.* **3**:123 with fig. (1927); *MSJ* **11**:37 (1971)
Series **Leucocephalae** M. GEMINISPINA Group

This is often misidentified in collections, but once known is unmistakable. It is solitary and ball-shaped at first, eventually clustering heavily. The tubercles are small and densely packed together, with wool and

numerous white bristles up to 1 cm long in the axils. The radial spines hide the body of the plant as they are so numerous and closely arranged because of the small tubercles; they number 30 to 35, and are up to 5 mm long, straight or a little curved, whitish; central spines 2 to 4 are only 2 mm long, whitish, red-brown at the tips. Flowers are rose-pink with deeper midstripe, about 1 cm long, 8 mm in diameter, stigma-lobes yellow. The fruit is small and red, seeds brown.

Reported from Tamaulipas, near Calebassas, about 15 km north of Jaumave, along the top edge of vertical limestone cliffs in indirect sun, or among rocks in thin undergrowth and from Palmillas.

Hunt allies it to *M. brauneana*.

M. klissingiana

M. knebeliana Boed., *Monatsschr. Deutsch. Kakt. Ges.* **4**:52 with fig. (1932); *MSJ* **11**:37 (1971)

Referred to *M. leucantha*.

M. knippeliana Quehl., *Monatsschr. Kakteenk.* **17**:59 (1907); *MSJ* **11**:35 (1971)
Series **Polyedrae** M. KARWINSKIANA Group

The identity of this species has been doubtful since its description, and its closeness to *M. karwinskiana* has led to it being merged by some authors. Currently it seems to be accepted again as distinct, having been rediscovered near Cuernavaca, the type locality. It makes a clustering plant in time, with individual bodies about 5 or 6 cm tall or more, 4 to 5 cm wide. Axils have both wool and prominent white bristles. The radial (or sub-central) spines number usually 6, sometimes 4, to 30 mm long, the lower longest, straight, white with brown or reddish tips. There are no real central spines. Flowers are smallish, about 1 cm wide, 1·5 cm long, straw-yellow with red-tipped petals and a faint reddish midstripe. Fruit is red, seeds brown.

Reported from Morelos, near Cuernavaca.

M. knippeliana

M. kraehenbuehlii Krainz, *Die Kakt. Lfg.* **46** sine pag. (1 June 1971); *MSJ* **11**:61(1971); *Cact. Amer.* **43**:270 (1971); *Cact. GB* **41**:103 (1979)
Series **Sphacelatae** M. SPHACELATA Group

This species has become widely available since its introduction a comparatively short time ago, mainly due to its clustering habit and readiness of the offsets to root. It clusters densely, with stems staying close together at the top; individually they are 3 to 12 cm long, but their length in older specimens is not apparent because of the clustering habit; they each measure about 3·5 cm in diameter. The axils are without wool or bristles. Radial spines number 18 to 24, 3 to 8 mm long, very thin, chalky white, brownish tipped, curving and interlacing. Central spine 1 (or

M. kraehenbuehlii

absent), thicker and longer than the radials, brownish tipped. Flowers are about 18 mm long, lilac-carmine, stigmas yellowish-white. Fruit is dark carmine, seeds black.

Reported from Oaxaca near Tamazulapan, on stony hillsides, mostly among grass or in the shade of low shrubs, often also on the top of rocks in indirect sun, in holes in the limestone growing in black, humus soil in tufts of moss! The flowers are not easily or prolifically produced in cultivation; they are indeed lilac-carmine, if that difficult to imagine colour combination means anything to you—perhaps a deep pink with a bluish quality is better—but all the plants I have seen in flower have in addition a white edge to the petals making for most distinctive flowers. The species was provisionally given the name *M. alpina*, but this turned out to be invalid through prior use long ago.

M. kuentziana Fearn, *Nat. Cact. Journ.* **18**:33 (1963); *MSJ* **11**:37 (1971)

Hunt equates this, with a scathing commentary on its erection, to synonymy with *M. vetula*.

M. kuentzii Hort., *MSJ* **7**:13 (1967)

A name for hybrids between *M. decipiens* and *M. elongata*.

M. kunthii Ehrenb., *Bot. Zeit.* **2**:835 (1844); *Die Cact.* **5**:3478 with fig. (1961)

Hunt equates this largely ignored specific name to *M. lanata*, itself a dubious species.

M. kunzeana Boed. & Quehl., *Monatsschr. Kakteenk.* **22**:177 with fig. (1912); *MSJ* **11**:38 (1971)

This species is sometimes ascribed to *M. bocasana* (see remarks under that name), but was described as having hair-like bristles in the axils (naked in *M. bocasana*), about 25 radial spines ('very numerous' in *M. bocasana*) to 13 mm long, bristle-like, white; central spines 3 or 4 (only 1 in *M. bocasana*), 1 hooked, white or yellow at base, tipped brown, purplish or blackish, 2 cm long (5 to 6 mm in *M. bocasana*). Flowers white or whitish-yellow, 2 cm long. Fruit is red, seeds brown. It is generally linked with sparser spined forms of *M. bocasana*, but its application is in doubt.

M. lanata (B. & R.) Orcutt, *Cactog.* **7** (1926); *The Cact.* **4**:104 (1923); *Cact. Amer.* **44**:169 with fig. (1972); *MSJ* **12**:7 (1972)

The description of this species by Britton and Rose calls for a short-cylindric stem with short tubercles; the areoles at the flowering area very woolly (Hunt suggests that this refers to the axils); the young flowers are surrounded by a mass of long, white hairs; radial spines 12 to 14 (Orcutt says up to 20) white with brown base; flowers very small, 6 to 7 mm (Orcutt: 10 mm) long, red (Orcutt: pink) with 3 short stigma-lobes (Orcutt: purplish-pink). No centrals are mentioned, and Orcutt adds that they are rudimentary or absent; he also gives the description of the fruit as 'elongate-globular, 5 mm long, scarlet with persistent perianth', and describes the seeds as brown.

Reported from Mexico, with no State given, from the Rio de Santa Luisa, now known to be from Puebla.

Lindsay found plants ascribed to this species in Tomellin Canyon, 50 miles south of Tehuacan, Puebla, towards Oaxaca on the north side of a deep canyon, occurring in clusters up to 25 cm wide, but the application of this name to these plants is doubtful.

It is a confused name best discarded, as no real idea of the true application of the name can be gleaned, and it is randomly applied to a variety of white plants, most of which resolve more readily under *M. albilanata*. Hunt allies this species to *M. supertexta*.

M. laneusumma Craig, *Mamm. Handb.* 310 with fig. (1945); *MSJ* **8**:40 (1968) & **14**:48 (1974)

Referred to *M. canelensis*.

M. lasiacantha Engelm., *Proc. Amer. Acad.* **3**:261 (1856); *Cact. Mex. Bound* 5 with fig. (1859); *MSJ* **12**:7 (1972); *Kakteen* 288 (1929)—var. *denudata*; *Cacti of the South-West* 145 (1972)

Series **Lasiacanthae** M. LASIACANTHA Group.

This species is an attractive, small member of the series, making slow clusters of globular to ovoid, button-mushroom sized stems completely covered with white spines. These are all radials and number from 40 to 80 per areole in several layers; they are 3 to 5 mm long, pubescent to smooth (the latter named as var. *denudata*). The flowers are white, prominently striped red in the centre of the petals. Fruit is scarlet, seeds black.

Reported from the USA in west Texas, around Leon

Spring and Camanche Spring, west of the Pecos, on low, limestone hills among herbage, and south-eastern New Mexico. Also reported by Glass and Foster from Marathon in Texas and in Mexico as far south as Zacatecas, and in the states of Chihuahua, Coahuila and Durango.

It is not the easiest plant to succeed with, being naturally slow-growing and compact. Seedlings develop painfully slowly, especially in the first year or two, and most plants seen in collections are wild-collected plants. The difficulty in cultivation is reflected in the infrequency of more than small, single-headed specimens being seen.

M. laui D. R. Hunt, *Cact. GB* **41**:100 (1979); *Cact. Amer.* **50**:180 (1978); *Kaktusy* **14**:78 (1978); *Mitteil. Arbeits. Mamm.* 1978. 186 (1978)

Series **Lasiacanthae** M. HUMBOLDTII Group

This delightful new species has been recently described by David Hunt, after its discovery by Alfred Lau, an account of which appeared in the American journal. He describes three forms, representing different altitudinal forms of the species, all worth obtaining. Firstly fa. *laui*, occurring at altitudes intermediate between the other two (about 1,000 to 1,600 m), with a heavily clustering habit, the individual heads in cultivation usually about 4 or 5 cm in height and width, but up to 6 cm tall. The axils are naked or a little woolly. The central spines intergrade inextricably with the radials, and there are 35 to 60 or more all told, with about 12 of these more or less central, white, bristle-like, about 7 to 10 mm long.

Reported from Tamaulipas, between Ciudad Victoria and Jaumave, La Reja, near an asbestos mine (*Lau 1171* and *Lau 1224*). (See colour plate.)

M. laui fa. *laui*

The form occurring at lower altitude (800 m approx.) is called fa. *subducta*, with well-marked central spines, more or less outstanding, 7 to 10 mm long, pale yellow or sometimes brown, at least in the upper half, thicker than in the previous form, but still

M. lasiacantha

intergrading with the radials, which are fewer and stronger than in the other forms.

Reported from the same locality, but at the lower level mentioned (*Lau 1222*). (See colour plate.)

M. laui fa. *subducta*

The last form named occurred at the highest points of the type locality, at 1,400 to 1,700 m, and was named as fa. *dasyacantha*, with very slender central spines, scarcely or indeed not distinguishable from the radials, which are very numerous, hair-like and glassy white, 6 to 9 mm long.

Reported from the same locality at the high levels mentioned above (*Lau 1219*).

This delightful new species in all three forms will undoubtedly be much sought after, and already Hunt has deplored the ravaging of the habitat by overcollecting. This is even more deplorable in view of the readiness of propagation from these naturally clustering plants and the availability of seed from continental seed merchants in the last year or two.

Hunt allies it to *M. humboldtii*, while recognising the

M. laui fa. *dasyacantha*

obvious differences of stem, spines, flower and seeds; this and *M. schiedeana* are close neighbours in Hidalgo and *M. carmenae* and *M. laui* are as close in Tamaulipas.

M. lengdoblerana Boed., Jahrb. *Deutsch. Kakt. Ges.* **1**:68 with fig. (1936); *MSJ* **12**:8 (1972)

From the description and lack of appearance in collections generally it must be assumed that this species is, as Hunt postulates, either *M. lasiacantha* or *M. magallanii*.

M. lenta Brandegee, *Zoe* **5**, 10:194 (1904); *Cact. Amer.* **42**:249 (1970); *MSJ* **12**:8 (1972); *Kakt. u. a. Sukk.* **27**:233 (1976); *The Cact.* **4**:129 (1923)—illustration incorrect
Series **Lasiacanthae** M. LENTA Group

This is one of the gems in the genus, with dense, fine, white spines covering the flattish heads. Slow-growing, it is not easy to cultivate successfully and needs a fair amount of light to induce a good show of flowers. It comes slowly from seed and is difficult to raise in the first few years, taking 5 or 6 years to reach full size before clustering. The individual heads are normally about 4 or 5 cm across and barely 1 or 2 cm high. The roots are thick, carrot-like. The covering of spines is complete, due to the closeness of the very narrow tubercles. The axils have a little wool and occasional bristles. The 30 to 40 spines are fine, glassy

M. lenta

white and from 3 to 7 mm long, radiating, all flat to the body. There are no centrals. Flowers open wide to about 2·5 cm across, glistening white with a prominent pink to purple midstripe to each petal. Fruit is red, seeds black. (See colour plate.)

Reported from Coahuila in rocks near Viesca, south of Parras and in the valley of Cuatro Cienegas.

M. leona Poselger, *Allg. Gartenz.* **21**:94 (1853)

This is a persistent synonym for *M. pottsii*.

M. lesaunieri Schum., *Gesamt. Kakt.* 553 (1898); *Mamm. Handb.* 245 (1945); *MSJ* **12**:9 (1972)

Referred to *M. heyderi.*

M. leucantha Boed., *Kakteenk.* 233 with fig. (1933); *MSJ* **12**:27 (1972)

Series **Stylothelae**   M. WILDII Group

Hunt now accepts this name, preferring it to *M. knebeliana.* It is not well-known in collections, although it is sometimes seen misnamed *M. aurihamata.* It was described as simple or rarely branching (clustering in cultivation) about 3·5cm wide and a little taller. Axils have white wool in youth, later naked. Radial spines number 18, 5 to 6mm long, straight, very thin, slightly pubescent, white with pale brownish yellow tip. Central spines number 3 or 4, 5 to 6 mm long, 3 hooked, the fourth when present straight, all stronger than the radials, dark amber yellow. Flowers are 15mm long and wide, white with faint olive-green midstripe. Fruit is red, seeds dark brown.

Reported from San Luis Potosi, Soledad Diez Gutierrez.

M. *leucantha*

M. leucocentra Berg., *Allg. Gartenz.* **8**:129 (1840); *MSJ* **12**:27 (1972)

The identity of the originally described species is in doubt, but Hunt believes it to be close to *M. geminispina.* The name is fairly constantly applied in error to plants in cultivation of *M. parkinsonii.*

M. lewisiana Linds. ex Gates, *Cact. Amer.* **27**:185 with fig. (1955); *Des. Pl. Life* **11**:167 (1939); *MSJ* **12**:17 (1972); *Int. Newer Mamm.* 8 with fig. (1973)

This is an attractive variant of *M. brandegei*, worth seeking out; see under *M. brandegei.*

M. lindsayi Craig, *Cact. Amer.* **12**:182 (1940); *Mamm. Handb.* 87 (1945); *MSJ* **14**:48 (1974)

Series **Macrothelae**   M. STANDLEYI Group

Hunt in his 'Review' vaguely suggests that this name is synonymous with *M. standleyi.* But in his paper

'Schumann & Buxbaum Reconciled' as revised, he retains the name at specific level. The description was of a plant forming clumps up to 1 m wide, with individual heads to 15 cm wide and tall. The axils have dense wool, especially in the growing area, and up to 8 tortuous, white bristles longer than the tubercles. Radial spines number 10 to 14, 2 to 8mm long, the upper 3 or 4 shorter and thinner, the lowermost a little heavier, straight, smooth, the upper white, the lower tan to golden-yellow. Central spines number 2 to 4 (usually 4), 4 to 12mm long, the upper shortest, the lower one longer and heavier, needle-like, straight, stiff, smooth, light golden-brown to reddish, becoming 'greyish-horn' in age. Flowers are 15 to 20 mm long, 10 mm wide, light greenish-yellow with an orange-yellow midstripe on the outer petals. Fruit is scarlet, seeds light brown.

Reported from south-west Chihuahua, in particular from Molina to Sierra Colorado, 10 to 15 miles northeast of the junction of the Rio Chinipas and Rio Fuerte, and along the Rio Watchera. Found in partial shade on canyon walls and slopes in leaf mould in rock crevices at about 1,200 m in altitude.

This is not a commonly seen plant in collections, but it is immediately distinguishable by its flowers which are unusually coloured for the type of plant.

M. *lindsayi*

M. lloydii (B. & R.) Orcutt, *Cactog.* 7 (1926); *The Cact.* **4**:89 with fig. (1923); *MSJ* **12**:18 (1972); Marsden, *Mammillaria*, photograph, plate 4, is not of this species

Series **Macrothelae** M. HEYDERI Group

The opinion expressed by Hunt that this species is no more than a straight-spined form of *M. uncinata* makes sense, and when the two are placed together the similarities are very apparent. He reports that it is found as a rarity among abundant *M. uncinata* north of San Luis Potosi: '*M. uncinata* occurs with 1, 2 or even 3 hooked centrals, so why not none at all?' Why not indeed? The description is of a plant with flattened-globular body, about 10 or 12 cm in diameter, axils woolly, tubercles four-angled. The spines are sub-central, 3 or 4, smooth, whitish, the uppermost red or dark brown and longer, 2 to 5 mm long, varying in length. Flower white, tinged red, and with dark red midstripes. Fruit is pink, seeds brown.

Reported from Zacatecas, and as indicated above as a rarity among *M. uncinata*, north of San Luis Potosi.

M. lloydii

M. longicoma (B. & R.) Berger, *Kakteen* 292 (1929); *The Cact.* **4**:146 with figs. (1923); *Cact. Amer.* **42**:175 with fig. (1970); *MSJ* **12**:18 (1972)
Series **Stylothelae**   M. WILDII Group

Here again we have a species which it has been suggested should be reduced to synonymy with *M. bocasana*. Plants grown as *M. longicoma* vary, but in general are less densely-woolled forms of what is grown as *M. bocasana*. The description was of a clustering plant forming broad clumps, with indi-idual heads 3 to 5 cm across, axils with long, white hair. Radial spines number 25 or more, weak and hairlike, more or less interlocking. Central spines number 4, 10 to 12 mm long, brown at the tips, a little paler below, 1

or 2 spines hooked. Flowers are white, sometimes tinged with pink, outer petals pinkish with darker midstripe. Fruit is red, seeds black.

Reported from San Luis Potosi.

Craig offers the distinguishing feature between this species and *M. kunzeana*, as the hairlike radial spines of this species as compared with the bristle-like, more substantial radials of *M. kunzeana*.

M. longiflora (B. & R.) Berger, *Kakteen.* 296 (1929); *The Cact.* **4**:163 with figs. (1923); *Cact. Amer.* **43**:24 (1971); *MSJ* **12**:19 (1972) & **20**:40 (1980); *Kakt. u. a. Sukk.* **30**:187 (1979); *Cact. GB* **41**:97 (1979)
Series **Longiflorae**   M. LONGIFLORA Group

This is a well-known species in collections and deservedly popular. It has a reputation, not entirely unjustified, of being short-lived. It does, however, make somewhat larger plants than Britton and Rose would have us believe, making globular to short-columnar specimens to about 8 or 9 cm in diameter (3 cm according to Britton and Rose, who must have been describing a seedling). Radial spines number about 30, needle-like, 10 to 13 mm long, pale yellow (almost white often in cultivation). There are 4 central spines, the upper 3 stronger and about the same length as the radials, the lower hooked and twice as long, yellow in the lower part, reddish-brown in the upper part, the colour varying considerably, some being completely yellowish-white (see below), others nearly wholly dark red-brown. The flowers, which are far too summarily dealt with by Britton and Rose, are breathtaking, and the species is generous with them from a very early age, producing them on incredibly small seedlings only one or two years old, the small plants seeming to stagger under the size of their proclamation of maturity. The flowers are long-tubed and open widely, to about 3 cm across. The colour of the petals varies from pale pink with faintly darker midstripe, to pink with deeper stripe. The fruit is small and remains sunken in the axils beneath the level of the

M. longicoma

M. longiflora fa. *longiflora*

M. longiflora fa. *stampferi*

radial spines; seeds are large and black, with a prominent white hilum as an appendage.

Reported from Durango around Santiago Papasquiaro, and at Coneto Pass. (See colour plate.)

David Hunt has recently referred to this species *M. stampferi*, described by Reppenhagen in *Kakteen und andere Sukkulenten* **30**:187 (1979). He has reduced it to *forma* level as follows: fa. *stampferi* (Reppenhagen) D. R. Hunt, described as earlier flowering in cultivation than the type, and with relatively short-tubed

M. longiflora (white-spined form)

uniformly coloured flowers of a soft mid-pink, larger tubercles and shorter central spines, about 11 mm long. This form was found by Josef Stampfer, an Austrian who works in the forest service of the Mexican Government, in Durango, near El Salto, at 2,600 m altitude (*Reppenhagen 1358*). It has also been collected by Alfred Lau, '*Lau 1250*'. There is too, as

indicated above, a completely white-spined form of this species, which comes true from seed, but whose origins are unknown.

M. longihamata Hort.—a misnomer sometimes applied to *M. bocasana* and sometimes to *M. poselgeri*

M. longimamma DC., *Mem Mus. Hist. Nat. Paris* **17**:113 (1828); B. & R. *The Cact.* **4**:62 with figs. (1923); *MSJ* **12**:19 (1972)
Subgenus **Dolichothele**

This is one of the more obviously separable species into the subgenus *Dolichothele*, with its long, flabby tubercles and large, yellow flowers. The spines tend to be weak and sometimes blacken with age, but the flowers more than compensate for the sometimes tatty appearance of plants, and if grown strongly and quickly this can in any case be avoided. It will often make a large sized individual head before clustering, up to about 10 or 12 cm wide. The very long (3 to 5 cm) and separately standing tubercles distinguish this species from others in the subgenus, as well as the comparatively large body size. Axils were reported as woolly but they are not prominently so. Radial spines number about 9 or 10 and are 12 to 18 mm long; the 1 central spine (rarely there are up to 3) is longer, up to 25 mm long, all whitish to pale yellowish, discolouring to brown or black with age, rough and slightly pubescent. Flowers 4 to 6 cm long and wide, clear lemon-yellow, fruit green to yellowish, swollen like a small grape and jostling with the tubercles, seeds dark brown.

M. longimamma var. *longimamma*

Reported from Hidalgo, between Ixmiquilpan and Tasquillo, also from Barranca de Venados, and from the area around Metzquititlan, near Venados.

Hunt refers back to Schumann in reducing *M. uberiformis* to a variety of *M. longimamma*, being a more westerly occurrence of the species, smaller in all its parts, and sometimes lacking a central spine.

M. longimamma var. *uberiformis*

M. louisiae Lindsay, *Des. Pl. Life* **11**:166 (1939) name only; *Cact. Amer.* **32**:169 with figs. (1960); *MSJ* **4**:76 (1964) & **7**:21 (1967) & **12**:20 (1972); *Int. Newer Mamm.* 9 with fig. (1973)
Series **Ancistracanthae** M. MICROCARPA Group

This species is rarely seen as a large plant in collections, being one of the touchiest to an excess of water at the wrong time. To grow it successfully in England, a long, dry period must be observed in the winter, allowing the plants to shrivel down considerably. With this treatment a modest-sized clump can be achieved after a few years when it will have formed a small mound of heads about 5 or 6 cm broad and tall. Each stem is about 3 or 4 cm in diameter, and little taller than it is broad, with no wool or bristles in the axils. Radial spines were described as numbering 11,

M. louisiae

but vary up to about 20; they are 5 to 7 mm long, needle-like, light tan coloured, tipped brown. Central spines number 4, brown, tipped darker, 8 to 10 mm long, the lowest hooked and the longest of the four. Flowers are large and open fully, 2·5 cm long and wide, entirely white or pale pink with a pinkish midstripe, olive- or brownish-green striped on the outer petals. The 6 to 8 stigma-lobes are long and prominent (7 to 11 mm), and were described by Lindsay as olive-green, but this colouring is less commonly seen than those with maroon or red-brown stigma-lobes. The fruit is bright red, fat and pear-shaped, the seed is black.

Reported from Baja California, 1 mile south of Socorro.

Hunt allies this species to *M. goodridgii*.

M. macdougalii Rose, Bailey, *Stand. Cycl. Hort.* **4**:1982 (1916); *Cacti of Arizona* **ed 2**:119 (1950) & **ed. 3**:22. 151 (1969); *MSJ* **11**:8 (1971) & **12**:36 (1972)

Hunt refers this species to subspecific level beneath *M. heyderi*—see under *M. heyderi*.

M. macracantha DC, *Mem. Mus. Hist. Nat. Paris* **17**:113 (1828); *MSJ* **12**:36 (1972)

Referred by Schumann to *M. centricirrha* and thence to *M. magnimamma*.

M. magallanii Schmoll in Craig, *Mamm. Handb.* 225 with fig. (1945); *MSJ* **12**:36 (1972)
Series **Lasiacanthae** M. LASIACANTHA Group

This diminutive species with its cream-coloured spines and cream-pink coloured flowers is always the first of the spring flowerers to open for me, usually in mid-February. It is slow-growing, and a plant up to 5 cm tall will be six years old or more. It is older than this usually before it clusters randomly from different levels on the stem.

It forms more or less globular stems, elongating with age, the axils a little woolly. The many radial spines—70 to 75—are very short, 2 to 5 mm long, creamy-white, very slightly tipped brown, fine and needle-like. Central spines not present, or only 1, variable in length from 1 to 6 mm, occasionally curved or hooked, orange-tan at base, tipped brown. Flowers are small, not opening very wide, recurving at the tips more, up to 10 mm long, cream with tannish-pink midstripe. Fruit is red, about 1·5 cm long, seeds black.

Reported from Coahuila, just north-east of the town of Parras, and to the west of Parras in the Sierra Bola (here with hooked spines—Backeberg's var. *hamatispina*).

This species is readily distinguished from *M. lasiacantha*, which it closely resembles when not in flower, by the more porrect (standing out) spines and the pinkish-cream overall colouring of the spines, compared with more close to the body spines, coloured dead white of *M. lasiacantha*. When in flower the difference is readily seen, since the last mentioned has flowers striped a distinctly deep pink. I have not seen a plant of *M. magallanii* with the longer, hooked centrals reported, and Hunt indicates that this may be a character which does not persist in cultivation.

M. magallanii

M. magneticola Meyran, *Cact. Suc. Mex.* **6**:17 with figs. (1961); *MSJ* **12**:37 (1972)

This name has now been firmly referred by Hunt to *M. vetula*.

M. magnifica Buchenau, *Cact. Suc. Mex.* **12**:3 with figs (1967); *MSJ* **12**:38 (1972)

Series **Polyacanthae** M. NUNEZII Group

This beautiful variation on the theme of densely spined species in this series has become rapidly available since its discovery, as it comes readily from

M. magnifica var. *magnifica*

seed, and grows quickly to form a slim column, about 7 to 9 cm in diameter, up to 40 cm tall. It clusters from the base or sides usually after it has reached about 15 cm in cultivation, to form in time a magnificent (!) clump. The axils have white wool and 8 to 15 bristles. Radial spines number about 18 to 24, 3 to 8 mm long, straight, glassy white or yellowish. The central spines give the plant its distinctly beautiful golden appearance; there are usually 4 or 5, or up to 8, strong, needle-like, clear yellowish-brown, varying in depth of colour, the lower one 35 to 55 mm long and usually hooked, the remainder shorter and straight. Flowers are typical of the series, purplish-red or deep pink, 20 mm long, 11 to 12 mm in diameter. The fruit is pink, green at the tip, the seeds brown.

var. *minor* Buchenau. This variety is smaller all round than the type: 5 cm wide, with less axillary bristles—1 to 5—and less strong spines. There are up to 8 central spines, shorter than the type, the longer one, usually hooked, being about 15 mm long, radials about 17 in number.

The type reported by Buchenau from Puebla, San Juan Bautista on the slopes of a 'cerro' on rocks in full sun or under shrubs, at 1,500 m altitude; var. *minor* is reported from a quite separate population at Puebla, Cerro de la Cruz, on cliff-tops in full sun or half-shade

M. magnifica var. *minor*

under trees, at the same altitude. Type localities are sometimes misreported to foil over-collecting, and Hunt tried to find this species and its variety without success until he stumbled across the type near the Cuautla-Izucar de Matamoros highway in the State of Morelos, close to the border with Puebla on the rocky slopes of a hill, El Penon de Amayuca. It was photographed there and pictured in the journal of the American Society, Vol. 43, page 272 (1971).

M. magnimamma Haw., *Phil. Mag.* **63**:41 (1824); *Cact. Gen. Nov. Sp.* 42 (1839) (*M. centricirrha*); *The Cact.* **4**:77 (1923); *MSJ* **12**:38 (1972)
Series **Macrothelae** M. MAGNIMAMMA Group

As ably set forth by Hunt in the *Mammillaria Society Journal* the determination of the application of this name is hidden in a maze of literary references since its erection in 1824. The confusion arises from incomplete descriptions, lack of habitat data and overall, a widespread, extremely variable species. The main contender by way of an alternative name is *M. centricirrha*, and this name is still widely applied either as an alternative or, particularly, it seems to have favour with collectors for either the yellow-flowered or the pink-flowered form—there seems to be no consistency.

M. magnimamma

M. magnimamma

In any case what we have here, call it what you will (although *M. magnimamma* is the correct name if you require only one) is an extremely variable species which could form an interesting collection of plants in itself. The basic description is of a plant forming large, flattish mounds (although it must be added that some forms tend to stay solitary—see Hunt's article mentioned above), with large individual heads about 10 to 12 cm in diameter. In cultivation I have seen clusters 40 or 50 cm across. The tubercles, as the name indicates, are large, well-spaced and often angled. The axils are densely woolly when young. The spines are more or less sub-central, greyish-white to yellowish, tipped dark brown, varying from 2 to 5 or more in number, spreading, and often curving this way and that, variable in length, the uppers short and often straight, only 5 mm or so, others longer, often 1 considerably longer, to 5 cm, curving back over the plant body. Flowers vary from deep pink to pale yellow, sometimes striped pink. Fruit is dark purple-red, flattened club-shaped, seeds brown.

Reported from Hidalgo and, according to Ehrenberg, from 'the plateau near Mexico City, San Mateo, Pachuca, Sinquiluca, Apam, near Zacualtepan,

Loma del Toro, Las Ranas am Doctor and in many other places, at 2,130 to 2,440 m altitude.'

I must emphasize again the variability of this species, and recommend that keen *Mammillaria* collectors do not, once they have a specimen, sit back and ignore others which become available to them; it is worth growing on seedlings acquired to compare their differences and to see perhaps whether you have a more attractive plant than that already in the place of honour. But be warned, they do get rather large, and quite quickly.

M. magnimamma

M. mainiae Brandegee, *Zoe* **5**:31 (1900); *Cacti of Arizona* ed. **3**:152 (1969); *MSJ* **9**:4, 68. (1969) & **12**:49 (1972)
Series **Ancistracanthae** M. MICROCARPA Group

The sight of a good-sized clump of this species in flower on a show-bench is enough to ensure its serious consideration for the accolade of 'Best in Show'. It has all the qualities which lead to such high rating: strong, colourful spination geometrically pleasing to the eye, large flowers with wonderfully colour-matched stigma-lobes, and, not least, it presents difficulties in cultivation with a shallow root-system and a correlating sensitivity to overwatering. It also has the annoying habit of forming buds prolifically but 'swallowing' them again if there is insufficient sunshine or perhaps water. But do not be deterred from growing it, as after the first few years from seed it grows well enough with a little care, and the reward is considerable. The species forms clusters to about 20 cm across or more in time; the individual heads are almost globular with a tendency to narrow towards the growing point, which is a little depressed, giving an egg-shaped appearance. The heads are 10 to 12 cm tall, and 6 to 7 cm across. The body colour is bright green, often with red colouring prominent in the axils, which have neither wool nor bristles. Radial spines number about 10 to 15, 6 to 10 (sometimes to 12) mm long, the upper shorter, yellowish becoming white, dark brown tipped, slender and needle-like. The 1, hooked, central spine is much stronger and longer (occasionally there is a second upper central also hooked, but weaker and shorter), about 15 mm long, brown with blackish tip or yellowish with brown tip, brightly coloured, shining and a little twisted. Flowers are up to 2 cm long and wide, pinkish-white with darker midstripe, stigma-lobes crimson and very prominent, enhancing the flower-colour. The fruit is small, staying beneath or level with the spines, coloured bright red, seeds dull black.

Reported from Sonora, south of Nogales, also south of Hermosillo and from near Fuerta, north of Sinaloa, and in the USA in Arizona near Sells, from Pima County, in the Papago Indian Reservation and Santa Cruz County near Nogales, in 'gravel or coarse, sandy soil of hill washes and alluvial pans in the desert or grassland at 610 to 1,220 m,' the latter according to

Benson; or 'open thorn-scrub to mesquite grassland; soil slightly rocky to very dry sandy,' according to Bleck. Bill Maddams (editor of the journal of the Mammillaria Society, see page 154) has also collected this species in Sonora near Hermosillo and Benjamin Hill.

M. mammillaris (L.) Karsten, *Hort. Med. Amst.* **1**: 105. with fig. (1697); *Sp. Pl.* **1**: 466. (1753); *Karsten in Deutsche Fl. 888*. (1882); *MSJ* **12**: 50 (1972)
Series **Macrothelae**   M. MAMMILLARIS Group

This is the name to be adopted by precedence for the type species of the genus, often seen labelled as *M. simplex*, which was an illegitimate name in view of the preceding *Cactus mammillaris* Linnaeus, acknowledged by Haworth, when setting up the name *M. simplex*, as a synonym.

The species, although known to cultivation since the seventeenth century, is not well represented in collections, having none of the attributes of the more sought after species these days, but it is an interesting plant historically as explained at length by Hunt in the *Mammillaria Society Journal* (ref. above).

Linnaeus described the species as '*Cactus subrotundus tectus tuberculis ovatis barbatis*—the nearly round cactus covered with ovate, bearded tubercles', which is grand if it happens to be the only *Mammillaria* in cultivation, which it may have been at that time. Later descriptions define the species as simple or clustering, globose to short-cylindrical, up to 20 cm tall (Britton and Rose's 4 to 6 cm is more like the size of most specimens in cultivation), axils with a little, whitish wool. Radial spines number 10 to 16, 5 to 8 mm long, straight, needle-like, smooth, reddish later grey, nearly horizontal to a little ascending. Central spines number 3 to 5, 7 to 8 mm long, the upper longer, all smooth and straight (the upper is occasionally bent), stronger than radials, reddish-brown with darker tip, becoming grey. Flowers are about 1 cm long, cream-coloured to pale yellow, outer petals brown to

M. mainiae

M. mammillaris

brownish-green, stigma-lobes 5 to 6, greenish-yellow. Fruit is carmine, seeds brown, very small and roughened.

Reported from Curacao by Dr Britton and Dr Shafer, 'common on the top of a limestone hill' and from neighbouring islands, as well as from Venezuela: near Cabo Blanco; La Vela de Coro; Estado Falcon 37 km south of Coro at 850 m altitude in 'limestone outcrops in chaparral and deciduous forest'.

M. maritima (Lindsay) D. R. Hunt, *Cact. GB* **33**:58 (1971); *Cact. Amer.* **8**:143 (1937); *MSJ* **14**:26 (1974)
Subgenus **Cochemiea**

This is one of the five species of the former genus *Cochemiea*, which Hunt has placed in a subgenus under *Mammillaria*. It is similar to *M. setispina*, but with reddish-brown, shorter and thicker spines. The stems grow up to 50 cm tall, and form clumps in habitat up to 1 m across, each stem 3 to 7 cm in diameter. Radial spines number 10 to 15, 10 mm long, reddish-brown. Central spines are 4 in number, the lowest one hooked, 10 mm long, reddish-brown too. Flowers are 3 cm long, scarlet, with petals curling back on themselves. Fruit is spherical, red, seeds black.

Reported from Punta Blanca in Baja California.

Hunt allies this species to *M. pondii*.

M. maritima

M. marksiana Krainz, *Sukkulentenkunde* **2**:21 with fig. (1948); *MSJ* **12**:52(1972); *Int. Newer Mamm.* 10 with fig. (1973); *Cact. y Suc. Mex.* **22**:66 (1977) & **24**:11 (1979)
Series **Macrothelae**   M. SONORENSIS Group

This is a very distinctive species, noted for its bright green body colouring and contrasting yellow flowers, unusual outside the subgenus *Dolichothele*. It was described as solitary, although in cultivation it eventually offsets from the body, flat-globose, about 5 cm tall and 8 cm across, with somewhat 4-sided, pyramidal tubercles, axils woolly in youth, areoles with dense yellow wool in the growing area. The spines are all alike, thin, needle-like, golden yellow, about 8 mm long, except the upper and lower radials (sub-centrals according to Sanchez-Mejorada), which are shorter; there are 8 to 10 radials and 1 central but these may vary considerably in number according to locality. Flowers are about 15 mm long and wide, greenish-yellow, the inner petals more distinctly yellow. Fruit is dark reddish-purple and 10 mm or less in length, the seed small and light brown.

Reported from Sinaloa, western Sierra Madre, on rocky slopes in sandy leafmould.

M. marksiana

M. marnierana Backeb., *Cact. (Paris)* **31** suppl. 2 (1952); *MSJ* **10**:34 (1970)

Referred to *M. oliviae*, which in turn is referred under *M. microcarpa*.

M. marshalliana Gates, *Cact. Amer.* **6**:4 (1934)

Referred to *M. baxterana*.

M. martinezii Backeb., *Cact. (Paris)* **31**. suppl. 6 (1952)

In spite of a certain mystique surrounding this name it usually turns out to be a flat-globular, less woolly form of *M. albilanata*.

M. mathildae Kraehenbuehl & Krainz, *Kakt. u. a. Sukk.* **24**:265 (1973); *Die Kakt. Lfg.* 55 (1973); *MSJ* **15**:33 (1975); *Cact. GB* **41**:99 (1979)
Series **Stylothelae**   M. BOMBYCINA Group

This recently described species, it is suggested by the authors in their description, is akin to *M. zeilmanniana* and *M. nana*, but Hunt asserts its individuality. It is described as clustering, with stems 5 to 6 cm tall and 5 cm wide. Axils are naked, rarely with a little white wool. Radial spines number 9 or 10, 5 to

14 mm long, white hair-like, more or less flexuous, pubescent. Central spines are 4 or 5 in number, one of which is 6 to 10 mm long and hooked, reddish-brown, the others are straight, sub-central, reddish-brown towards the tip, all pubescent. Flowers are 2 cm long and wide, white, outer petals with pinkish-green midstripe, stigma-lobes yellowish. Fruit is scarlet, seeds black.

Reported from Queretaro, south east of Queretaro city, near La Canada, among stones and shrubs.

M. mathildae

This easy to grow species has been surprisingly tardy in getting itself distributed among *Mammillaria* enthusiasts, in England at least, but seedlings are at present being offered, and its clustering habit will lead to its rapid dispersal once the seedlings reach any size.

M. matudae Bravo, *Cact. GB* **18**:83 with fig. (1956); *MSJ* **12**:52 (1972); *Int. Newer Mamm.* **11** with fig. (1973)

Series **Polyacanthae**   M. SPINOSISSIMA Group

This is one of the most beautifully spined species to emerge in recent years, and it has proved equally as floriferous in cultivation as its close relatives in the series. It grows readily and fairly rapidly from seed, and will flower within three years at about 5 cm tall. The description by Dra. Helia Bravo is of plants either simple or clustering from the base (one would expect it maybe to offset from the stem as well in keeping with related species), cylindrical, elongated, 10 to 20 cm (or taller in cultivation) by 3 cm wide. Axils are naked. Radial spines number 18 to 20, 2 to 3 mm long, the lower longest, white, translucent with yellowish base. There is 1 central spine about 5 mm long, thicker than the radials, pointing upwards, white at first and translucent with a pinkish tinge and reddish tip, later dirty white and sometimes brown, needle-like and slightly flattened. The contrast in colour of the spines and their neat regularity make this a distinctive, sought-after species, without the bonus of the flowers, which are funnel-shaped, 12 mm long, purplish-

brown outside and light reddish-purple inside. Fruit is green tinged reddish, seeds light brown.

Reported from the state of Mexico at La Junta, at 686 m altitude, and from the state of Guerrero at 1,150 to 1,500 m by Fittkau, who described the plants found at this latter locality as var. *serpentiformis*, one stem of which was reported as 155 cm long! Fittkau also named forma *duocentralis*, for some plants of this variety which sported 2 central spines. Seed-raised plants of var. *serpentiformis* have made 20 to 30 cm of narrower columnar growth than the type, for which it was named, in only five years, but have made no offsets; I have resisted the temptation to put several in a hanging basket to see if they will attain 1·5 m with gravity encouragement.

M. matudae var. *matudae*

M. matudae var. *serpentiformis*

M. maycobaensis Schreier, *Kakt. u. a. Sukk.* **27**:40 (1976)

A provisional name for plants found in Chihuahua by Kurt Schreier, which seem to be very close to *M. hertrichiana*.

M. mayensis Craig, *Mamm. Handb.* 116 (1945); *MSJ* **12**:54 (1972) & **14**:48 (1974)

Referred to *M. canelensis*; reported from near Rio Mayo.

M. mazatlanensis Schum. ex Guerke, *Monatsschr. Kakteenk.* **15**:154 with fig. (1905); *MSJ* **5**:19 (1965) & **12**:54 (1972); *Kakt. u. a. Sukk.* **27**:85 (1976)
Series **Ancistracanthae** M. MICROCARPA Group

There is considerable confusion in collections between this species and *M. occidentalis*. If Hunt's theorizing is correct—that the hooked spine plants from Mazatlan referred to *M. occidentalis* by Craig, as well as *M. occidentalis* var. *sinalensis*, are referrable to *M. mazatlanensis*—the concept of the variability of this species is very much widened. Hunt has recently confirmed this view and identified *M. occidentalis* as distinct—see remarks under that name. *M. mazatlanensis* was described as heavily clustering, with narrow cylindrical stems, 4 cm in diameter and up to 12 cm tall. Axils are bare or have 1 or 2 short bristles. Radial spines number 13 to 15, white, slender, needle-like, 5 to 10 mm long. Central spines are 3 or 4 in number, reddish-brown, paler below, up to 15 mm long, the upper shorter and lying in the same plane as the radials, the lower longer, standing out straight or sometimes weakly hooked. Flowers are 3 to 4 cm long, carmine-red to purplish, really intensely coloured, and very bright compared with the depth of colour in many species of similar ilk. Fruit is brown becoming reddish-yellow, seeds black. Reported from Sinaloa, Mazatlan, and Nayarit, Tres Marias Islands, the latter locality for *M. mazatlanensis* var. *patonii* (syn. *M. patonii* and *M. occidentalis* var. *patonii*).

M. meiacantha Engelm., *Proc. Amer. Acad.* **3**:263 (1857); 'Descr. Cact.' in *US Senate Rep. Expl. Surv. Railroad Pacific Ocean. Bot.* **4**:27 (1857); *Cact. Bound.* **9**. t9 (1859); *MSJ* **12**:56 (1972)

Referred to *M. heyderi*.

M. meissneri Ehrenb., *Bot. Zeit.* **2**:834 (1844); *Allg. Gartenz.* **12**:402 (1844); *MSJ* **9**:8 (1969)

A narrow and clustering form of *M. haageana*, known also as *M. elegans* var. *schmollii*—see under *M. haageana*.

M. melaleuca Karw. ex Salm-Dyck, *Cact. Hort. Dyck.* 108 (1850); *Mamm. Vergl. Schluss.* 19 (1933); *Cact. Amer.* **40**:20 (1968) & **44**:86 (1972); *MSJ* **12**:56 (1972)
Subgenus **Dolichothele**

This attractive species is not well-known in collections, which is a pity, since it has the edge on most other *Dolichothele* species. It forms a globose stem, not so readily clustering as its near relatives, with naked axils and stout tubercles about 10 mm long and 7 mm in diameter. Radial spines number 6 or 7 or up to 9, and are slender and rigid, evenly spreading and recurved, about 12 to 14 mm long, the upper 4 a little longer, brown, the lower white. There is 1 central spine, similar to the radials and dark brown, but occasionally this is not present. The flowers are yellow, smallish for the subgenus, about 2 cm long. Fruit is green, seeds black.

Reported from Tamaulipas, south-west of

M. mazatlanensis

M. melaleuca

Jaumave—not Oaxaca, as earlier reports suggested, which was the place from which Karwinski despatched his plants.

M. melanocentra Poselger, *Allg. Gartenz.* 23:17 (1855); *MSJ* 12:57 (1972)
Series **Macrothelae** M. HEYDERI Group
This is a very distinctive species with long, central spines. Hunt dismisses as synonymous *M. runyonii*, a weak spined form, and *M. euthele*, a name invalidly published, which Backeberg offered only as a provisional name for a strong spined form with tubercles more rounded at the apex. It is a solitary species usually, becoming quite large, to about 10 or 12 cm in diameter, flattish-globular, with a glaucous green body colour, and large 4-sided tubercles. The axils are woolly in youth. Radial spines number 6 to 9, strong, unequal in length, the upper shorter, the lowest the longest, ranging from 6 to 22 mm long, black at base to grey tipped black. There is 1 central up to 3 cm long, black becoming brownish-grey as it ages. Flowers are bright deep pink, about 2 cm long and wide. Fruit is pink to scarlet, seeds brown.

Reported from Nuevo Leon, near Monterrey, and from Huasteca Canyon.

M. melanocentra

M. melispina Werderm., *Notizbl. Bot. Gart. Berlin* 12:226 (1934); *MSJ* 12:57 (1972)
Referred to *M. winterae*. Reppenhagen uses this name for a distinctive, pale flowered species.

M. mendeliana (Bravo) Werderm., *Neue Kakt.* 100 (1931); *An. Inst. Biol. Mex.* 2:195 with fig. (1931); *MSJ* 12:57 (1972)
Hunt ascribes this name to *M. hahniana*, as a form with poorly developed radials and long centrals (2 to 4) the lowest up to 2 cm long. Found at Guanajuato, without precise locality, this name is often applied to plants without any real regard to the requirements of the original description.

M. mercadensis Patoni, *Bol. Alianza Cient. Univ. Durangol.* 54 (1910); *The Cact.* 4:145 (1923); *MSJ* 12:58 (1972)
Series **Stylothelae** M. BOMBYCINA Group
According to Glass and Foster this species is one of a large complex involving '*M. sinistrohamata, guillauminiana, barbata, pennispinosa, zacatecasensis,* along with numerous others, many of which should be dumped into synonymy.' The names specified have not yet been discarded and are mostly well-known and firmly attached to distinct plants in collections, but there are strong similarities between them especially this species, *M. sinistrohamata* and *M. guillauminiana*, the only apparent difference being in coloration of the spines or flowers. Their proximity to each other also points to 1 large, variable species, but considerable legwork needs to be done in the field to establish their true relationships; *M. pennispinosa* and *M. barbata* are more distinct.

M. mercadensis is particularly noteworthy with a reddish cast to the spines, accompanied by cleverly colour-matched, pale, shell-pink flowers. Plants of this species make flat-globular heads clustering from the base after reaching apple size. The axils are naked. Radial spines number 25 to 30, white, slightly pubescent, 5 to 8 mm long. Central spines number 4 to 7, 15 to 25 mm long, one hooked, needle-like, stronger than the radials, deep red to light reddish-brown. Flowers are pale, shell-pink, described as 3 cm wide, but this is reckoned to be an error—they are more often about 1·5 to 2 cm wide. Fruit is red, seeds black.

Reported from the state of Durango, near the city of Durango, Cerro Mercado, and in the volcanic area known as the Brena.

M. mercadensis

M. meridiorosei, Castetter, Pierce & Schwerin, *Cact. Amer.* 50:176 (1978); *MSJ* 19:44 et seq. (1979); *Cact. GB* 41:97 (1979)
In papers which are as baffling as they are long, these authors advance this new name for the plant known for

some time now as *M. wilcoxii* (or more recently as *M. wrightii* var. *wilcoxii*), maintaining that this latter epithet more correctly applies to what has been known as *M. viridiflora*; they discard the latter name altogether. This theory has not yet met with general acceptance by either collectors or botanists, and the taxon *M. wrightii* var. *wilcoxii* is maintained here in preference to *M. meridiorosei*.

M. mexicensis Craig, *Mamm. Handb.* 311 with fig. (1945); *MSJ* **12**:58 (1972)

Hunt equates this incomplete description of a juvenile plant with 'probably' *M. grusonii* or *M. zeyerana*.

M. meyranii Bravo, *Cact. GB* **18**:84 with fig. (1956); *MSJ* **12**:58 (1972); *Cact. y Suc. Mex.* **14**:75 & 93 (1969)—var. *michoacana*

Series **Polyacanthae** M. SPINOSISSIMA Group

This is a narrow stemmed species in the series, differing little from *M. pilcayensis*, except in the lesser number of central spines.

The very full description by Dra. Helia Bravo is condensed here: it called for a clustering plant, with eventually very long, individual stems—to 55 cm long—only 4 to 5 cm wide, the body completely hidden by the spines. Axils in youth are sparsely woolly. Central spines number 2, pointing upwards and downwards, to 10 mm long, straight, needle-like, orange-yellow tipped chestnut-brown in youth, becoming greyish. Radial spines number 17 to 19, similar to the centrals, but shorter, 3 to 6 mm long and thinner. Flowers are purple inside, purplish-brown outside, nearly 2 cm long, narrow with the petals reflexing at the tips. Fruit is pinkish-purple, seeds light brown. Plants in cultivation are often at variance with the description.

Reported from the state of Mexico, the valley of the Rio Tilostoc, Santa Barbara, near the Miguel Alcman

M. meyranii

hydro-electric plant, at 1,500 to 1,700 m altitude. Buchenau erected a variety—var. *michoacana*—in 1969, largely ignored since then, although the use of the name specifically has persisted in seed catalogues. It is close to *M. bella* The differences are minor, and with the spiny nature of this species difficult to determine, except perhaps for the flower which is yellowish-brownish, and the fruit, red.

Reported from Michoacan, near San Jose Purua.

M. microcarpa Engelm., Emory, *Mil. Rec.* 157 (1848); *MSJ* **12**:59 (1972); *Proc. Amer. Acad.* **3**:262 (1856)—*M. grahamii*; *West Amer. Sci.* **12**:50 (1902)—*M. oliviae*

Series **Ancistracanthae** M. MICROCARPA Group

This species is exceedingly widespread in habitat, but is not so commonly seen attaining any real size in collections. This is due to its propensity for regarding life in cultivation as often not comparable in some way to the wastelands of Mexico and southern USA; it returns with astonishing rapidity and regularity westwards, leaving collectors fondly regarding their photographs in memory of its short stay. But with extra care, in the form of a gritty compost and judicious watering especially in the spring, it will grow happily into a clump of stems and wring your withers with its show of large pink flowers.

Because of its wide range it is one of the most variable species, and the differences have prompted the separation at one time or another of various elements: *M. grahamii*, *M. milleri*, *M. oliviae* and *M. microcarpa* var. *auricarpa*. Benson in the third edition of his *Cacti of Arizona*, maintains *M. grahamii* as a distinct species, with *M. oliviae* treated as a straight-spined variety of it; at the same time he regards *M. milleri* as synonymous with *M. microcarpa*. The differences do not make identification easy, but they come down to *M. microcarpa* being more inclined to cluster as it gets on in life, while *M. grahamii* tends to stay solitary, the former with cylindroid stems compared with ovoid to spheroid in *M. grahamii*, and *M. grahamii* has generally thinner spines than *M. microcarpa*. Hunt is sceptical of the separation, especially since Benson says that these species intergrade where they overlap, which, as Hunt points out, from Benson's distribution maps means apparently much of southern Arizona! The species are therefore treated as synonymous here, with varietal status maintained for *M. grahamii*, and for var. *auricarpa*, which maintains its coloration of central spines (yellow rather than the normal red-brown to black) in plants raised from seed. *M. oliviae* is also regarded here as a variety of *M. microcarpa*. Descriptions, where not covered above, are as follows:

var. *microcarpa*, cylindroid stems, solitary or often clustering, 7·5 to 15 cm long, 4 to 5 cm wide. Radials number 18 to 28, 6 to 12 mm long, white to whitish tipped brown; centrals 1 or 2, 1 hooked, red-brown to black; flowers 18 to 28 mm wide, lavender-pink. Fruit is red, seeds black.

Reported from the south-eastern corner of Mojave County to western Graham and Pima Counties in Arizona, USA, and from Mexico in the north of Sonora.

Reported from Yavapai County to southern and eastern Pima County, and to Cochise County in Arizona, USA, from south-western New Mexico State and from El Paso County and (rarely) Presidio County in Texas. Also from the northern parts of Chihuahua and Sonora, Mexico.

var. *auricarpa*. Habit as for var. *grahamii*, but with yellow central spines and fruit, and more readily clustering.

Reported from Pinnacle Peak, Maricopa County, Arizona, USA.

M. microcarpa var. *microcarpa*

var. *grahamii*, solitary, seldom clustering, with ovoid to globular stems, 5 to 10 cm tall, 4·5 to 11·5 cm wide. Radials 20 to 35, 6 to 8 mm long. Centrals 2 to 4, 12 to 25 mm long, 1 hooked, red-brown to black. Flower is 18 to 23 mm wide, pale pink or white. Fruit is red, seeds black.

M. microcarpa var. *auricarpa*

M. microcarpa var. *grahamii*

M. microcarpa var. *oliviae*

var. *oliviae* (Orcutt) Benson. Habit as for var. *grahamii* but more readily clustering, central spines usually 3 in number, white or the lower sometimes dark-tipped, and straight (occasionally an odd hooked central, but rarely), about 5 to 8 mm long.

Reported from Pima County and (rarely) in Santa Cruz and Cochise Counties in Arizona, USA, and from northern Sonora in Mexico.

M. microceras Lem., *Cact. Nov. Hort. Monv.* 6 (1838); *MSJ* **12**:60 (1972)

According to Hunt a synonym for *M. magnimamma*.

M. microhelia Werderm., *Monatsschr. Deutsch. Kakt. Ges.* 236 with fig. (1930); *MSJ* **12**:61 (1972)
Series **Leptocladodae** M. ELONGATA Group

'Little sun' the specific name means, and the golden-yellow radials, especially in youth, live up to the name, setting off the darker centrals wonderfully. It has too the distinction of being one of the earliest to flower in the year, with distinctive, greenish-yellow flowers, sometimes tinged pink or wholly pink to purple. Described shortly after this species was *M. microheliopsis*, which seems by most authorities to be accepted merely as a form of this species with more numerous, persistent central spines, and purplish flowers. Another form of the species more inclined to cluster was identified by Craig as *M. droegeana*, a species otherwise very obscure. *M. microhelia* makes a columnar stem to about 25 cm tall or more and about 6 cm wide, clustering when reaching this height or sometimes beforehand, from the base and lower stem. Axils are a little woolly in youth only. Radial spines number 30 to 50, 4 to 6 mm long, evenly radiating,

straight or more often a little curved back to the plant body, white to reddish-yellow. Central spines up to 4 (to 8 in '*M. microheliopsis*' or sometimes not present at all), up to 11 mm long, stout and needle-like, straight or curved, varying degrees of reddish or yellowish brown. Flowers are about 16 mm long and wide, whitish-cream, through lemon yellow to reddish-pink or purplish. Fruit is whitish, greenish or pale pink, seeds brown.

Reported from Queretaro, Sierra de Zamorano, at 2,000 m altitude, in rocky soil.

M. microheliopsis Werderm., *Notizbl. Bot. Gart. Mus. Berlin* **11**:278 (1931); *MSJ* **12**:61 (1972)

Referred to *M. microhelia*.

M. micromeris Engelm., *Proc. Amer. Acad.* **3**:256 (1857)

This is the well-known *Epithelantha micromeris*.

M. microthele Muehlenpf., *Allg. Gartenz.* **16**:11 (1848)—(not *Cactus microthele* Spreng., or *M. microthele* Mart.); *MSJ* **4**:65 (1964) & **12**:61 (1972)
Series **Leucocephalae** M. SEMPERVIVI Group

This name is often seen applied to *M. pseudoperbella* or *M. perbella*, which both have pink flowers compared with white in this species. *M. microthele* differs too from *M. pseudoperbella* (usually short-columnar and solitary) in its flatter, many-headed habit of growth, and in this respect is more like *M. perbella*, or *M. formosa*, the latter suggested by Hunt as a more likely candidate for comparison. Muehlenpfordt's description gives 22 to 24 radial spines, white and bristle-like, 3 to 4 mm long. The 2 central spines are shorter still at 2 mm but stronger, directed upwards and downwards and white (usually tipped brown in cultivated plants

M. microhelia

M. microthele

seen). The flowers are white with a reddish-yellow midstripe only on the outer segments. Fruit is red, seeds brown.

Reported from Tamaulipas, and from San Luis Potosi east of Huizache near the turning to Tula on highway 80.

M. miegeana W. H. Earle, _Saguaroland Bull._ **26**:77 with fig. (1972); _MSJ_ **14**:49 (1974)
Series **Macrothelae** M. STANDLEYI Group
This is a recently described species with affinities to _M. johnstonii, M. standleyi_ and _M. sonorensis_, and is becoming widespread in collections from collected seed made available in the trade. As with similar species growth is not fast, and it will be 8 years or so before a plant of mature size, 10 cm in diameter, is achieved.

Earle described it as usually solitary, globular to short-columnar, axils with white wool only in the growing area. Radial spines number 10 or 11, 8 to 9 mm long, straight or slightly curving, grey-white, giving the plant an overall whitish appearance. Central spines are usually 2 in number, 7 to 8 mm long, straight and brown. Flowers are 20 mm long, 25 mm wide, reddish-pink with scarlet midstripe, brownish outer segments, stigma-lobes yellow, 5 in number. Fruit is cherry-red, seeds reddish-brown.

Reported from Sonora, 14 km west of Moctezuma. Hunt comments that this is the most northerly of this group, from the Sierra Madre foothills.

M. miegeana

M. mieheana Tiegel, _Deutsche Gartenz._ **48**:397 with fig. (1933); _MSJ_ **12**:62 (1972) & **18**:13 (1978)
Series **Leptocladodae** M. ELONGATA Group
This beautiful species is like a thick-stemmed, whitish-yellow spined _M. elongata_. It has a heavily clustering habit, with stems up to about 15 cm long and 5 cm wide; the axils have white wool in youth. Radial spines number 18 to 20, with 3 to 6 similar centrals, up to 15 mm long, pale yellow, almost white at the

growing points, the centrals slightly darker yellow, sometimes brownish. Flowers are yellow, about 15 mm long, fruit whitish, semi-translucent, so that the light brown seeds are discernible (fruit in cultivated plants is a whitish pink colour).

Reported from Queretaro.

Tiegel named as var. _globosa_ a more globose form, which could well be the all yellow spined form of _M. densispina_, sometimes seen labelled as _M. esaussieri_. Hunt is inclined to regard _M. mieheana_ as relating more closely to _M. densispina_, and it may be the connecting link between this species and _M. elongata_. Certainly plants in cultivation of _M. mieheana_ flower and fruit at the same time as _M. elongata_, and the flowers and fruit are very similar.

M. mieheana

M. milleri (B. & R.) Boed., _Mamm. Vergl. Schluss._ 30 (1933); _The Cact._ **4**:156 with fig. (1923)
See under _M. microcarpa_.

M. mitlensis Bravo, _Cact. Suc. Mex._ **1**:86 (1956); _MSJ_ **13**:77 (1973)
Referred to _M. rekoi_.

M. mixtecensis Bravo, _An. Inst. Biol. Mex._ **25**:534 (1954); _MSJ_ **12**:80 (1972); _Cact. Amer._ **44**:98 with fig. (1972)
Referred to _M. mystax_.

M. moellerana Boed., _Zeitschr. Sukk._ **1**:213 with fig. (1924); _Cact. Amer._ **42**:111 (1970); _MSJ_ **12**:75 (1972)
Series **Stylothelae** M. BOMBYCINA Group
The difference in colour of the central spines of this species gave rise to the erection of _M. cowperae_, which name was applied to a plant with dark red-brown central spines. Contrarily it is often applied in collections to those with yellow spines.

With the natural reluctance of collectors to let go a name once one is available for a distinctive form, the wrangling over the suggested synonymy of the two has continued. But there seems no doubt that what we have

M. albicans

M. candida

M. carmenae

M. dioica and *M. brandegei* in habitat

M. erythrosperma

M. elongata (various forms)

M. guelzowiana

M. herrerae var. *albiflora*

M. geminispina

M. guillauminiana

M. hahniana

M. humboldtii

M. Lau 1186 *(M. glassii* affinity)

M. laui fa. *laui*

M. laui fa. *subducta*

M. lenta

M. longiflora fa. *longiflora*

M. pectinifera

M. poselgeri

M. petterssonii

M. saboae fa. *saboae*

M. rekoi

M. senilis

M. ruestii

M. setispina

M. slevinii

M. spinosissima

M. tegelbergiana

M. solisioides

M. stella-de-tacubaya

M. tetrancistra

M. wrightii var. *wilcoxii*

here are variable populations of one species, with sometimes yellow, sometimes brown central spines, varying flower colour from white to yellowish to pink, and variable density and angle of the spination.

The description to embrace the variation is as follows: stem solitary, flat-globular to short-columnar in time, with naked axils. Radial spines number 35 to 50, 7 to 9 mm long, smooth, white, yellowish at base, needle-like. Central spines are 8 or 9 in number, occasionally 10, the lower 2 to 4 hooked, 20 to 30 mm long, the upper shorter and straight, smooth, thickened at base, 'splendid, bright honey-yellow to a beautiful dark red-brown', yellow at base. Flowers are clear pink, with darker midstripe, or white with yellowish midstripe, about 15 mm long and wide. Fruit is greenish-white, seeds black.

Reported from Durango, Sierra de Santa Maria, under pine trees, but Glass and Foster report the type locality is due east of the city of Durango, and that it occurs throughout the high rocky summits of the mountains at least as far as Jerez in Zacatecas.

M. moellerana

M. mollendorffiana Shurly, *Cact. GB* **10**:19 with fig. (1948); *Cact. Amer.* **43**:73 with figs. (1971); *MSJ* **12**:75 (1972); *Int. Newer Mamm.* 12 with fig. (1973)
Series **Heterochlorae** M. RHODANTHA Group

The standing of this species is very doubtful, and it probably resolves under the widespread, variable *M. rhodantha*. It was described from plants discovered in 1937 in Hidalgo by Schwarz, without precise locality. Glass and Foster commented on rediscovering it near Cardonal, a few miles north of Ixmiquilpan in Hidalgo, that it is unlikely that such an accessible species had not been described previously. But maybe its close resemblance to *M. rhodantha* led to its being overlooked.

It tends to remain solitary, making eventually a slender column about 7 cm or more wide and up to 30 cm or more tall. Axils are woolly and later have 4 or 5 bristles too. Radial spines vary in the two plants in Kew received from Shurly—from 18 to 20 in that

preserved in the herbarium, and from 24 to 28 in the other, now older plant which was grown on—3 to 5 mm long and glassy white (chalky white in the preserved one). Central spines are 4 or 6 in number, 6 to 14 mm long, stout and needle-like, light yellow-brown with darker tip. Flowers are smallish, 10 to 13 mm long, 8 mm wide, purplish-red. Fruit is purplish-red, seeds brown.

M. mollendorffiana

M. mollihamata Shurly, *Cact. GB* **22**:52 with figs. (1960); *MSJ* **13**:66 (1973)
Referred to *M. pygmaea*.

M. monancistracantha Backeb., *Die Cact.* **6**:3897 (1962); *MSJ* **9**:25 (1969)
Referred to *M. nana*.

M. monancistria Berg. ex Schum., *Gesamt. Kakt.* 533 (1898); *Mamm. Handb.* 157 (1945); *MSJ* **12**:76 (1972)
A dubious species referred to *M. erythrosperma*.

M. monocentra Jacobi, *Allg. Gartenz.* **24**:90 (1856); *Mamm. Handb.* 74 (1945); *MSJ* **12**:76 (1972)
Hunt dismisses this name as dubiously valid because of its unknown source and dubious identity.

M. montensis Craig, *Mamm. Handb.* 311 with fig. (1945); *MSJ* **14**:48 (1974)
An incomplete description of a dubiously determinable species.

M. morganiana Tiegel, *Deutsch. Gartenz.* **48**: 397 with fig. (1933) *MSJ* **12**:76 (1972)
Series **Leucocephalae** M. GEMINISPINA Group

According to Hunt this is a variety at most of *M. perbella*, but the name is likely to persist, as the plants it is applied to are quite distinctive. The body of the solitary, eventually dichotomously dividing stem is about 8 cm wide, globose to short-cylindric. Axils have dense white hair, to 2 cm long in the growing area. Radial spines number 40 to 50, up to 12 mm long, white, fine, needle-like to hair-like, tortuous and

M. morganiana

interlacing. Central spines number 4 to 6, sometimes oddly 3, 10 mm long, straight, stronger than the radials, but not so strong or long as in *M. parkinsonii*, white with brown tips. Flowers are about 1 cm long and wide, pink with deeper pink midstripe. Fruit is red, seeds brown.

Reported from Guanajuato without locality.

M. morricalii Cowper, *Cact. Amer.* **41**:208 with fig. (1969); *MSJ* **14**:66 (1974)

This name is referred to the prior *M. barbata*, with which both Hunt and the Zimmermans agree in principle it is conspecific.

M. movensis Craig, *Mamm. Handb.* 312 with fig. (1945); *MSJ* **14**:48 (1974)

Hunt tentatively ascribes this species name to *M. craigii*, itself dubiously identifiable.

M. muehlenpfordtii Foerst., *Allg. Gartenz.* **15**:49 (1847); *Cact. Amer.* **42**:266 with fig. (1970); *MSJ* **12**:77 (1972)

Series **Leucocephalae** M. GEMINISPINA Group

Names associated with this species include *M. potosina*, later described as *M. neopotosina* by Craig, *M. nealeana*, invalidly published, and *M. celsiana*, an indeterminate species, which in collections invariably turns out to be what was described as *M. muehlenpfordtii*.

Although collectors have baulked at accepting this name, the reasons are more linguistic I think, rather

than anything to do with taxonomy, and since Backeberg has resurrected what is generally agreed to be the correct name for the species, it should be adopted without further demur. The variability is superficial and is mainly in regard to the varying length of the central spines, which leads to further confusion as some collectors label their long-spined plants *M. celsiana*, without really bothering to check them out. Comparison of such plants with the original descriptions invariably shows that they are ascribable to *M. muehlenpfordtii* with the lower spine longer, while the description of *M. celsiana* calls for the upper spine to be the longer. Craig's illustration no. 251, captioned *M. celsiana* in his *Handbook* is also of *M. muehlenpfordtii*. In view of the confusion and the complete absence of plants fitting the description of *M. celsiana* as originally portrayed the latter is a name best discarded.

Coming back to *M. muehlenpfordtii*, the body tends to remain single-stemmed, branching dichotomously to form a massive, top-heavy plant with individual heads 12 to 15 cm in diameter. The axils have white bristles and the areoles have pale yellow to white wool in the young growth. Radial spines are very numerous (about 40 or 50) up to 4 mm long and almost hiding the plant body, whitish and bristle-like. Central spines

M. muehlenpfordtii

number 4, standing out from the body, brown-yellow to pale yellow, slightly darker sometimes at the tips, the upper 3 only 3 to 4 mm long, the lower varying a great deal, up to 16 mm long. Flowers are about 1 cm long, deep pink. Fruit is red, seeds light brown.

Reported from Queretaro, Guanajuato and the southern part of San Luis Potosi.

M. multicentralis Craig, *Mamm. Handb.* 313 (1945); *MSJ* **12**:78 (1972)

One of the numerous, closely relating *Stylothelae* series, dead before it could be photographed by Craig, it should now at last be decently buried, since no one has been able to positively identify it in the 30 years since Craig published the name in his *Handbook*.

M. multiceps Salm-Dyck, *Cact. Hort. Dyck* **7**:81 (1850); *MSJ* **13**:63 (1973)
See under *M. prolifera*.

M multidigitata Radley ex Lindsay, *Cact. Amer.* **19**:152 with figs. (1947) & **12**:5 (1940); *MSJ* **12**:78 (1972); *Int. Newer Mamm.* 13 with fig. (1973)
Series **Ancistracanthae** M. DIOICA Group
A species not widespread in collections, although its clumping habit may lead to its being so in a few more years. It forms clusters early in life, and gives the impression of a white-spined, stubby form of *M. elongata*. In some plants the individual stems will reach up to 20 cm in height, while others stay below 10 cm, sometimes only about 5 cm tall; they vary from 2 to 5 cm in diameter, according to the height, the taller ones being that much thicker-stemmed. The axils are slightly woolly. Radial spines are straight and white, numbering from 15 to 25, 6 to 8 mm long. Central spines are usually 4 in number, white with brown tips, about 8 mm long, straight and needle-like, although on new growth they are occasionally hooked. Flowers are white, about 15 mm long and wide, with an olive green stripe on the outer petals and green stigma lobes, which combine to give the appearance sometimes of a greenish-yellow flower. Fruit is red, seeds black.

Reported from Baja California on the steep slopes of San Pedro Nolasco Island in profusion, sometimes growing in pure guano—not recommended as a cultivation tip!

M. multidigitata

M. multiformis (B. & R.) Boed., *Mamm. Vergl. Schluss.* 26 (1933); *The Cact.* **4**:148 with fig. (1923); *MSJ* **12**:79 (1972)
This name has been unknown in cultivation for many years, no doubt due to its synonymy with *M. erythrosperma*, from which the original description differed only slightly.

M. multihamata Boed., *Monatsschr. Kakteenk.* **25**:76 with fig. (1915); *MSJ* **12**:79 (1972)

An uncertain species of the series *Stylothelae*, characterized by several hooked central spines. This is a character which occurs variously in this series, and the description points towards *M. erythrosperma* as its most probable placing.

M. multiseta Ehrenb., *Allg. Gart.* **17**:242 (1849); *MSJ* **11**:35 (1971)
Referred by Hunt to *M. karwinskiana*.

M. mundtii Schum., *Monatsschr. Kakteenk.* **13**:141 with fig. (1903); *MSJ* **12**:80 (1972)
Referred to *M. wiesingeri*.

M. mutabilis Scheidw., *Allg. Gartenz.* **9**:43 (1841); *MSJ* **12**:80 (1972)
A synonym of *M. mystax*.

M. muy-rosa Hort., *MSJ* **12**:80 (1972)
A catalogue name which appears to refer to *M. parkinsonii*.

M. mystax Mart., *Nov. Act. Nat. Cur.* **16(1)**:322. t21 (1832); *Hort. Reg. Monac.* 127 (1829) name only; *MSJ* **12**:80 (1972)
Series **Polyedrae** M. MYSTAX Group
This is a well-known species in collections, desirable if only for its free flowering, producing several rings of flowers readily each year, deep pink with brown outer petals. The stem is simple, and will reach a considerable size in time, 30 cm or more tall and about 15 cm wide. The original description tells us that the tubercles are angled, and Hunt adds the information that the sap is milky and the axils have bristles. These white bristles are most apparent in the growing area. Radial spines are variable, from 8 to 12 in number, and from 3 to 10 mm long and in colour from grey-white

M. mystax

tipped darker to purple-grey in youth. Central spines number 3 or 4, to 7 in *M. mixtecensis*, sometimes only 1, 15 to 20 mm long, occasionally with one up to 70 mm long, dark purplish tipped dark brown. Flowers are numerous in several rings around the top of the stem, deep purplish-pink with brown stripes on the outer petals, largish (to 2·5 cm long) but not very wide-spreading. Fruit is red, seeds brown.

Reported from Ixmiquilpan and San Pedro Nolasco at 1,830 m altitude, and subsequently from Puebla, widespread; also Oaxaca at Suchixtlahuaca (*casoi*), east of Huajuapan de Leon (*huajuapensis*), and between Tejupan and Suchixtlahuaca (*mixtecensis*).

Hunt equates *M. casoi*, *M. huajuapensis*, *M. atroflorens*, *M. crispiseta* and *M. mixtecensis* here.

M. nana Backeb., *Descr. Cact. Nov.* **3**:8 (1963); *Kakteenlex.* 249. fig. 215 (1966); *MSJ* **13**:10 (1973); *Cact. Amer.* **42**:269 (1970)
Series **Stylothelae** M. WILDII Group

This name persists, in spite of its reduction to synonymy with firstly *M. haehneliana*, by Glass and Foster, secondly *M. monancistracantha*, by Hunt, and in the same breath by Hunt with 'possibly' *M. eschanzieri*. But Hunt has swung back to the more accepted name amongst collectors, *M. nana*, for this species in his latest published opinion, to a sigh of relief from those who had not altered their labels. The problem is exacerbated for the collector by the persistence of *M. nana* in remaining solitary and small, while plants grown as *M. monancistracantha* often strongly cluster and fill a large pan. Apart from that the plants are identical, and Hunt's reduction to one species name makes good sense. The description of *M. eschanzieri* calls for a somewhat different plant, and the name should be regarded with suspicion. Hunt dismisses it as a dubious species, and certainly the

M. nana

name is not applied to any plants in collections I have seen, unless in error to plants of *M. nana*. The species *M. nana* was described as only 2·5 cm in diameter at most, and about 1·5 cm tall, but in cultivation plants grow to about 5 cm across and as tall, and as indicated above the habit varies from solitary to clustering and forming quite large clumps. Axils with wool in youth later have bristles too. Radial spines number about 35, very thin, shining white, a little pubescent (more in '*M. trichacantha*'). Centrals are sometimes absent, or 1 to 2 in number, the lower hooked, brownish, pubescent, to about 5 mm long. Flowers are about 1 cm long, 1·5 cm wide, creamy-white to pale yellow with faint pinkish midstripe. Fruit is pink to dark red, seeds black.

Reported 25 km south of San Luis Potosi and at El Balneario de Lourdes.

M. nana (monancistracantha)

M. napina Purpus, *Monatsschr. Kakteenk.* **33**:161 (1912) and **23**:123 with fig. (1913); *MSJ* **13**:11 (1973)
Series **Longiflorae** M. NAPINA Group

Here is one of the rare gems of the genus, which combines beauty and the beast in one species, being difficult to grow successfully and reluctant to flower, but rewarding care and skill in meeting its needs with stupendous flowers. Hunt relates this 'old' species with the recently named *M. deherdtiana*. The stem which surmounts a large, carrot-like root, is solitary, as tall as it is wide, about 5 cm at most usually, with sometimes a little wool in the axils, radial spines number about 12, 8 to 9 mm long, a little recurved, glassy white, yellowish at the base. There are usually no centrals, but Britton and Rose mentioned some plants collected as having central spines, which Craig also mentions in his *Handbook*, describing it as var. *centrispina*, with solitary central spines. The large flowers, up to 4 cm in diameter, but not very long tubed, are pale carmine or pink, with deeper midstripe. Fruit and seed was not described, but a plant in my collection set fruit in the characteristic way of others in this series, the fruit remaining embedded in the plant body with just the end showing between the tubercles; the seeds were black.

Reported from Puebla, near Tehuacan, on hills south of San Lorenzo.

Until more fieldwork is done the relationship with *M. deherdtiana* and var. *dodsonii* remains in question, but I shall happily retain them separately for the present.

M. napina

M. nealeana Hort. (Schmoll), Neale, *Cacti & other Succ.* 91 (1935); *MSJ* **13**:11 (1973)

An invalidly published name referred to *M. muehlenpfordtii*.

M. nejapensis Craig & Dawson, *Allan Hancock Found. Occ. Papers* **no. 2**:57 (1948); *MSJ* **11**:36 (1971); *Int. Newer Mamm.* 14 with fig. (1973)
Series **Polyedrae** M. KARWINSKIANA Group

This close relative of *M. karwinskiana* is said by Hunt to occur between that species and *M. collinsii*, and may well be the connecting link between the two.

M. nejapensis

It is a readily recognised and accepted plant in collections with its long, axillary bristles, bright green body colour and pale yellow flowers, and if reduced in status will hopefully be retained at some level. It makes clusters of stems about 15 cm tall and 7·5 cm wide, clustering dichotomously or offsetting. Axils have dense wool and long twisting bristles. Radial spines number usually 4, sometimes 3 or 5, 2 to 5 mm long, except for the lower 1 which varies up to 5 cm long, white, tipped reddish-brown. There are no central spines. Flowers are about 1·5 cm across, whitish with reddish or reddish-brown midstripe. Fruit is light red, seeds pale brown.

Reported from Oaxaca, north-west of Nejapa.

M. nelsonii (B. & R.) Boed., *Mamm. Vergl. Schluss.* 37 (1933); *The Cact.* **4**:163 with fig. 182 (1923); *Cact. Amer.* **43**:202 (1971); *MSJ* **13**:11 (1973)

Referred to *M. beneckei*.

M. neobertrandiana Backeb., *Cact. (Paris)* **33**:82 (1952); *Die Cact.* **5**:3433 with figs. (1961); *MSJ* **13**:11 (1973)

This is apparently a synonym for *M. magallanii*.

M. neocoronaria Knuth, *Kaktus ABC.* 392 (1935); (syn. *M. coronaria* Schum., *Gesamt. Kakt.* 555 (1938), but not *M. coronaria* Haw., *Rev. Pl. Succ.* 69 (1821)); *MSJ* **13**:11 (1973)

This name crops up in collections variously applied to plants of *M. spinosissima* affinity or *M. duoformis*. It is best discarded as indeterminable. The description was of a clustering plant with stems 6 to 7 cm wide, 7 to 15 cm tall, with naked axils, 16 to 18 radial spines, 8 to 10 mm long, transparent to white, and 6 (sometimes 4) centrals, the upper longest, to 15 mm, the lower hooked, dark ruby red, later brown then yellowish to grey. Flowers are 16 mm long, 10–12 mm wide, light carmine, with darker midstripe. Fruit and seeds undescribed.

M. neocrucigera Backeb., *Die Cact.* **5**:3426 (1961); *MSJ* **13**:12 (1973)

Not validly published and probably just a short-spined form of *M. parkinsonii*.

M. neomystax Backeb., *Cactus (Paris)* **no. 30**:133 (1951); *MSJ* **11**:35 (1971)

Hunt equates this name to *M. karwinskiana*. It is often applied to plants of *M. mystax* in error.

M. neopalmeri Craig, *Mamm. Handb.* 267 with fig. (1945); *Cact. Amer.* **24**:82 with fig. (1952); *MSJ* **7**:37 (1967) & **13**:12 (1972)
Series **Ancistracanthae** M. DIOICA Group

This is a good-looking species, not well represented in collections, mainly appealing in its dense spines, which, with the axillary wool, almost hide the body of the plant. It clusters fairly early in life, with globular stems each about 5 cm tall and across, and has dense wool in the axils with occasional bristles. Radial spines number from about 15 to 30, and are up to about 5 mm long, slender, needle-like, white or pale yellow and interlacing. Central spines often number 2, but up to 5 are found, from 4 to 8 mm long, straight, or sometimes hooked, brown with darker tip, stronger than the radials. The flowers are smallish, to 12 mm long, pale greenish-white to light cream with an olive-green midstripe, sometimes tinged with pink, outer petals with reddish-tan midstripe. The fruit is scarlet, seeds black.

Reported from Baja California, on San Benito Island.

M. neopalmeri

M. neophaeacantha Backeb., *Blatt. Sukk.* **1**:5 (1949); *Cactus (Paris)* **33**:84 (1952); *Die Cact.* **5**:3437, 3438 with fig. (1961); *MSJ* **13**:13 (1973)

A name referred to *M. kewensis*.

M. neopotosina Craig, *Mamm. Handb.* 117 with fig. (1945); *MSJ* **12**:77 (1972)

Referred to *M. muehlenpfordtii*.

M. neoschwarzeana Backeb., *Blatt. Sukk.* **1**:5 (1949); *Cactus (Paris)* **7, no. 30**:135 (1951); *Die Cact.* **5**:3405, 3407 with fig. (1961); *MSJ* **7**:79 (1967) & **14**:62 (1974); *Int. Newer Mamm.* 16 with fig. (1973).

Hunt refers this name to *M. bocensis* or *M. tesopacensis*.

M. nivosa Link, *Enum. Cact.* 11 (1837); *MSJ* **13**:14 (1973)

Series **Macrothelae** M. MAMMILLARIS Group

One of the few species endemic to the islands of the West Indies, this handsome species, although a little difficult to grow sometimes, is becoming widespread in collections after some years of comparative obscurity. In cultivation it is usually a heavily clustering plant from around the base, with more or less globular heads

about 6 or 7 cm in diameter (to 18 cm in habitat), the offsets often appearing at the tips of the tubercles rather than as more commonly in the axils. The body colour is a dark olive-green, bronzing in full light, and the axils are densely woolly, white with a yellowish tinge. The spines are similar, with one more centrally positioned, numbering 6 to 8 (or up to 13) around the central, up to 2 cm long, straight, bright yellow becoming dark brown. Flowers are cream-coloured to yellow, up to 2 cm long. Fruit is red, seeds light brown.

Reported from Tortola Island in the West Indies (the type plant) and from southern Bahamas, Mona Island, Puerto Rico, Desecheo, Culebra, Buck Island, St Thomas, Little St James Island, Antigua and Turks Island.

Its more tropical origins suggest somewhat higher temperatures are needed for successful cultivation, although lower temperatures are tolerated.

M. nivosa

M. nolascana Craig, *Mamm. Handb.* 82 (1945), *Cact. Amer.* **12**:5 (1940) & **47**:173 (1975)

Referred now to *M. tayloriorum*.

M. nunezii (B. & R.) Orcutt, *Cactog.* 8 (1926); *The Cact.* **4**:120 and 142 with figs. (1923); *Mamm. Vergl. Schluss.* 35 (1933); *Die Cact.* **5**:3374 (1961); *MSJ* **13**:14 (1973)

Series **Polyacanthae** M. NUNEZII Group

This species is an attractive variation on the theme of *M. spinosissima*, with a suggestion of *M. rhodantha* in its appearance. It takes in *M. solisii*, which, according to Hunt is synonymous, with fewer radials and more consistently hooked central spines. As with others in this series both straight and hooked central spines occur, with permutations between the two in some plants, which often produce odd hooked or straight central spines in contrast with their general habit. The plant body is globular to cylindrical, usually solitary, in time reaching a height of 15 cm or more, 6 to 8 cm wide, with bristles in the axils. Radial spines usually number from 25 to 30, 20 to 25 for *M. solisii*, 5 to 7 mm long, bristle-like, white and stiff. The central spines are 2 to 4 in number, occasionally 5 or 6, stouter than the radials, 8 to 15 mm long (one hooked and up to 2 cm long, *M. solisii*), straight or occasionally hooked, brown to nearly black at the tips. Flowers magenta red, 15 mm wide. Fruit is greenish-white tinged pink, seeds brown.

Reported from Guerrero, Cerro de Buenavista de Cuellar, and from Taxco on shaded cliffs.

M. nunezii

M. obconella Scheidw., *Hort. Belge* **4**:93 with fig. (1837); *Die Cact.* **5**:3341 (1961); *Cact. Amer.* **43**:121 with fig. (1971); *MSJ* **13**:23 (1973)
Series **Heterochlorae** M. POLYTHELE Group

M. obconella

Hunt upholds this name in preference to the previously named *M. tetracantha*, which he rejects as a source of confusion, and equates here too the later described *M. dolichocentra* and *M. ingens*. It is a handsome, large-growing species with strong, yellowish-brown spines. The body will eventually make a large, egg-shaped plant about 25 cm tall and 15 cm wide—an ostrich's egg! The axils are woolly in youth. In time it will offset from the base. Central spines (or sub-central—there are no real radials) number 4, occasionally up to 6, 10 to 30 mm long, the lower longer, tending to recurve, yellowish-brown at first, later grey. Flowers are about 15 mm long and wide, pink with whitish margins. Fruit is red, seeds light brown.

Reported from the Barranca de Venados and from near Metzquititlan.

M. obscura Hildm., *Monatsschr. Kakteenk.* **1**:52 with fig. (1891); *MSJ* **13**:24 (1973)
(Not *M. obscura* Loudon, for which see *M. obconella*)

Hunt ascribes this name to synonymy with *M. hamiltonhoytea*, and thence to *M. gigantea*.

M. obvallata Otto (ex Dietr.), *Allg. Gartenz.* **14**:308 (1846); *MSJ* **13**:24 (1973)

A name referred by Craig to *M. fuliginosa*, but this in turn is obscure and doubtfully identifiable.

M. ocamponis Ochot., *Bol. Dir. Estud. Biol.* **2**:355 with fig. (1918); *MSJ* **12**:58 (1972)

Referred to *M. mercadensis*.

M. occidentalis (B. & R.) Boed., *Mamm. Vergl. Schluss.* 36 (1933); *The Cact.* **4**:161 with figs. (1923); *MSJ* **13**:24 (1973)

M. occidentalis

Series **Ancistracanthae** M. MICROCARPA Group

There is considerable confusion in collections between this species and *M. mazatlanensis*. The latter is now taken to embrace former varieties incorrectly ascribed to *M. occidentalis*, i.e. var. *patonii* (syn. *M. patonii*) and var. *sinalensis*. This leaves the identity of *M. occidentalis*, confused for some time by these equations, clearer and applying to altogether paler and smaller-flowered plants. It was described by Britton and Rose (whose photographs of this species and *M. bombycina* on page 160 of Volume 4 of *The Cactaceae* are transposed) as clustering, with 'slender' branches 10 cm tall, densely spiny. Radial spines number about 12, yellowish. Central spines 4 or 5, reddish or brown, one longer and hooked. Flowers small, 1 cm long, pink. Fruit is red, seeds undescribed, but should be black.

Reported from near Manzanillo, Colima.

M. ochoterenae (Bravo) Werd., *Neue Kakt.* 98 (1931); *An. Inst. Biol. Mex.* **2**:127 with fig. (1931); *Cact. Amer.* **43**:75 with fig. (1971); *MSJ* **13**:25 (1973)
Referred to *M. discolor*.

M. ocotillensis Craig, *Mamm. Handb.* 314 with figs. (1945); *MSJ* **13**:25 (1973)
Hunt equates this name to *M. gigantea*. It is a fewer spined form with 1 to 3 centrals and 2 to 4 radials.

M. oliviae Orcutt, *West Amer. Sci.* **12**:50 (1902); *MSJ* **10**:34 (1970) & **13**:25 (1973)
Hunt follows Benson in regarding this species as a variation of *M. grahamii* and thence of *M. microcarpa*—see under *M. microcarpa*.

M. orcuttii Boed., *Kakteen* 323 (1929); *Monatsschr. Deutsch. Kakt. Ges.* **2**:258 with fig. (1930); *MSJ* **13**:25 (1973)
Series **Macrothelae**?

Plants grown under this name accord well with the original description, but hail from San Luis Potosi, not Puebla near Esperanza as cited, where only *M. carnea* grows, according to Hunt. The body is dark blue-green and plants remain solitary, in maturity reaching 11 cm wide and 12 cm or more tall. Axils have dense white wool and the areoles in youth are also very woolly. There are no radial spines except for occasionally 6 to 8 very short ones on young areoles. Central spines number 4, occasionally 5 or 6, 8 to 20 mm long, the lower the longest. Flowers are 12 mm long and wide, bright carmine with darker midstripes to the petals. Fruit is red, seeds brown.

M. orestera Benson, *Cacti of Arizona* **ed. 3**:22, 155 (1969); *Cacti. Amer.* **49**:23 & 51 (1977); *MSJ* **13**:26 (1973)
This name is offered by Benson in preference for *M. chavezei*, but it is apparent that this species, call it what you will, falls into synonymy beneath *M. viridiflora*—see comments under that name.

M. ortegae (B. & R.) Orcutt, *Cactog.* 8 (1926); *The Cact.* **4**:83 with fig. (1923); *MSJ* **13**:26 (1973)
Another doubtful name, unknown (or unidentified) in collections.

M. ortiz-rubiona (Bravo) Werderm., *Neue Kakt.* 95 (1931); *An. Inst. Biol. Mex.* **2**:193 with figs. (1931); *MSJ* **8**:45 (1968)
Hunt refers this name firmly to synonymy with *M. candida*.

M. oteroi Glass & Foster, *Cact. Amer.* **47**:24 with figs. (1975); *MSJ* **15**:51 (1975); *Cact. GB* **41**:99 (1979)
Series **Stylothelae** M. OTEROI Group
Freely clustering, even at a year old from seed, this recently described species will become rapidly available. The stems are only 2 to 3 cm tall, 3 to 4 cm wide, axils with a tuft of wool and a few hairlike

M. orcuttii

M. oteroi

bristles. Radial spines 12 to 14, 6 to 8 mm long, slender, needle-like, white tipped brown. There is 1 central spine, about 11 mm long, hooked, reddish-brown, whitish at base. Flowers are about 15 mm long, whitish with brownish-cerise midstripe. Fruit is bright red, seeds black.

Reported from Oaxaca, Alta Mixteca, near Buenavista de Concepcion, at about 1,800 m altitude, under oak trees in black, humus soil.

M. pachycylindrica Backeb., *Cact. GB* **21**:82 with fig. (1959); *MSJ* **13**:35 (1973)
Series **Macrothelae**   M. HEYDERI Group
Although Hunt declares this name 'probably conspecific' with *M. grusonii*, it is a very distinctive plant from a collector's point of view, making a thick column, to about 25 cm tall and about 11 cm in diameter, with a dark, grey-green body and little wool in the axils. Radial spines number about 20 to 23, 4 to 8 mm long, straight, whitish-grey and slender. Central spines, about 6 in number, are straight, about 12 mm long, black at first, fading to grey. Flowers are quite large, about 2 cm long and wide, dark, dull pink with deeper midstripe. Fruit is pale purplish-pink, seeds brown.

Reported from Mexico, but with no locality—probably from the State of Coahuila.

M. pachycylindrica

M. pachyrhiza Backeb., *Beitr. Sukk. u. Pflege.* **2**:39 with fig. (1939); *Cact. Amer.* **43**:75–76 with fig. (1971) *MSJ* **13**:35 (1973)
Referred to *M. discolor*.

M. pacifica (Gates) Boed., *Kaktus. ABC* 398 (1935); *MSJ* **7**:41 (1967)
Hunt equates this name with *M. baxterana*.

M. painteri Rose, *Monatsschr. Kakteenk.* **27**:22 with fig. (1917); *Cact. Amer.* **43**:7 (1971); *MSJ* **7**:41 (1967)
Series **Stylothelae**   M. WILDII Group
The original description of this species is of a globular plant 2 cm (sic) in diameter—plants are very shrunken in habitat, subsequently increasing girth rapidly in cultivation—with up to 25 thin, white radial spines, 5 mm long, and 4 or 5 central spines, 1 cm long, dark brown, one hooked and, with the radials, puberulent, i.e. having tiny hair-like bristles on the spines, like *M. pennispinosa*. Flowers were described as 15 mm long, greenish white, outer segments brownish.

It was reported from Queretaro, north of San Juan del Rio, on sheer faces of rocky cliffs. Glass and Foster recollected at what they thought was the type locality in 1968.

Plants in cultivation, probably resulting from this collection, show as they develop fine bristles in the axils, and the flowers are pinkish; they are regarded by Hunt as closer to *M. pygmaea*.

M. painteri

M. palmeri (Coult.) Boed., *Mamm. Vergl. Schluss.* 43 (1933) *not* Jacobi, 1856; Coult., *Contr. US Nat. Herb.* **3**:108 (1894); *MSJ* **13**:36 (1973)
Because of the prior (but unidentified) use of this name by Jacobi, the subsequent use of it by Coulter and Boedeker is invalid. The correct epithet for the species described is *M. neopalmeri*, by which name this species is now commonly known.

M. paradensis Hort., a catalogue name for plants referrable to *M. stella-de-tacubaya*.

M. parensis Craig, *Mamm. Handb.* 316 with fig. (1945); *MSJ* **13**:36 (1973)
Hunt equates this name to *M. pringlei*.

M. parkinsonii Ehrenb., *Linnaea* **14**:375 (1840); *MSJ* **13**:36 (1973)
Series   **Leucocephalae**   M.   GEMINISPINA Group
Hunt ascribes a number of names to synonymy with this species. Most are practically unknown in collect-

ions, due no doubt to their ready identification with this well-known, very distinctive species. Others, differing somewhat in spine length, are less easily discarded.

The names suggested as synonymous include *M. aljibensis*, *M. auriareolis*, *M. avila-camachoi*, *M. leucocentra*, *M. pseudocrucigera*, *M. queretarica*, *M. tiegeliana*, *M. vonwyssiana*, *M. morganiana*, *M. rosensis*, *M. cadereytensis*, and *M. infernillensis*. Of these 12 names few are worth arguing about from a collector's viewpoint. The differences in mature plants are mostly slight, and seedlings of most are notably indistinguishable. But one or two names persist, the most noteworthy being *M. morganiana*, see description under that name.

M. parkinsonii was described as at first solitary, later dichotomously dividing, 10 to 15 cm wide; plants in cultivation rarely reach a height of more than about 15 cm, although they will divide and form quite wide clusters eventually. Axils have wool and bristles. Radial spines number 30 or more, fine, white, about 4 to 6 mm long. Centrals number 2 to 4, rarely 5, upper 6 to 8 mm long, lowermost variable to 38 mm long, usually recurved, stiff, milk-white or reddish, dark

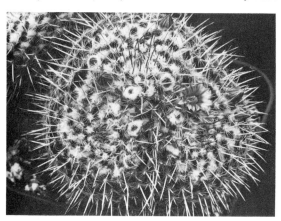

M. parkinsonii

brown at tip, a good deal stronger than the radials. Flowers are yellowish, small, with red stripe. Fruit is scarlet, seeds brown.

Reported from Hidalgo, near San Onofre in the Mineral del Doctor, on limestone rocks.

M. parriana Hort., *Cact. Amer.* **43**:273 (1971);
Referred to *M. mixtecensis*, and thence to synonymy with *M. mystax*.

M. patonii (Bravo) Boed., *Mamm. Vergl. Schluss.* 33 (1933); *An. Inst. Biol. Mex.* **2**:129 with fig. (1931)
Referred to *M. mazatlanensis*.

M. pectinifera F. A. C. Weber, *Bois Dict. Hort.* 804 (1898); *The Cact.* **4**:64 with fig. (1923) as *Solisia*

pectinata; *MSJ* **13**:36 (1973); B. Stein, *Gartenflora.* **34**:25 (1885) as *Pelecyphora pectinata*.
Series **Lasiacanthae** M. PECTINIFERA Group

This is the name we must perforce use to describe the well-known *Solisia pectinata* if Hunt's submerging of this monotypic genus into *Mammillaria* is accepted, as indeed it seems to have been. With the sole real difference lying in the elongated areoles there is little doubt that this is where it belongs.

Plants are solitary, globular and grow up to about 4 or 5 cm more in cultivation. The milky sap of this species is the one differentiating factor from other species in the series *Lasiacanthae*, except for *M. aureilanata*, which has it also. Axils are naked. The areoles are narrow and elongated vertically, with 20 to 40 white, short spines, about 2 mm long, arranged like a comb, and hiding the plant body. Flowers are about 25 mm long and wide, white to pale pink with deeper pink midstripe, not yellow as reported by Hunt in error. Fruit is small and greenish, barely protruding beyond the spines, seeds are black, pitted, dome-shaped with a broad basal hilum.

Reported from Puebla from a few localities only, near Tehuacan. (See colour plate)

M. pectinifera

M. peninsularis (B. & R.) Orcutt, *Cactog.* 8 (1926); *The Cact.* **4**:85 (1923); *MSJ* **13**:37 (1973)
Series **Macrothelae** M. PETROPHILA Group

This is not a well-known species in cultivation, due perhaps to the remoteness of its occurrence in the wild: the very end of the Baja California peninsula, although other species from the area are fairly well represented. But seedlings have become available in recent years.

The nearest related species in habitat are *M. baxterana* and others associated with that species—*M. petrophila* and *M. gatesii*. Britton and Rose described it as solitary or clustering, sitting deeply in the ground in habitat, nearly flat topped. Axils are woolly only in young growth. Radial spines number 4 to 8, nearly

M. peninsularis

erect, one sometimes nearly central, short and pale brown with brown tips. Apart from the occasional more central spine mentioned above there is usually no central spine at all. Flowers are 1·5 cm long, pale yellow or greenish, outer petals reddish. Fruit is purplish-pink, thickening considerably at the tip. Seed is brown.

Reported from Cape San Lucas and Cape Migrine at the tip of Baja California, where it grows on rocks immediately by the sea.

M. pennispinosa Krainz, *Sukkulentenk.* **2**:20 with fig. (1948); *MSJ* **13**:37 (1973) & **15**:51 (1975);
var. *nazasensis* Glass & Foster, *Cact. Amer.* **47**:96 with figs. (1975); *Cact. GB* **41**:99 (1979)
Series **Stylothelae**   M. BOMBYCINA Group
This feathery-spined beauty is one of the most sought-after species in the genus, and presents, as is often the way of nature, some difficulty in cultivation, mainly being lost through overwatering, especially overhead, when the plumose spines soak up and retain the moisture on the body. At the beginning and end of the growing season it is better left drier than most species.

It will eventually cluster, but remains solitary for many years, forming a low, globular body about 3 or 4 cm tall and wide, with a carrot-like taproot. The axils are woolly in the growing area. Radial spines number 16 to 20, 5 to 8 mm long, greyish-white, slender, straight and pubescent. There is 1 central spine, hooked, 10 to 12 mm long, or sometimes there are 3, with 1 hooked and 2 upper ones straight, yellow at the base, brownish-red above and, like the radials, pubescent. Flowers are 15 mm long, white with a pink midstripe, stigmas 3 or 4, yellowish. Fruit is not as originally described—'5 mm long and green'—which must have been immature, but about 15 to 20 mm long and red. Seeds are black with a very large hilum (a corky appendage).

Reported from south-west Coahuila among bare, red-brown stones. Recollected by Glass and Foster in north Durango, between Bermejillo and Mapinsi in shade in deep crevices in red-brown boulders, near the tops of hills and on eastern slopes, and further south-west in Durango, near the Rio Nazas, the latter described as:

var. *nazasensis* Glass & Foster, which differs in having less pubescent spines, yellow in colour. Hunt expresses a doubt on this placing, in view of its distance (160 km) from *M. pennispinosa*, and the lack of conspicuous hilum to the seed. It may be that this is a distinct species, or perhaps a variety of another of the many *Stylothelae* in the area.

M. pennispinosa var. *pennispinosa*

M. pennispinosa var. *nazasensis*

M. pentacantha Pfeiff., *Allg. Gartenz.* **8**:406 (1840); *MSJ* **13**:38 (1973)
Referred by Britton and Rose to *M. magnimamma*, the name is obstinately persistent.

M. perbella Hildm. ex Schum., *Gesamt. Kakteenk.*
567 (1898); *MSJ* **13**:38 (1973)
Series **Leucocephalae** M. GEMINISPINA
Group

This species forms beautiful, low-growing mounds
of dichotomously dividing heads, with short, stout
spines and rings of small deep pink flowers forcing
their way between the small, tightly-packed tubercles.
The axils have white wool, more especially in youth.
There are 14 to 18 radial spines, white and thin, up to
3 mm long (longer at the sides of the areole and black-
tipped sometimes here). Central spines number 2, the
upper a little longer, 4 to 6 mm long, thick and rigid,
reddish-white later ivory white. Flowers are about
10 mm long, deep pink, outer petals greenish-brown.
Fruit is red, seeds brown.

Reported from near Toliman in the state of Hidalgo
on rocky hilltops; and San Pablo in Queretaro.

Hunt equates here the name *M. aljibensis*, an
obscure name which has appeared on several different
species over the years, but originally, it is believed,
referring to a plant of this ilk.

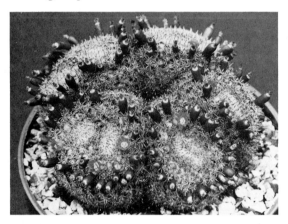

M. perbella

M. petrophila K. Brandegee, *Zoe* **5**:193 (1904); *MSJ*
13:38 (1973)
Series **Macrothelae** M. PETROPHILA Group

Hunt now accepts this name for a distinctive species,
which has become available in the last few years again,
after some years of obscurity. It is at first simple,
clustering randomly after a few years, with stems about
8 to 10 cm, later up to 15 cm wide. Axils have persistent
brownish-yellow wool and a few bristles. Radial spines
number 8 to 10, 10 to 15 mm long, slender but stiff,
needle-like, standing out, brown, darker at the tips.
There is 1 central spine, occasionally 2, to 20 mm long,
dark chestnut brown, nearly black at the tip, and a little
stronger than the radials. Flowers are about 2 cm long
and wide, bright greenish yellow with darker midstripe. Fruit is red, seeds brown.

Reported from Baja California, at the Sierra de la
Laguna and Sierra Francisquito in the Cape area.

M. petrophila

M. petterssonii Hildm., *Deutsch. Gartenz.* (**5**):185
with fig. (1886); *Cact. Amer.* **44**:198 with fig. (1972);
MSJ **13**:39 (1973)
Series **Macrothelae** M. PETTERSSONII Group

Hunt expresses some doubt on the separation of this
species from *M. gigantea*, but if declared conspecific it
would be this species name which would take
precedence. The description was of a large, solitary,
globose plant with large tubercles, 1 cm long and broad
at the base, 3-angled, and with woolly axils. Large is a
relative term, but specimens up to about 30 cm in
diameter have been reported. Radial spines numbering
10 or more were described as white, 2 to 10 mm long,
the uppermost shorter and weaker. Central spines
number 4, brown with darker tips, becoming whitish,
the lowermost much longer, to 20 mm long, the others
10 to 15 mm long. Flowers, fruit and seed were not
described and no locality was given. Craig's cited
locality of San Moran is thought to be a mistranslation

M. petterssonii

of the Indian name 'Zamorano'. Glass and Foster reported the species from the hills above Guanajuato, and Hunt subsequently saw plants in this locality which 'were the largest, single-stemmed *Mammillarias*' he had seen, 'very variable in shape, colour and spination.' Plants in cultivation under this name tend to have thinner spines than the usually cultivated form of *M. gigantea*, and are often brown or orange-brown spined without the black tip called for. They are very handsome plants if grown on strongly. Flowers are pink with darker pink midstripe, about 2·5 cm long and wide. Fruit is purplish-pink, seeds brown. (See colour plate.)

M. phaeacantha Lemaire, *Cact. Gen. Nov. Sp.* 47 (1839); *MSJ* **13**:51 (1973)

A dubious species of *M. rhodantha* or *M. discolor* affinity.

M. phitauiana (Baxter) Werderm., *Neue Kakteen* 96 with figs. (1931); *Cact. Amer.* **2**:471 (1931); *MSJ* **13**:51 (1973) & **14**:77 (1974); *Cact. GB* **39**:40 (1977)
Series **Ancistracanthae** M. DIOICA Group

With clustering, cylindrical stems only about 4 to 4·5 cm wide, to 15 cm or more tall, this is not a common plant in collections, although seedlings have come on the market in recent years. It appears too to be somewhat reluctant to flower in England. Axils have about 20 bristles. Radial spines number 24, 4 to 12 mm long, the lower the longest, white, bristle-like; centrals 4, 4 to 6 mm long, straight or one hooked in young plants, white with brown upper half. Flowers are 12 to 15 mm long, white, outer petals with red midstripe. Fruit is red, seeds black.

Reported from Baja California east of Todos Santos, at 800 m altitude on north-facing slopes, in almost full shade of trees.

M. phitauiana

This name is preferred to the former, but vaguely described, *M. verhaertiana*.

M. phymatothele Berg., *Allg. Gartenz.* **8**:129 (1840); *MSJ* **13**:51 (1973)

A name lost in obscurity, probably ascribable to *M. magnimamma*.

M. picta Meinshausen, *Wochenschrift* **1**:27 (1858); *MSJ* **13**:52 (1973)
Series **Proliferae** M. PROLIFERA Group

This is generally seen as a small, dark green gem, with dark, bristle-like spines, contrasting with the white flowers produced often on seedlings no bigger than a fingernail. The globose to a little elongated stem surmounts a thick taproot and, except for a huge many-headed plant in Bill Maddams's collection, all the plants I have seen have been no taller than about 4 or 5 cm, and about the same in diameter. Axils have a few bristles. All the spines are pubescent and straight, the radials number 10 to 14, the upper ones yellow at the base, whitish in the middle and tipped a dark purplish brown, about 10 mm long, the lower radials are white, to 10 mm long. The 1 central spine (occasionally there are 2), is stronger and more completely dark brown. Flowers are greenish-white. Fruit is elongated and red, seeds black.

Reported from the Jaumave Valley, and by Glass and Foster 32 km east of Matehuala in Nuevo Leon. Hunt suggests that *M. viereckii* is merely an ecotype of this species with paler spines; it comes from Tamaulipas. He also refers Backeberg's *M. aurisaeta* to this species.

M. picta

M. pilcayensis H. Bravo, *An. Inst. Biol. Mex.* **28**:37 with fig. (1958); *Cact. Amer.* **43**:200 (1971); *MSJ* **13**:54 (1973)—all as *M. pitcayensis*.

Series **Polyacanthae**   M. SPINOSISSIMA Group
   This attractively close-spined species is related to
M. spinosissima, and has become increasingly available
over the last few years. It is as variable in the colour of
the spines as is *M. spinosissima*, and the most
commonly seen in collections are a yellow-spined form
and one with white spines tipped red. Dra. Bravo's
description is of a clustering plant, with stems up to
14 cm long and 4 cm in diameter, and with woolly axils
having 8 to 10 slender bristles. The sap was described
as milky and thus out of character with the section *Subhydrochylus*, where Hunt places it, in spite of Dra.
Bravo's placing in *Galactochylus* and proposing a
separate series for it. This may be accounted for by
Hunt's definition of the section *Subhydrochylus* in
which he says: 'sap of tubercles watery, or at most
thinly milky, but milky sap typically present, if only
seasonally, in the stem or its lower part.' It does not
require much imagination to allow this species to fit the

M. pilcayensis

M. pilcayensis (yellow spined form)

bill. Central and radial spines similar and merging,
about 17 outer and about 14 inner, all 5 to 6 mm long,
translucent dirty white, straight and slender, tipped
red or sometimes all yellow. Flowers purplish-red,
2 cm long. The fruit and seed were not described; for
the plants pictured it is similar to that found in *M.
spinosissima*, greenish to pale pinkish-purple fruit and
light brown seeds.
   Reported from Guerrero, Barranca de Pilcaya
('Pitcaya') at 1,400 m altitude, also from the state of
Mexico, in the Barranca de Malinaltenango.

M. pilensis Shurly ex Backeb., *Die Cact.* **5**:3408 with
fig. (1961); *Cact. GB* **21**:66 (1959) illustration only;
MSJ **13**:52 (1973);
   Referred to *M. petterssonii*.

M. pilispina J. A. Purpus, *Monatsschr. Kakteenk.*
22:150 (1912); *MSJ* **7**:6 (1967) & **13**:53 (1973)
Series **Proliferae**   M. PROLIFERA Group
   Hunt ascribes to synonymy with this species the
later described *M. sanluisensis*—the one with straight
spines, see remarks under that name—and *M. subtilis*.
The species forms clusters of semi-globose stems
about 4 cm in diameter. The axils are woolly and have a
few, long, hair-like bristles. The radial spines are very
fine, hair-like, white and pubescent. There are 4 or 5
sub-central spines placed at the top and sides of the
areoles, 6 to 7 mm long, needle-like, pubescent, yellow
at the base, white in the middle and tipped brown, and
1 central spine similar to the sub-centrals. Flowers,
fruit and seed are not described by Purpus. John Bleck
collected plants from the locality given for *M. subtilis*
and supplied the missing characters: flowers 10 to
15 mm long, 10 mm wide, creamy-white with sometimes a faint pink midstripe on the inner petals. Fruit is
pale red-orange, seeds black.
   Reported from north of San Luis Potosi, Minas de
San Rafael.
   The plant pictured by Britton and Rose as *Neolloy-*

M. pilispina

dia pilispina, who erroneously assumed it to be Purpus's *M. pilispina*, has not yet been satisfactorily identified.

M. pitcayensis H. Bravo—this mis-spelling is corrected as permitted by the *International Code of Botanical Nomenclature (ICBN)*, see under *M. pilcayensis*.

M. plumosa Weber, *Bois. Dict. Hort.* 804 (ca. 1897); *Gesamt. Kakt.* 535 (1898); *MSJ* **13**:54 (1973) & **17**:33 (1977)

Series **Lasiacanthae** M. SCHIEDEANA Group

This well-known, well-loved species hardly needs any recommendation, and there is probably little I can include here by way of fresh information, except to underline the variability of the species, about which not much seems to have been written, and its flowering habits, which to say the least are sporadic. Its variability lies mainly in its form, which varies from an even mound of level-topped heads, as shown in the illustration, through intermediates to quite distinct, separate heads, popularly known as the 'golfball' form.

All its forms are worth growing, and will make quite rapidly large, snowy mounds up to 40 cm or more in cultivation. Such large plants may be grown and kept satisfactorily if watering is carefully carried out so as not to wet the spine clusters too much: the feathery nature of the spines tends to hold the water over the plant, which in cold, humid conditions can be disastrous. Flowers are sparingly produced in cultivation in England, often in winter if they do appear, but their appearance is nothing to get excited about, as they are small and white or at most flushed pink.

An interesting phenomenon is that this species can be propagated fairly easily from detached tubercles, which will form roots and then a plant. I have found this more readily achieved if the detached tubercles are kept in enclosed conditions, after a dip in hormone rooting powder, at least until the tiny single root has got well down into the compost and caused the tubercle to plump up. Schumann, who provided the first formal description of the species, referred to individual heads 6 to 7 cm in diameter, with woolly axils, about 40 radial spines, 3 to 7 mm long, plumose, white, with whitish flowers about 15 mm long. He did not describe the fruit, but said the seeds were black. A description of the fruit was reported in the *Mammillaria Society Journal* by Elsie Graydon of New Zealand, where I am sure no *Mammillaria* presents any problems in flowering. She described it as 'about 15 mm long, club-shaped and a deep purplish-rose in colour . . . develops from light green through a whitish pink to the purplish rose shade. These fruits are usually hidden by the spines.'

Reported from Coahuila, near the border with Nuevo Leon, at Mariposa near Los Muertos, and recently by Glass and Foster from Huasteca Canyon in Nuevo Leon.

M. plumosa

M. plumosa (golfball form)

M. polyedra Mart., *Nov. Act. Nat. Cur.* **16(1)**:326 with fig. (1832); *Hort. Reg. Monac.* 127 (1829) name only; *MSJ* **13**:54 (1973)

Series **Polyedrae** M. POLYEDRA Group

A little known member (albeit the type) of the series,

M. polyedra

described as simple, later clustering, with stems up to 30 cm tall, 10 to 12 cm across, with 6 to 7-sided tubercles, and axils with wool and bristles. Spines in only 1 series, more or less subcentral, 4 to 6 in number, 6 to 25 mm long, the uppermost being the longest and strongest, straight, pale yellow tipped dark purple. Flowers are about 25 mm long and pink. Fruit is red, seeds brown.

Reported from Oaxaca.

M. polygona Salm-Dyck, *Cact. Hort. Dyck* 1849:120 (1850); *MSJ* **13**:55 (1973)

A name of uncertain identity.

M. polythele Mart., *Nov. Act. Nat. Cur.* **16(1)**:327 with fig. (1832); *Hort. Reg. Monaco* 127 (1829) name only; *MSJ* **13**:55 (1973)

Series **Heterochlorae**   M. POLYTHELE Group

Apart from some difficulties in reconciling the consistency of the sap of this species, which, according to the season, can be either watery or milky, there is not much doubt that what is grown today under this name is usually correctly identified.

Plants are solitary, reaching 60 cm tall and about 8 or 10 cm in diameter, eventually collapsing under their own weight and becoming decumbent as others in this series will. The tubercles are prominent, and dark, bluish green; axils and areoles are woolly. Spines number 2 at first, pointing up and down, later 3 or 4 or more, the lowest longest, up to 25 mm, pale brown in youth, becoming dark brown, sometimes reddish. Flowers are about 1 cm long, pinkish purple. The fruit is red, the seeds brown.

M. polythele

Reported from Hidalgo, near Ixmiquilpan and subsequently from the same state 'between Actopan and Zimapan on barren, stony hills, also on clayey soils.'

Hunt equates *M. hidalgensis* to this species.

M. pondii Greene, *Pittonia* **1**:268 (1889); *Cact. Journ.* **2**:51 (1899)—as *Cochemiea pondii*; *The Cact.* **4**:23 with figs. (1923); *MSJ* **13**:60 (1973)

Subgenus **Cochemiea**

This species is said to branch sparingly with cylindrical stems up to 30 cm tall, and about 3 or 4 cm wide, with wool and bristles in the axils. Radial spines number 20 to 30 (15 to 25 according to Britton and Rose), slender and white, sometimes brownish. Central spines number 4 or 5 (8 to 11, Britton and Rose), the longest more than 25 mm long, rigid and strongly hooked (1 or 2 hooked, Britton and Rose), whitish, dark brown in the upper half, the others longer and stronger than the radials. Flowers are nearly 5 cm long, bright scarlet, stamens exserted. Fruit is purplish-red, seeds black. Specimens seen in cultivation, although small have been freely branching, and although slow-growing, seem to present no difficulty in cultivation.

Reported from Cedros Island off Baja California.

M. pondii

M. poselgeri Hildm., *Gart. Zeit.* **4**:559 with fig. (1885); *Zoe* **2**:19 (1891)—as *M. roseana*; *The Cact.* **4**:22 with figs. (1923); *MSJ* **13**:61 (1973)

Subgenus **Cochemiea**

At present this is the commonest of the subgenus in cultivation, as seed has been readily available in the last few years, and raising this species from seed presents no problems. Perhaps the same will some time be true of others in the subgenus, but for the present seed is rarely offered. Seedlings grow quite rapidly and several flowering specimens at about 20 or 30 cm tall and about 3 cm in diameter have been known in England. It makes a cluster of cylindrical stems, branching usually early from the base, the stems in habitat, sometimes pendulous from rocks, can reach about 2 m long and about 4 cm in diameter. Axils are woolly and rarely have a few bristles too. Radial spines number about 8, about 10 mm long, white tipped brown. There is only 1 central spine, 15 to 20 mm or longer, similar to the radials but hooked. Flowers are 3 cm long, scarlet, stamens and style exserted. Fruit is red, globular to fat-elongate, seeds black.

Reported from Puerto Escondido, Baja California. (See colour plate.)

M. poselgeri

M. posseltiana Boed., *Monatsschr. Deutsch. Kakt. Ges.* **4**:99 with fig. (1932); *MSJ* **13**:61 (1973)

Referred to *M. rettigiana*. Some plants received under this name have a strong affinity with *M. zacatecasensis*.

M. pottsii Scheer, *Cact. Hort. Dyck* 1849:104 (1850); *The Cact.* **4**:137 with fig. (1923); *Allg. Gartenz.* **21**:94 (1853)—as *M. leona*; *MSJ* **13**:61 (1973); Weniger, *Cacti of the South-West* 143 (1972)
Series **Leptocladodae** M. POTTSII Group

This is not an easy species to grow well, and good sized specimens are not often seen in collections, but its unusual steely-blue, young spines and red flowers make it worth the extra effort. A gritty compost and a light hand with the water seem to give best results. Stems are slim and cylindrical or club-shaped, thicker at the top, to about 20 cm tall, 2·5 to 3 cm wide, branching mainly at the base. Axils are somewhat woolly. Radial spines are very numerous (about 45 in cultivated plants observed), slender, white, straight and about 6 mm long. Centrals are 7 in number, stronger than radials, 7 to 12 mm long, the uppermost longer and recurving, coloured white tipped brown with bluish sheen in youth, later greyish. Flowers are

small, 12 to 15 mm long and wide, not opening widely, rust-red or maroon with paler margins to the petals. Fruit is light red, seeds black.

Reported from Durango, about 30 km south-west of Torreon, and in the Big Bend region of Texas, around Terlingua.

M. leona is a synonym for this species, somewhat persistent with nurserymen.

M. pottsii

M. praelii Muehlenpf., *Allg. Gartenz.* **14**:372 (1846); *MSJ* **13**:62 (1973)

Plants seen under this name are indistinguishable from either *M. nejapensis* or *M. karwinskiana*. Hunt ascribes it to synonymy with the latter.

M. pringlei (Coulter) K. Brandegee, *Contr. US. Nat. Herb.* **3**:109 (1894); *Cact. GB.* **39**:74 (1977); *Cact. y Suc. Mex.* **21**:36 (1976)
Series **Heterochlorae** M. RHODANTHA Group

This is the species with long curling yellow spines associated with *M. rhodantha*. Other species associated are *M. fera-rubra*, with orange-brown or gingery-red spines and *M. aureiceps*, with shorter yellow spines.

M. pringlei is a more globose plant than *M. rhodantha* or *M. aureiceps*, making a fair sized large egg-shaped plant before offsetting around the base, about 16 cm tall and 7 to 10 cm wide. Axils have white wool and an occasional bristle. Radial spines number 15 to 20, 5 to 8 mm long, yellow, straight or slightly curved, fine needle-like. Central spines number 5 to 7, usually 6, 18 to 20 mm long or longer, golden yellow and shining, recurving and interlacing over the top of the plant. Flowers are deep purplish-pink to reddish-pink, 8 to 10 mm long, barely making their way through the tangle of spines. Fruit is greenish to purplish-pink, seeds brown. Reported from San Luis Potosi and the state of Mexico in Tultenango Canyon, also further east in the Barranca of Jiltepec and further north-east from the Barranca of Metztitlan and near Huayacocotla, Veracruz.

M. pringlei

M. prolifera (Mill.) Haw., *Syn. Pl. Succ.* 177 (1812); *Gard. Dict.* **ed. 8**:(sp. no. 6) (1768); *MSJ* **13**:63 (1973); *Cacti of the South-West*, 147 (1972); *Cact. GB* **40**:11 (1978)
Series **Proliferae**   M. PROLIFERA Group

Next to *M. gracilis* this species is probably the most widely distributed *Mammillaria* in cultivation. As its name implies it forms offsets with gay abandon, which are easily detached and rooted. A well-grown clump in flower is an impressive sight, especially if it is in fruit at the same time, with bright red, prominent fat berries, contrasting with the yellow spines and flowers. There is considerable variation in the colour of the spines, and many collections sport '*M. multiceps*', with much darker spines than the type, but essentially the same species (see var. *texana* below).

The individual stems are about 4 or 5 cm in

diameter, and (taking away the offsets, which tend to hide the true length of the stem) about 9 cm tall. The axils usually have fine white hairs extending to or beyond the ends of the tubercles. Radial spines are white, merging with the centrals, numbering 25 to 40,

M. prolifera var. *texana*

3 to 12 mm long, bristle-like or more hairlike, straight or sometimes twisted. Central spines number 5 to 12, 4 to 9 mm long, straight, slender, needle-like, white to yellow or reddish, sometimes dark-tipped, with tiny pubescent hairs on the spines. Flowers are 10 to 18 mm long, cream-coloured or pinkish-yellow, with a brownish midstripe on the outer petals. Fruit is red, to about 2 cm long, fat; seeds are black.

Reported from a wide range: the type (with yellow spines) from the West Indies; var. *haitiensis* (K. Schum.) Borg, with larger stem, 7 cm thick, and more spines with a more whitish appearance, from Haiti; var. *texana* (Poselger) Borg, (syn. *M. multiceps*), with white and brown spines, from Texas and north-east Mexico; var. *arachnoidea* D. R. Hunt, with more

M. prolifera var. *prolifera*

M. prolifera var. *arachnoidea*

slender, fine central spines and unusually narrow, funnel-shaped flowers, from Tamaulipas, 8 km from Antiguo Morelos on the road to San Luis Potosi, and from Hidalgo, east of Jacala, in the barranca of Rio Moctezuma. In its various forms it is also reported from the Dominican Republic, Cuba, Mexico around Jaumave in Tamaulipas as well as above Victoria on the road to Jaumave, and Nuevo Leon at Huasteca Canyon. There is too in cultivation a very small bodied form, with almost a monstrose habit of growth, not known to flower, but very prolifically clustering; its origins are unknown.

M. prolifera var. *haitiensis*

M. prolifera (small form)

M. pseudoalamensis Backeb., *Cactus (Paris)* **no. 37**:210 (1953); *Die Cact.* **5**:3460 with fig. (1961); *MSJ* **7**:35 (1967) & **10**:34 (1970) & **13**:64 (1973)

Apart from some aberrantly named seedlings of *M. discolor*, which appear under this name, the plants usually seen are the same as *M. marnierana*, referred by Hunt to synonymy with *M. oliviae*, a straight spined variety of *M. microcarpa*—see under *M. microcarpa*.

M. pseudocrucigera Boed., *Kakteenk.* 1936:237; *Cact. Amer.* **43**:6 with figs. (1971); *MSJ* **13**:64 (1973)

An invalid name referred to *M. sempervivi*—see also below.

M. pseudocrucigera Craig, *Mamm. Handb.* 101 with fig. (1945); *Cact. Amer.* **43**:6 (1971); *MSJ* **13**:64 (1973)

Asserted to be described from juvenile plants of *M. sempervivi*, the 4 centrals in maturity giving way usually to 2—see also above.

M. pseudoperbella Quehl., *Monatsschr. Kakteenk.* **19**:188 with fig. (1909) & **26**:94 (1916); *The Cact.* **4**:109 (1923); *MSJ* **13**:65 (1973) & **18**:2, 7, 46 (1978)

Series **Leucocephalae** M. GEMINISPINA Group

Hunt has said that he regards this species as probably conspecific with *M. perbella*. But plants in cultivation under this name are almost invariably stout, shortly columnar plants with dense, white radial spines, 20 to 30, about 3 mm long, obscuring the stem, and usually 2 central spines, 3 to 5 mm long, black at first, becoming greyish-white, tipped black, with 3 or 4 annual rings of flowers, pale pink striped prominently deeper pink, about 15 mm long and wide. Fruit is red, seeds brown.

M. pseudoperbella

With the consistency of application of the name, and the conformity of progeny produced from cultivated plants, it is maintained here under this name, wanting a better one.

M. pseudorekoi Boed, Mamm. *Vergl. Schluss.* 34 (1933); *MSJ* **13**:65 (1973)

Hunt equates this name with *M. rekoi*.

M. pseudoschiedeana Hort.

This is a catalogue name for *M. dumetorum*—see under *M. schiedeana*.

M. pseudoscrippsiana Backeb., *Cactus (Paris)* **no. 30**:132 (1951); *Notes Jard. Bot. Les Cedres* **1**:4 (1951);

Die Cact. **5**:3410 with fig. (1961); *Cact. Amer.* **74**:198 with fig. (1972); *MSJ* **13**:65 (1973)
Referred to *M. scrippsiana.*

M. pseudosimplex W. Haage & Backeb., *Die Cact.* **6**:3888 (1962); *MSJ* **5**:55 (1965) & **13**:65 (1973)
An invalid name, apparently a form of *M. columbiana*, but possibly intermediate between this species group and the *M. mammillaris* group, according to Hunt.

M. pseudosupertexta Hort., *MSJ* **13**:66 (1973)
A catalogue name (Schwarz) for a form of *M. haageana* with short, close-set spines.

M. pubispina Boed., *Monatsschr. Deutsch. Kakt. Ges.* **61** (1930); *Cact. Amer.* **43**:73 with fig. (1971); *MSJ* **13**:66 (1973)
Referred to *M. pygmaea.*

M. pullihamata Backeb., *Die Cact.* **6**:3898 with fig. (1962) nom. prov.
A provisional name, not subsequently validated, which Hunt refers to *M. rekoi.*

M. purpusii K. Schum., *Monatsschr. Kakteenk.* **4**:165 (1894); *The Cact.* **3**:90 (1922); *MSJ* **13**:66 (1973)
Referred by Britton & Rose to *Pediocactus simpsonii.*

M. pusilla (DC) Sweet, *Hort. Brit.* 171 (1826); *MSJ* **13**:66 (1973)
A synonym of *M. prolifera.*

M. pygmaea (B. & R.) Berg., *Kakteen* 296 (1929); *The Cact.* **4**:142 (1923); *MSJ* **13**:66 (1973)
Series **Stylothelae**   M. WILDII Group
A well-known, widespread species under different names, including *M. cadereytana*, *M. pubispina*, *M. mollihamata* (and *M. seideliana* as grown in cultivation). It ıs fast-growing and clustering with thick tuberous

M. pygmaea

roots. The individual heads were, according to the original description only 2 to 3 cm wide, but in cultivation they will reach 5 or 6 cm; they are globular with a tendency to become pyramidal. The axils have bristles. Radial spines number about 15, white, stiff, bristle-like. Central spines number 4, golden yellow, the lower one hooked, 5 to 6 mm long, stouter than radials (young spines in '*M. pubispina*' with purplish tinge). Flowers are about 1 cm long, cream, outer petals with faint reddish midstripe. Fruit is reddish, seeds black.

Reported from Queretaro near Cadereyta on stony hills. The locality for *M. pubispina* at Hidalgo, near Ixmiquilpan is about 70 km from Cadereyta, but the plants agree fairly closely with the description of *M. pygmaea*. *M. mollihamata*, locality unknown, is similar, but with considerably more radial spines (28).

M. pyrrhocephala Scheidw., *Allg. Gartenz.* **9**:42 (1841); *MSJ* **11**:34 (1971)
Referred by Hunt to synonymy with *M. karwinskiana* in his paper 'Schumann & Buxbaum Reconciled.' But he now regards this as a dubious species.

M. pyrrhochrantha Lem., *Cact. Gen. Nov. Sp.* 51 (1839); *Mamm. Handb.* 232 (1945); *MSJ* **13**:67 (1973)
An inadequately described species, not known in cultivation.

M. queretarica Craig, *Mamm. Handb.* 316 with fig. (1945); *MSJ* **13**:76 (1973)
Referred to *M. parkinsonii.*

M. quevedoi Hort. (Schmoll), *Mamm. Handb.* 113 (1945); *MSJ* **13**:76 (1973)
Craig says this is a variant of *M. bravoae* with darker central spines. Plants in cultivation have been indistinguishable from *M. bravoae* or *M. woodsii.*

M. radiaissima Lindsay in Craig, *Mamm. Handb.* 292 with figs. (1945)
Glass and Foster (and Hunt) assert that this was a redescription of *M. baumii* with unusual stigmas.

M. rawlii Hort., *MSJ* **13**:76 (1973)
Plants obtained through the trade under this name are inseparable from *M. nana.*

M. redleri Hort., *MSJ* **9**:14 (1969) & **13**:76 (1973)
An unpublished name, and practically unknown in collections now.

M. rekoi (B. & R.) Vaupel, *Nat. Pflanzenfam.* ed. 2. **21**:633 (1925); *The Cact.* **4**:141 with figs. (1923); *Cact. Amer.* **44**:97 with fig. (1972); *MSJ* **13**:76 (1973)
Series **Polyacanthae**   M. NUNEZII Group
Hunt refers several other species here, including *M. rekoiana*, separated by Craig on the basis of straight central spines, not an unknown character in this series,

M. rekoi

M. pseudorekoi, an inadequately described species with no photograph nor type preserved, *M. mitlensis*, which Hunt dismisses as a redescription of *M. rekoi*, and *M. pullihamata*, a provisional name not subsequently validated, which he says appears to be referrable also to *M. rekoi*.

M. rekoi was described as globular to short-cylindrical, up to 12 cm tall and 5 to 6 cm wide. In cultivation it clusters freely after a few years; axils have a woolly tuft and several long, white bristles. Radial spines number about 20, white, fine needle-like, 4 to 6 mm long. Central spines number 4, brown, much stronger than the radials, 10 to 15 mm long, the lower one strongly hooked, but sometimes straight (*M. rekioana* above). Flowers are 1·5 cm long, deep purple-pink to pink with deeper midstripe. Fruit is red, seeds brown.

Reported from Oaxaca, in the mountains above Mitla; *M. pseudorekoi* was reported from Puebla and Morelos, *M. mitlensis* from Mitla, Oaxaca, *M. pulliha-mata* from the Chontal slopes, south-east of Oaxaca. (See colour plate.)

M. rekoi affinity (Lau 1314)

M. rekoiana Craig, *Mamm. Handb.* 128 (1945); *MSJ* **13**:76 (1973)

A synonym of *M. rekoi*, with straight spines.

M. reppenhagenii D. R. Hunt, *Kakt. u. a. Sukk.* **28**:129 with figs. (1977); *Cact. Amer.* **49**:210 (1977); *Cact. GB* **41**:105 (1979)

Series **Supertextae** M. SUPERTEXTA Group

This very recently described species has not found its way into many collections as yet, but it will no doubt be appearing in the next few years, as it is an attractive, densely white-spined species.

It has affinities to *M. albilanata*, and was described

M. rekoi var. *aureispina* n.n. (Lau 1055)

M. reppenhagenii

as simple, globose to elongated, sometimes branching. Stems are about 6 cm in diameter, the top depressed and covered in white wool; areoles and axils have persistent, plentiful white wool, especially in the growing area. Radial spines are white, 19 to 26 in number, usually 22 or 23, longest at the sides, 2 to 3 mm long, bristle-like, straight or irregularly curved. Central spines number 2 to 5, usually 4, reddish-brown in youth with darker tips, later whitish. Flowers, sitting deeply in the axils, are 10 to 12 mm long, tubular bell shaped, carmine with narrow, deeper midstripe, paler towards the edges of the petals. Fruit is red, seeds brown.

Reported from Colima, near the Rancho Tecuan, Cerro Barrigon at 2,000 m altitude, found in humus pockets in limestone rocks, and from Tuxpan near Michoacan.

The description and single plant seen by the author strongly suggest *M. tegelbergiana*. Hunt allies both these species to *M. albilanata*.

M. rettigiana Boed., *Monatsschr. Deutsch. Kakt. Ges.* **2**:98 with fig. (1930); *MSJ* **13**:77 (1973)
Series **Stylothelae**   M. BOMBYCINA Group

Not common in cultivation at present, this species is one of the earliest to flower in England, with the biscuit-pink flowers pushing their way through dense spination. It is solitary (mine has remained so for at least 10 years) forming a short, thick column in time,

pink), about 15 mm across. Fruit is small, red, seeds brownish-black.

Reported from Hidalgo and Guanajuato.

Hunt equates *M. posseltiana* here.

M. rhodantha Link & Otto, *Ic. Pl. Rar. Hort. Berol.* 51 with fig. (1829); *MSJ* **13**:77 (1973); *Cact. Suc. Mex.* **20**:89 (1975) & **21**:3 & 31 (1976)
Series **Heterochlorae**   M. RHODANTHA Group

Although there are several species associated with *M. rhodantha*, they are maintained separately for the present, pending a thorough exploration of the range of the species involved. See associated species *M. aureiceps*, with short yellow spines, *M. pringlei*, with long yellow spines, *M. fera-rubra*, with orange-brown or gingery-red spines.

M. rhodantha is simple or offsetting, or dichotomously branching, although the more normal habit in cultivation is a tall, solitary column about 7 to 10 cm wide, and up to 30 cm tall. Axils have white wool and bristles. Radial spines number 16 to 24, 6 to 10 mm long, thin, white to yellowish. Central spines number 4 to 7, 10 to 15 mm long, straight or slightly curved, red to reddish-brown, shining. Flowers are 20 mm long, 16 mm wide, deep purplish-pink. Fruit is greenish to pale pinkish-purple, seeds are brown.

Reported from the east side of the valley of Mexico, over a wide area in the states of Mexico, Morelos and Hidalgo mainly, at 2,300 to 3,000 m altitude.

M. rettigiana

M. rhodantha

about 4 cm in diameter, with slightly woolly axils. Radial spines were reported as 18 to 20 in number, up to 10 mm long, white, smooth, thin and needle-like. Central spines number 3 to 4 (more in older plants), the lowermost hooked, stronger than the radials, up to 15 mm long, the straight spines about 12 mm, red or blackish-brown. Flowers are pale pink (or yellowish-

M. ritterana Boed., *Monatsschr. Deutsch. Kakt. Ges.* **1**:73 with fig. (1929); *MSJ* **13**:79 (1973)
Referred by Hunt to *M. chionocephala*.

M. roseana T. S. Brandegee, *Zoe* **2**:19 (1891); *MSJ* **13**:79 (1973)
A synonym for *M. poselgeri*.

M. rosensis Craig, *Mamm. Handb.* 317 with fig. (1945); *MSJ* **13**:79 (1973)

A local form of *M. parkinsonii* with very flattened growth, from San Juan de Las Rosas, Guanajuato.

M. roseo-alba Boed., *Monatsschr. Deutsch. Kakt. Ges.* **1**:87 with fig. (1929); *MSJ* **13**:80 (1973)
Series **Macrothelae** M. MAGNIMAMMA Group

This name is attached to various different-looking plants, so that it should be viewed with suspicion at all times. The situation is not helped by Craig's picture and description of this species in his *Handbook* being somewhat at variance with the original!

It was described as simple, flattish ball-shaped, with angled tubercles, and densely woolly axils. Spines are in one series (sub-central), 4 to 5, rarely 6, to 8 mm long, unequal, a little recurved, needle-like, whitish, pink at the base. Flowers are 3 cm long, whitish, outer petals brownish-pink. Fruit is 1·5 cm long, red, seeds brown.

Reported from Tamaulipas, Progreso, 'near Victoria'. Hunt has expressed some doubts on the locality, since the only Progreso shown on maps is 161 km north-east of Victoria.

The plant pictured, of unknown origin, bears out the description; the body-colour is notably dark green, and the flower a beautiful pale shell-pink overall, and in the style of *M. heyderi*.

M. roseo-alba

M. roseocentra Boed. & Ritter, *Mamm. Vergl. Schluss.* 21 (1933); *MSJ* **13**:80 (1973)

The identity of this specific name is uncertain. Hunt refers it with some reservation to *M. magallanii*, but the description of *M. roseocentra* calls for 25 radial spines, compared with about 70 for *M. magallanii*. Its application is therefore doubtful, and with no cited locality it is unlikely to be positively identified.

M. rossiana W. Heinrich, *Kakt. u. a. Sukk.* **9**:119 (1958); *MSJ* **13**:80 (1973)

Referred to *M. duoformis*.

M. rubida Schwarz, *Blatt. Sukk.* **1**:5 (1949), *MSJ* **13**:81 (1973)

Hunt equates this name with *M. bocensis*. Seedlings raised under this name have a purple-red body colouring.

M. rubrograndis Reppenhagen & Lau, *Kakt. u. a. Sukk.* **28**:281 (1977) & **30**:82 (1979)
Series **Macrothelae** M. PETTERSSONII Group

This recently described species is compared by the authors of the description to *M. melanocentra*, from which they say it differs mainly in its flowers and to some extent in its spination.

It is always solitary in habitat, and although often seen in the type locality, was never plentiful. The body is flat-globular in shape, up to 10 cm tall and 18 cm wide. The axils are more or less woolly at first, later naked, the areoles with large white wool tufts at first too. Radial spines number 11 to 13, 4 to 12 mm long, the upper shortest, horn coloured with dark tips, fairly straight, smooth, thin, needle shaped. Centrals number 1 to 4, often 2, 10 to 20 mm long, light brown to dark brown, lighter and slightly thicker at the base, straight or slightly upward curving, needle-shaped. Flowers are bright carmine, wide funnel-shaped to urn-shaped, about 4 cm long and 4·5 cm wide, petals lighter coloured at the edges, outer petals olive-green, white edged. Fruit is dull carmine-red, greenish at the tip, whitish at the base, seeds dark brown.

Reported from Asbestos in Tamaulipas at 800 to 1,600 m on south-facing slopes on rocks in half-shade, growing in coarse oak leafmould.

M. rubrograndis

M. ruestii Quehl, *Monatsschr. Kakteenk.* **15**:173 (1905); *The Cact.* **4**:115 (1923); *Mamm. Handb.* 234 (1945); *MSJ* **13**:81 (1973)
Series **Supertextae** M. SUPERTEXTA Group

The original description calls for a solitary plant, but clustering later in life from the base, globose to elongate, with bristles in the axils, and 4 central spines, 7 mm long, needle-like, fox-red; radial spines 16 to 18, unequal in length, up to 6 mm long, white; flower deep carmine, 20 mm long, 15 to 20 mm wide, fruit red, seeds brown. This throws out most plants in cultivation under this name, with no bristles in the axils and with longer, dark honey-yellow central spines, which usually turn out to be *M. yucatanensis*. (See colour plate.)

Reported from Honduras and Guatemala.

Hunt allies this species to *M columbiana*.

M. ruestii

M. runyonii (B. & R.) Boed., *Mamm. Vergl. Schluss.* 52 (1933); *The Cact.* **4**:81 with fig. (1923); *MSJ* **12**:57 (1972)

Referred to *M. melanocentra*.

M. rutila Zucc. ex Pfeiff., *Enum. Cact.* 29 (1837); Zucc., *Pl. Nov. Monac.* 706 (1837); *MSJ* **13**:79 (1973)

Referred to *M. rhodantha*, although some plants seen in cultivation under this name are referrable to *M. obconella*.

M. saboae Glass, *Cact. Suc. Mex.* **11**:55 with figs. (1966); *Int. Newer Mamm.* 19 with fig. (1973); *MSJ* **14**:5 (1974) & **19**:18 & 30 (1979); *Cact. Amer.* **51**:123 (1979); *Cact. GB* **41**:97 (1979)

Series **Longiflorae** M. SABOAE Group

According to David Hunt (last ref. above) the reduction by Glass and Foster of *M. haudeana* and *M. goldii* to varietal rank beneath this species *and* the reduction by Gordon Rowley of these two species plus *M. theresae* in May and June 1979 respectively is invalid under the *International Code for Botanical Nomenclature* article 33.2. Hunt goes on to reduce *M. haudeana* to forma status beneath *M. saboae*, with a sideways threat at *M. goldii* for the future. He makes no mention of *M. theresae* as a candidate for reduction and this pleases at least one person, as I was discomforted by *M. theresae's* reduction; it is considerably different from the other three species mentioned, as well as being separated by a much greater distance, and until the fieldwork to establish the extent of the various

species in this group is done, it is best left at specific level. *M. goldii* too, although bearing a close affinity in spination with *M. saboae* and fa. *haudeana*, has a very different mode of growth, and I am happy to see its reduction at least deferred for a while.

We have then under *M. saboae* at present the two forms: fa. *saboae*, which since its introduction has pervaded collections rapidly, due to its proliferating habit and ease of propagation, cuttings rooting readily. It forms many-headed clumps of small stems, with fine gold and white spines and relatively enormous flowers usually generously produced. The individual stems are 1 to 2 cm tall and wide, tapering slightly at the apex, almost acorn-shaped, with naked axils. The spines are all radial (although an odd similar central appears now and again) numbering 17 to 25, about 2 mm long, glassy white, thin, slightly recurving, yellowish at the base where they emerge from a conspicuous pale yellow areole. The flowers are up to 4 cm long and wide, deep rose-pink. The seeds are black. The fruit does not emerge from the stem, in the infuriating way of this complex, and the desire to propagate this delightful species from seed must be balanced against the risk of damaging the plant body when extracting the seed within it.

This form is reported from south-west Chihuahua, near Terrero at 2,100 m altitude in soil pockets in porous volcanic rock, and was found by Kitty Sabo, of whose collecting adventures one can read in the American Society's journal. (See colour plate.)

The other form—fa. *haudeana*—was known for a long time as *Lau 777*, before its erection to specific status. It had a brief life as a species before being shot at from both sides of the Atlantic, and finally reduced to forma level by Hunt as indicated above.

This form clusters like fa. *saboae* to form flat clumps with fleshy roots. Individual stems are about 2 cm wide and 4 cm tall, fresh green, reddish at base, with naked axils. Radial spines (there are no centrals) number 18 to 27, glassy white, thin and slightly recurved, and are 5 to 6 mm long, 'the tips regularly turned to the right'.

M. saboae fa. *saboae*

The flowers are large, up to 65 mm wide, the tube 45 mm long, naked and slender (3·5 mm in diameter) coloured lilac-pink. The fruit stays in the plant body, or when showing slightly is red. Seeds are black. The main differences are in slightly larger bodies, generally observed to be a shinier green, thicker and longer radials and a more lilac coloured flower than in fa. *saboae*. Reported from Sonora at Yecora in humus pockets on lava fields in extremely arid conditions.

M. saboae fa. *haudeana*

M. saetigera Boed. & Tiegel, *Mamm. Vergl. Schluss.* 49 (1933); *Kakteenk.* 191 with fig. (1934); *MSJ* **14**:5 (1974)

Plants in cultivation under this name do not often accord with the original description. Hunt refers the name to synonymy with *M. brauneana*. Recent seed-raised plants are referrable to *M. hahniana* in one of its less hairy manifestations.

M. saffordii (B. & R.) Bravo, *Las. Cact. Mex.* 613 (1937); *The Cact.* **4**:149 with fig. (1923); *MSJ* **14**:6 (1974)

See under *M. carretii*.

M. saint-pieana Backeb., *Descr. Cact. Nov.* **3**:8 (1963); *MSJ* **14**:6 (1974)

See under *M. petterssonii*.

M. sanluisensis Shurly, *Cact. GB* **11**:57 with fig. (1949); *MSJ* **12**:6 (1972) & **13**:53 (1973)

This straight-spined plant has been referred to synonymy with *M. pilispina*. The plant often seen under this name with orange-brown, hooked central spines is a misnomer allied to *M. leucantha*.

M. santaclarensis Cowper, *Cact. Amer.* **41**:248 (1969); *MSJ* **15**:64 (1975)

See under *M. barbata*.

M. sartorii J.A. Purpus, *Monatsschr. Kakteenk.* **21**:50 with fig. (1911); *MSJ* **11**:35 (1971) & **14**:6 (1974)

Series **Polyedrae** M. MYSTAX Group

Almost unknown since its original description this species has recently been sought out by David Hunt, his explorings being reported in the *Mammillaria Society's Journal* (ref. above).

Two forms were originally described (*brevispina* and *longispina*) and Hunt's observations confirm the variability of the species in its spination. It is described as clustering, which it does with vigour in cultivation, although Hunt says plants in the wild are not so inclined to cluster, with stems to 13 cm in diameter, globular to somewhat elongate. Axils have wool and bristles, the wool coloured brownish-yellow to white, the latter in more glaucous plants, but some have no wool or bristles. Radial spines are small and white, up to 12 in number, but sometimes not present. Sub-central and central spines (1 or 2 are more central) number 4 to 6, 5 to 8 mm long, 1 sometimes much longer, brownish-white with brown tips. Flowers are about 2 cm long, pale carmine with darker midstripe to the petals. Fruit is carmine-red, seeds brown.

Reported from Veracruz on rocky walls of barrancas near 'Zaenapam' (correctly Zacuapam), specifically

M. sartorii

M. sartorii (large cluster)

from the Bárranca of Tenampa and Atlayae near Zacuapam; by Hunt from this area and specifically also on rocks near Puente Nacional and near the village of Palo Rocho on the highway between Veracruz and Jalapa.

M. scheidweilerana Otto ex A. Dietr., *Allg. Gartenz.* **9**:179 (1841); *MSJ* **14**:8 (1974)
    Referred to *M. erythrosperma*.

M. schelhasii Pfeiff., *Allg. Gartenz.* **6**:274 (1838); MSJ **14**:8 (1974)
    Plants seen under this name in collections usually turn out to be one of the sparser-woolled forms of *M. bocasana* or *M. longicoma*, with prominent, reddish central spines, of which one at least is hooked. The original plant described (from a well collected area) may well be sitting unsuspected in our collections, having taken advantage of the intervening years to change its name. The description comes near, allowing for variation, several members of the series *Stylothelae*, and failing the emergence of a more definite link-up between collected plants and this name as originally described it is best discarded as a source of confusion.
    For the record Pfeiffer's description called for a clustering plant, with stems nearly globose, tubercles cylindric, 20 mm long, 8 mm thick, pale below, dark green above, axils with very little white wool; radial spines 16 to 20, 8 to 10 mm long, white, bristle-like; central spines 3, brown, 1 hooked; flowers white with red filaments.
    Type locality is Hidalgo, near Actopan and Ixmiquilpan in nooks amongst lava blocks, not as reported by Britton and Rose and others at Mineral del Monte, which was the home of Ehrenberg, who sent the species to Pfeiffer.
    Hunt rejects the name as confused.

M. schiedeana Ehrenb., *Allg. Gartenz.* **6**:249 (1838); *Linnaea* **19**:344 (1846); *MSJ* **14**:9 (1974)
Series **Lasiacanthae**   M. SCHIEDEANA Group
    This species is now a little passé in fashion, but should not be ignored or overlooked on account of its common occurrence. Although it has been a little outshone by the magnificent flowers of the more recently discovered species like *M. saboae* and friends, it still puts them all in the shade when not in flower, because of the shining, gold, fine spines radiating like spokes of sunshine from the areoles to cover the plant; the popular name in Germany translates as 'gold mouse'. The flowers are unimpressively white and small, but appear intermittently throughout most of the year, particularly in autumn; they are often accompanied by the long curling bright carmine fruits which contrast well with the spines.
    It is eventually a clustering plant with flattish round stems 5 or 6 cm in diameter, and although from top to bottom on clustering plants the heads may measure up

to 10 cm or more, the part that shows is seldom more than about 5 or 6 cm tall. The axils have long white wool-like hairs protruding beyond the ends of the narrow dark green tubercles. Radial spines were described as 'very numerous' (a random count showed an average on the plant pictured of above 80); they are 2 to 5 mm long, in several series (layers), very slender, straight and bristle-like, white in the upper part grading to yellowish and golden-yellow at the base, the tip often tapering to a flexuous hair, adpressed (flattened) to the body of the plant, and hardly projecting at all.
    No central spines are present. Flowers are 8 mm long, white and quite insignificant. Fruit is bright carmine-red, seeds black.
    Reported from Hidalgo, Puente de Dios and the barrancas around Metztitlan in leafmould on limestone at 1,200 to 1,500 m altitude.
    A more predominantly white and more plumose form is often seen (usually labelled *M. schiedeana* var. *plumosa,* a name without description in a nursery catalogue—Rebut's). It tends to cluster more readily and be of a flatter disposition, with more plumose

M. schiedeana

M. schiedeana (var. *plumosa*)

spines than commonly seen (but no more plumose than early photographs accompanying descriptions of *M. schiedeana*).

Hunt ascribes *M. dumetorum* to synonymy with this species; this was reported from an area about 64 km east of San Luis Potosi, in steep, silty banks of shaded ravines. It has much less dense spination, and may well justify separate recognition.

M. schieliana Schick, *Sukkulentenk.* **3**:27 with fig. (1949); *MSJ* **14**:9 (1974)

Hunt refers this species to synonymy with *M. picta*, along with *M. viereckii*, with which it is identical.

M. schmollii Bravo, *An. Inst. Biol. Mex.* **2**:123 with fig. (1931); *MSJ* **14**:9 (1974)

See under *M. discolor*—not to be confused with '*M. elegans* var. *schmollii*', referred to *M. haageana*.

M. schumannii Hildm., *Monatsschr. Kakteenk.* **1**:101 (1891); *Zoe* **5**:8 (1900) as *M. venusta*; *The Cact.* **4**:58 with fig. (1923) as *Bartschella schumannii*; *MSJ* **14**:9 (1974)

Series **Ancistracanthae** M. MICROCARPA Group

This is a species only recently returned to *Mammillaria* from its excursion into a monotypic genus on account of the flower-size, the position of the flower—at the top of the plant—black seeds and 'circumscissile' fruit (i.e. fruit that separates by breaking off in part rather than falling or shrivelling as a whole), all characters which are not now so unknown in the genus. Hunt reasons that the pods remain partly embedded, as in some other species, and the fact of the pod partly breaking away is not so significantly characteristic as might at first appear.

It is placed by Hunt in the series *Ancistracanthae*, and it certainly has some of the more wayward characteristics of that series, in that it is not a plant to be treated carelessly, early or overwatering being liable to bring premature, squashy death. Small clumps with

their freely produced, large, comely flowers are not uncommon, although I have yet to see a really large one. As already indicated it is a clustering plant, with heads usually 4 or 5 cm or more tall, and about 3 cm wide, with axils woolly only in youth. Radial spines number 9 to 15, 6 to 12 mm long, white with brown tips, thin, needle-like. Central spines number 1 to 4, hooked, usually only 1 present, stouter than radials, but similarly coloured. Flowers are 3 to 4 cm in diameter, clear pink. Fruit is scarlet or orange, seeds black.

Reported from the cape area of Baja California, widespread near San Jose del Cabo, and between Bahia de las Palmas and Cabo San Lucas.

M. schwartzii (Fric) F. Buxb., *Gentes Herbarum* **8**:324 (1953); Krainz, *Die Kakteen Lfg.* 16 (1961); Backeb., *Kakteenlex.* 258 (1966); *MSJ* **14**:10 (1974)

This is an illegitimate name for *M. coahuilensis*. Due to the similarity with the name *M. schwarzii*, the name was changed on transfer to this genus (formerly it was *Porfiria schwartzii*).

M. schwarzii Shurly, *Cact. GB* **11**:17 with fig. (1949); *Int. Newer Mamm.* 20 with fig. (1973); *MSJ* **14**:11 (1974)

Series **Proliferae** M. PROLIFERA Group

This species will quickly make a number of small heads, each about 2 or 3 cm across, fitting together evenly to form modest-sized clumps, about grapefruit size, with glistening, white spines completely hiding the plant bodies. It is not difficult to induce to flower, but needs good light to ensure a good number of flowers and encourage tight growth, when the beauty of the spines is shown to advantage. Axils have up to 12 thin, white bristles about 5 mm long, adding to the density of the spination. Radial spines number 35 to 40, 8 mm long, straight, shining white, very thin, hairlike. Central spines number 8 or 9, standing a little apart from the radials, which encroach from a flat, radial position to nearly upright from the areoles; the

M. schumannii

M. schwarzii

M. schwarzii (red-spined form)

centrals are also shining white, occasionally tipped red-brown (see photograph) and occasionally hooked. Flowers are 15 mm long, predominantly white, with a red or pink midstripe to the petals. Fruit is red, seeds black.

Reported from Guanajuato, in the north, at about 1,200 m altitude on cliffs in good soil pockets, but not yet found again. The red-tipped central spined form is a distinctive form to look out for.

M. scrippsiana B. & R., *The Cact.* **4**:84 with fig. (1923); *Cact. Amer.* **44**:198 with fig. (1972); *MSJ* **14**:22 (1974)

Series **Macrothelae**   M. SONORENSIS Group

Perhaps because its spination is not outstanding and its flowers are not large this species is not often encountered, except in the *Mammillaria* fancier's collection. But these are considerations which apply more to small plants than large, as a well-grown large, clump of this species with dense wool in axils and areoles is an impressive sight. Radial spines number 8 to 10, slender, bristle-like, pink with reddish tips, about 7 mm long. Central spines are a little stronger and longer, usually 2 in number, brown and a little recurved, pointing upwards and downwards. Flowers pale pinkish-yellow to deep purplish-pink, stigma-lobes about 6, cream-coloured. Fruit is red, seeds brown.

Reported from Jalisco, the Barranca of Guadalajara and the Barranca Oblatos near Guadalajara and widespread throughout much of Jalisco and Nayarit; var. *autlanensis* Craig and Dawson (*Cact. Amer.* **20**:126 with fig. 1948) was reported from Jalisco, south-west of Autlan on cliffs and slopes of hills near the top of the pass on the road to La Resolana, a caespitose variety with cylindrical stems, 1 central

spine 9 to 12 mm long, 6 radial spines 3 to 10 mm; for var. *rooksbyana* Backeb. (*Cactus, Paris* **no. 30** 132. 1951) no more specific locality was given than 'Jalisco' and it was described as having 12 to 14 radials and 4 central spines.

As well as these two varieties, Hunt also reduces *M. pseudoscrippsiana* to synonymy.

M. scrippsiana

M. seideliana Quehl, *Monatsschr. Kakteenk.* **21**:154 (1911) & 107 (1916); *MSJ* **14**:22 (1974)

Plants grown under this name are referred to *M. pygmaea*.

M. seitziana Martius ex Pfeiff., *Enum. Cact.* 18 (1837); *Pl. Nov. Monac* 716. (1837); *MSJ* **14**:23 (1974)

Referred to *M. compressa*.

M. sempervivi DC., 'Rev. Fam. Cact.' in *Mem. Mus. Hist. Nat. Paris* **17**:114 (1829); *Memoire* **8**:13 with fig. (1834); *Cact. Amer.* **43**:7 with fig. (1971); *MSJ* **14**:24 (1974); *Cact. GB* **39**:99 (1977)

Series **Leucocephalae**   M. SEMPERVIVI Group

Although this species eventually clusters, it is more often than not seen as a solitary plant, thickly tap-rooted, and forming a flattish ball-shape, prominently woolly in the axils, often 7 or 8 cm in diameter or larger. Radial spines, when present (often only on young stems) are small white bristles to 3 mm long, usually up to 6 in number, occasionally more. Central spines, 2 (to 4, var. *tetracantha* DC) are short, 4 mm and stout, brown to black, later grey. Flowers were described as 'outer segments dirty olive, inner dirty white', which conflicts with most plants in cultivation under this name at the present time, which have a prominent pink central stripe, not an important difference in view of the distinctive appearance of the species, which cannot easily be confused with any other. Hunt described the fruit as red and the seeds as brown.

Reported from Hidalgo in calcareous soils in various locations; near Zimapan in the Barranca de Metztitlan near Venados, in the Barranca Sierra de la Mesa and near Santuario. Hunt's reference to seeing it growing 'as an epiphyte on trees' (*MSJ* **14**:24. 1974) refers of course to chance seeds germinating in favourable conditions rather than a general propensity of the species. This may seem an unnecessary statement, but I have heard serious reference to this with regard to cultivation requirements of this species.

var. *tetracantha* referred to above is a consistently 4-spined form, although its standing as a variety is doubtful.

M. caput-medusae is referred under *M. sempervivi*, although some plants seen under this name are referrable to *M. lloydii*.

M. sempervivi

M. senilis Salm-Dyck, *Cact. Hort. Dyck* 1849:8:82 (1850); *The Cact.* **4**:19 with figs. (1923); *MSJ* **14**:24 (1974) & **19**:7 (1979)
Subgenus **Mamillopsis**
Hunt returns this species and *M. diguetii* to the genus *Mammillaria* from their placing in *Mamillopsis*.

There is a mystery here, as plants in cultivation under this name invariably have red flowers, whereas the description of *M. senilis* calls for orange-yellow flowers. The companion species *M. diguetii* is described as having more rigid dark straw-coloured spines and red flowers, but the colour of the spines rules out the possibility of confusion merely over the flower colour. I have never seen, nor know of anyone who has a plant resembling this latter description. Nor for that matter have I seen or heard of a '*M. senilis*' with orange-yellow flowers.

As *M. diguetii* is never applied to plants in collections the sensible solution is to stick to the well-known name *M. senilis* and amplify the description to embrace the red flowers as follows: plants clustering,

stems globular to short-columnar, each up to 15 cm tall and 6 cm wide, axils naked (according to Salm-Dyck) pubescent and bristly (Britton and Rose); plants seen in cultivation usually naked. Radial spines number 30 to 40, 2 cm long, white, more slender than the central spines, which number 4 to 6, white, with yellow tips, at least the upper and lower hooked. Flower is 6 to 7 cm long, red, or doubtfully orange-yellow, with a straight, slender, scaly tube and spreading petals. Stamens and style are exserted from the tube. Fruit is red with a metallic golden sheen, seeds are black.

Reported from near Chihuahua and near El Salto between Mazatlan and Durango, as well as the mountains of Jalisco at 2,500 m, and in the Sierra de Chabarra, near Concordia, Sinaloa. (See colour plate.)

M. senilis

M. setispina (Coulter) Engelm. ex K. Brandegee, *Erythea* **5**:117 (1897); *Contr. US Nat. Herb.* **3**:106 (1894); *Cact. Journ.* **2**:51 (1899); *MSJ* **14**:25 (1974)
Subgenus **Cochemiea**
Another of the five former *Cochemiea* species, this one stands out with its white, black-tipped spines. It needs to be a fair size (20 cm or more) before any flower can be expected, and in England at least it appears that only the sunnier glasshouses will permit enough light to achieve this.

It is a clustering species with stems to 30 cm tall 3 to 6 cm in diameter, with wool in the axils but no bristles. Radial spines number 10 to 12 varying considerably in length from 10 to 34 mm long, slender, flexuous, white with black tips. Central spines number 1 to 4, 2 to 5 cm long, the upper straight, the lowest longest, hooked and often curved and twisted, coloured like the radials. It is implied that younger stems have the single central. Flowers are up to 5 cm long, red with exserted anthers and stigma. Fruit is scarlet, 3 cm long, seeds black, pitted.

Reported from Baja California, San Borgia (or Borja) and San Julio Canyon in rocky or gravelly soil.

Hunt allies this species to *M. pondii*.

M. setispina

M. sheldonii (B. & R.) Boed., *Mamm. Vergl. Schluss.* 30 (1933); *The Cact.* **4**:156 with fig. (1923); *MSJ* **14**:26 & 51 (1974)
Series **Ancistracanthae** M. MICROCARPA Group

This is a common species in collections, far more common than *M. swinglei*, with which it is sometimes confused. *M. sheldonii* is, however, a smaller growing species, with stems often only 8 or 10 cm tall, clustering from the base to form small clumps, body colour dull green turning reddish. Axils are without bristles (*M. swinglei* has axils 'more or less setose' i.e. bristly). Radial spines are 12 to 15, pale with dark tips, the upper 3 or 4 darker and a little stronger, and one or

two placed sub-centrally. There is 1 true central, darker, stouter and hooked. Flowers are light purple-pink with very pale margins, filaments and style light purple; stigma-lobes 6, green. Fruit is 2·5 to 3 cm long, clavate, pale scarlet.

Reported from near Hermosillo, Sonora.

M. shurlyana, Gates ex Shurly, *Cact. Journ.* **4**:14 (1935); *MSJ* **8**:13 (1968) & **14**:27 (1974)

A provisional name which persists, although it has long since been referred to *M. blossfeldiana.*

M. shurlyi F. Buxb., Krainz, *Die Kakteen Lfg.* 16 (1961); *MSJ* **14**:10 & 27 (1974)

Referred to *M. schwarzii.*

M. simplex Haw., *Syn. Pl. Succ.* 177 (1812); *MSJ* **14**:27 (1974)

Another illegitimate name, under modern rules, for *M. mammillaris.*

M. sinaloensis Rose ex J. G. Ortega, *Apuntes Fl. Indig. Sinaloa Fam. Cact.* (no page numbers) (1929); *MSJ* **14**:27 (1974)

See under *M. mazatlanensis.*

M. sinistrohamata Boed., *Monatsschr. Deutsch. Kakt. Ges.* **4**:162 with fig. (1932); *Cact. Amer.* 42:110 with figs. (1970); *MSJ* **14**:27 (1974)
Series **Stylothelae** M. BOMBYCINA Group

In spite of various suggestions that this and other species (*M. mercadensis*, *M. seideliana*, *M. zacatecasensis* to name a few) should be declared synonymous, no one has done the dirty deed, and collectors still happily acquire the different species since they are readily distinguishable. The outstanding character of this species is its overall yellow spination. It is a clustering plant (despite the original description as solitary, which must have been based on young plants),

M. sheldonii

M. sinistrochamata

flatly globose, heads about 4 to 5 cm in diameter, with naked axils. Radial spines number about 20, 8 to 10 mm long, very slender, needle-like, white and smooth. Central spines number 4, pale yellow, the lowest hooked, to 14 mm long, the others straight, about 10 mm, smooth and much thicker than the radials. Flowers are about 15 mm long, cream with a greenish tinge, faintly reddish striped on the outer petals. Fruit is red, seeds black.

Reported from the conjunction of Zacatecas, Durango and Coahuila states, and from Santa Clara, near San Miguel de Mezquital, Zacatecas, and from north-east of Zacatecas.

M. slevinii (B. & R.) Boed., *Mamm. Vergl. Schluss.* 44 (1933); *The Cact.* **4**:139 with fig. (1923); *MSJ* **7**:36 (1967) & **14**:34 (1974); *Kakt. u. a. Sukk.* **27**:140 (1976) Series **Ancistracanthae** M. DIOICA Group

Craig's placing of this name into synonymy with *M. albicans* has been seriously questioned in recent years, and it is here treated separately, as the name persists in collections, and there remains some doubt as to the synonymy of the two, or indeed their correct identification.

It is not at all well-known in collections. It is generally solitary, cylindrical, 10 cm tall or more and 5 to 6 cm in diameter, more slender than *M. albicans*, which latter species also seems to offset more readily. Axils have wool and occasional bristles. Radial spines are numerous (in cultivated plants about 17), white to pinkish in new growth, with brown to blackish tips. Central spines are about 6 in number, a little longer and stouter than the radials, coloured similarly but with more prominent dark tips, and an occasionally hooked spine. Flowers are about 2 cm across, white with pinkish stripe. Fruit is red, seeds black with large hilum.

Reported from San Josef Island and nearby San Francisco Island in the Gulf of California off Baja California. (See colour plate.)

M. soehlemannii W. Haage & Backeb., *Kakteenlex.* 259 (1966); MSJ. **14**:34 (1974)

A provisional name now referred to *M. columbiana*.

M. solisii (B. & R.) Boed., *Mamm. Vergl. Schluss.* 35 (1933); *The Cact.* **4**:142 with figs. (1923); *MSJ* **14**:34 (1974)

A form of *M. nunezii* with hooked spines, not upheld.

M. solisioides Backeb., *Cactus (Paris)* **7.30**:131 (1951) & no. **31** suppl. 3 (1952); *Die Cact.* **5**: 3434 with fig. (1961); *Cact. Amer.* **43**:16 (1971); *Int. Newer Mamm.* 21 with fig. (1973); *MSJ* **14**:34 (1974) & **19**:7 (1979) Series **Lasiacanthae** M. PECTINIFERA Group

A challenge to grow for any length of time, this beautifully spined species is much sought after. Seed is difficult to obtain, and even more difficult to raise, the young plants being painfully slow-growing and prone to damp off. Mature plants too have a nasty habit of dying in the spring after carrying their half-emerged buds through the winter, looking for enough sunshine to encourage them to push them out; perhaps the temptation to give a drop of water to hasten the process is too much. But it is as though this species cannot accept captivity, refuses to believe the English cloudy winter, and finally succumbs, pining for Mexico. An open gritty compost is necessary, with a smallish pot and light touch with the watering can.

Described as solitary (I have one, aged clustering plant) the stems are usually no more than 5 or at most 6 cm in diameter and height. Axils are naked. Radial spines number about 25, 5 to 20 mm long, chalky or dirty white, arranged in a comb-like manner, and flat to the body. There are no central spines. Flowers as indicated sometimes emerge in winter, or through to June or July, described as 14 mm long and yellowish-white, although most cultivated specimens I have seen (usually collected plants) are more pronouncedly yellow with a reddish midstripe on the outer petals. Fruit is retained half within the plant body, or barely protruding beyond the spines, greenish with the dead flower persisting; seeds are large and black, similar to that of *M. pectinifera* (but like no other *Mammillaria*) which is found within 100 km of this species—and the two have other points of similarity.

Reported from Puebla south of Petlalzingo, 'in humus on low stony hills in full sun' and from Oaxaca, Tomellin Canyon. Don't let the reference to humus in habitat fool you—they will not tolerate a damp-retentive rooting medium. (See colour plate.)

M. solisioides

M. sombreretensis Hort., *MSJ* **14**:34 (1974)

A trade name for plants unidentified, but not seen now for some years.

M. sonorensis Craig, *Cact. Amer.* **12**:155 with fig. (1940) & **44**:201 with fig. (1972); *Mamm. Handb.* 90 with figs. (1945); *MSJ* **14**:34 (1974)

Series **Macrothelae**   M. SONORENSIS Group

It is evident from the range of spination seen on plants of this species that it varies considerably, and this is borne out by the five varieties set up by Craig (albeit invalidly) based on differing spination and tubercle length. As with other plants in the series *Macrothelae* this species is in the large category, with individual heads flatly globular and about 6 to 8 cm or more in diameter, clumping to form large, flat mounds in time, similar to *M. magnimamma* in overall appearance. The body-colour is a dark bluish-green, not shining; the axils are woolly and occasionally, but seldom, have a few hair-like bristles. Radial spines are 8 to 10 (14 or 15 in var. *longispina*) varying from 1 to 20 mm long, the upper the shortest, slender and needle-like, sometimes thicker, whitish to cream with reddish-brown tip. Central spines number 1 to 4, 5 to 20mm long or longer (35 to 45 mm) in var. *longispina* and var. *gentryi*, needle-like, reddish-brown. Flowers are 20 mm long, deep pink, stigma-lobes olive-green. Fruit is scarlet, seeds brown.

Reported from Sonora, south-east of Alamos, near Guirocoba, also in north-east Sinaloa and south-west Chihuahua.

M. sonorensis

M. sphacelata Mart., *Nov. Act. Nat. Cur.* **16(1)**:339 with fig. (1832); *Hort. Reg. Monac.* 127 (1829) name only; *Cact. Suc. Mex.* **11**:41 (1966); *MSJ* **14**:35 (1974)
Series **Sphacelatae**   M. SPHACELATA Group

It seems clear that the close resemblance of this species and *M. viperina*, and the existence of inter-mediate forms where the 2 species meet must lead to their being recognised as a single species.

M. sphacelata is a clustering plant with thick, finger-like stems 2 to 3 cm wide and up to 20 cm long, but usually in cultivation only 5 to 10 cm long. Axils are a little woolly or naked. Radial spines number 10 to 15, 5 to 8 mm long, ivory to chalky white, red-speckled at the tip becoming darker with age. Central spines are similarly coloured, and number 1 to 3 or 4, 4 to 8 mm long, stronger than the radials. Flowers are 15 mm

long, not opening very wide, carmine to dark purplish-red. Fruit is scarlet, seeds black.

Reported from Altapexi, east of Tehuacan, Puebla, and by various authors from Oaxaca. The intergrading with *M. viperina* occurs at the southernmost range of the species near Zapotitlan de las Salinas and Calipan.

M. sphacelata

M. sphacelata (viperina)

M. sphaerica A. Dietr., *Allg. Gartenz.* **21**:94 (1853); *MSJ* **14**:36 (1974)
Subgenus **Dolichothele**

This is a small-headed, clustering species, which has been likened to *M. longimamma*, a much larger, less readily offsetting species, but it has maintained its separate identity. It has the common resilience of members of this subgenus to maltreatment, but if grown well will quickly make flat clusters to 50 cm or more of heads each about 5 cm across. Axils are a little woolly, but not significantly. Radial spines number 12 to 14, 6 to 8 mm long, straight, whitish to pale yellowish, needle-like. There is 1 central spine, 3 to 6 mm long, yellowish, like the radials. Flowers are yellow and large, 6 to 7 cm wide. Fruit is green to purplish, seeds black.

Reported from the USA, Texas near Corpus Christi, and near the coast. Also reported from Tamaulipas, Mexico, 24 to 30 km south of Ciudad Mier, by Glass and Foster, and further south at Progreso, north of Victoria, by Hunt.

M. sphaerica

M. spinosissima Lem., *Cact. Aliq. Nov.* 4 (1838); *MSJ* **14**:36 (1974)

Series **Polyacanthae** M. SPINOSISSIMA Group

Much has been written about the difficulty of equating plants in cultivation under this name with the original sparse description. The main discrepancy is in the spine count, which, according to the original description, should be 20 to 25, whitish, bristle-like radials, and 12 to 15 stronger, dark pink centrals. Most plants in collections under this name have less than this—up to 18 radials and 8 centrals.

The confusion does not give headaches to most collectors however, who mostly have a very clear idea of this species, with its straight, thin, needle-like spines, varying in colour in different plants, from almost completely white or yellowish to deep red-brown, and forming eventually handsome clumps of thick stems each 20 cm or more tall and 6 or 7 cm in diameter. The only two species which might be confused with it are *M. nunezii*, a squatter, more deeply coloured species with fewer centrals, and *M. pilcayensis*, a more slender species with denser and shorter spination. Flowers, in common with others in this series, are freely produced in several rings each year, so that the plants when mature are in flower for two months or more, a fresh ring of flowers opening as the ring below it fades. The quantity of berries produced presents a problem, in England at least, as it

encourages the formation of moulds and the consequent unsightly marking of the spines. They should be removed before the onset of the dark, dank days of winter. Flowers are purplish-pink, with brown outer petals, about 1·5 cm long and wide. Fruit is green to purplish-pink, seeds reddish-brown.

Reported variously from near El Parque (a railway station) in the mountains between Mexico City and Cuernavaca (Britton and Rose), from cliffs near Pilenya, Guerrero (Glass and Foster), and a yellow-spined form on limestone cliffs of the Sierra de Tepoxtlan in the State of Morelos (Hunt). Hunt regards the name *M. auricoma* for this last form as confused and best discarded. (See colour plate.)

M. spinosissima

M. stampferi Reppenhagen, *Kakt. u. a. Sukk.* **30**:187 (1979); *Cact. GB* **41**:97 (1979)

Referred to *M. longiflora* as a form by Hunt.

M. standleyi (B. & R.) Orcutt, *Cactog.* 8 (1926); *The Cact.* **4**:97 with fig. (1923); *MSJ* **14**:48 (1974)

Series **Macrothelae** M. STANDLEYI Group

This is not a well-known species, and it occurs in an area where several indeterminate species have been erected and promptly lost, in the sense that they have been unknown in collections since. A few have remained; *M. canelensis*, under which Hunt refers several of the aforementioned 'species', *M. hertrichiana*, which Maddams considers inextricably intermingled with *M. sonorensis*, and *M. standleyi*, and more recently *M. miegeana* with close affinities here as well. A thorough examination in the field is needed before the relationships of these species will be understood.

As described by Britton & Rose, *M. standleyi* is

usually a solitary plant, nearly globular, about 10 cm in diameter, with white bristles in the axils and wool especially at the top of the plant. Clustering plants with more spines were described by Craig. Radial spines are white with brown tips, about 16 in number, but up to 20 have been recorded. Central spines number 4, reddish-brown, longer and stronger than the radials. Flowers are purplish, about 12 mm long, stigma-lobes green. Fruit is scarlet, seeds brown.

Reported from Sonora, Sierra de Alamos in dry, stony places.

M. standleyi

M. stella-de-tacubaya Heese, *Gartenflora* **53**:214 with fig. (1904); Fedde, *Just. Bot. Jahresb.* **33(1)**:443 (1906)—as *M. tacubayensis*; *Zeitschr. Sukk.* **3**:75 with fig. (1927)—as *M gasserana; Cact. Amer.* **42**:73 with fig. (1970); *MSJ* **14**:49 (1974)
Series **Stylothelae**   M. BOMBYCINA Group
This is a little-known species, and Hunt has expressed the opinion that it may be a borderline species with the series *Lasiacanthae*.

The description was of a solitary plant (specimens I have seen have been clustering), 4 to 5 cm

M. stella-de-tacubaya

tall, 3 to 4 cm wide, with sparsely woolly axils. Radial spines 35 to 50, 3 to 5 mm long, whitish, interlacing, bristle-like. Central spines 1 or 2, hooked, whitish tipped dark brown to black, not always present. Flowers are about 15 mm long, reddish-white (to yellowish with reddish stripe). Fruit is brownish-red, seeds black.

Reported from Coahuila at a ranch near Tacubaya, and by Glass and Foster from northern Durango.

Plants distributed recently under the name *M. paradensis* have been this species. (See colour plate.)

M. strobilina Tiegel, *Deutsch. Gart. Zeit.* **48**:329, 367 with fig. (1933); *Cact. Amer.* **42**: 182 (1970); *MSJ* **14**:50 (1974)
A freak form of *M. collinsii* or *M. karwinskiana*.

M. stueberi Foerster, *Handb. Cact.* 517 (1846); *MSJ* **14**:50 (1974)
Dismissed by Hunt as a dubious species.

M. subdurispina Backeb., *Blatt. f. Sukkulentenk.* **1**:5 (1949); *Die Cact.* **5**:3438 with fig. (1961); *Int. Newer Mamm.* 39 (1973); *MSJ* **14**:50 (1974)
Hunt and Maddams equate this name to *M. kewensis*.

M. subpolyedra Salm-Dyck, *Hort. Dyck.* 1834. 155, 343 (1834); *MSJ* **14**:50 (1974)
Referred to *M. polyedra*.

M. subtilis Backeb., *Cact. GB* **12**:81 (1950); *MSJ* **7**:6 (1967) & **12**:6 (1972) & **13**:53 (1973) & **14**:50 (1974)
Referred to *M. pilispina*.

M. supertexta Mart. ex Pfeiff., *Enum. Cact.* 25 (1837); *Act. Acad. Nat. Cur.* **16(1)**: 322–362 (1832);

M. supertexta

Pl. Nov. Monaco 706 (1837); *Hort. Reg. Monac.* 128 (1829) name only; *MSJ* **14**:50 (1974) & **18**:3 & 46 (1978); *Cact. GB* **39**:97–99 (1977)

Series **Supertextae**

This name has been randomly applied for many years to plants of *M. haageana* and *M. albilanata* affinity. But it has been recently more rationally applied by Hunt to discoveries by Alfred Lau in the Tomellin Canyon, near Quiotepec, Oaxaca, (Lau 061 and 1158) much more in line with the original description and according well with the contemporary drawing of *M. supertexta* in the herbarium at Munich. The species forms narrow stems, about 5 cm in diameter and to 8 cm or more tall, clustering from the base and sides. Radial spines number about 14, slender, chalky white, 3 to 6 mm long, the lower the longer. Central spines are thicker, 2 in number, developing more readily when plants are older, white with brown tips, only about 3 mm long. Flowers are small, purplish-red. Fruit and seed not yet recorded.

M. surculosa Boed., *Monatsschr. Deutsch. Kakt. Ges.* **3**:78 (1931); *MSJ* **1**(4): **12** (1961) & **14**:50 (1974)

Subgenus **Dolichothele**

This species make really large mats of hundreds of small heads surmounting thick tap-roots, and, if potted on regularly, will fill a washing-bowl within a few years. It is a delightful species, and may be split up and started again from a single head or a small clump if space is at a premium. It is one of the more attractive of the subgenus with predominantly yellow spines, which show up well if the plant is grown a little hard, so that the many small heads remain pulled down tight on the root. This treatment also seems to encourage the generous production of flowers, which will cover the top of the plant with their butter yellow petals. The individual heads are about 3 cm tall and 2 cm wide, sometimes a little taller if grown in less light, with tubercles 8 mm long, 4 mm wide. Axils are naked. Radial spines number about 15, 8 to 10 mm long, fine, needle-like and white. There is 1 central spine,

M. surculosa

stronger and longer than the radials, up to 20 mm long and hooked, amber yellow and brownish-yellow at the tip. Fruit is greenish-brown, seeds yellowish-brown.

Reported from Tamaulipas, Miquihuana, and from San Luis Potosi, ½ km south of Pres de Guadalupe.

M. swinglei (B. & R.) Boed., *Mamm. Vergl. Schluss.* 33 (1933); *The Cact.* **4**:158 (1923); *MSJ* **14**:51 (1974)

Series **Ancistracanthae** M. DIOICA Group

Constantly confused with *M. sheldonii*, this species is generally larger growing with stems 10 to 20 cm tall, 3 to 5 cm wide, clustering less readily than *M. sheldonii*, and with a dark green body colour, reddening in strong light. Axils sometimes have bristles. Radials number 11 to 18, stout for the group, dull white with dark tips. Centrals number 4, ascending, dark brown to black, the lowest longer, 1 to 1·5 cm long, hooked or sometimes straight. Flowers are whitish to pale pink with brown midstripe. Fruit is dark red, seeds black.

Reported from Guaymas, Sonora.

M. swinglei

M. tacubayensis Fedde, *Just. Bot. Jahresb.* **33**(1):443 (1906(; *MSJ* **14**:49 & 61 (1974)

A later, illegitimate name for *M. stella-de-tacubaya*.

M. tamayonis Killip ex Schmee, *Bol. Acad. Cienc. Fis. Nat. y Nat. Venez.* **12**, no. **38**:62 (1949); *MSJ* **14**:61 (1974)

Hunt refers this name to *M. hennissii*, which is merely the Venezuelan occurrence of *M. columbiana*.

M. tayloriorum Glass & Foster, *Cact. Amer.* **47**:173 (1975)

Series **Macrothelae** M. STANDLEYI Group

This has not long been described, and there has been

little availability of plants to collectors yet. With its island location it is not likely to be a common plant for some time, although seed has been offered in recent times. The stem is solitary or clustering from the base and sides with age, globose to thick cylindric, 10 to 11 cm wide, and up to 25 cm or more tall in time. Axils are very woolly in youth, later sparsely woolly and with an occasional bristle. Radial spines number 12, slightly recurved, 9 mm long, orange-brown in youth, becoming white with brownish tips. Central spines are 2 or 3, occasionally 4 or 5 similar to the radials. Flowers are cerise with white margins, 15 mm long, about 12 mm wide. Fruit is red, seeds pale brown. *M. nolascana* is referrable here.

Reported from San Pedro Nolasco Island, Sonora.

The captions of the pictures of *M. evermanniana* and this species accompanying Glass and Foster's description are transposed (*Cact. Amer.* **47**:194 (1975) corrects the error).

M. tayloriorum

M. tegelbergiana Lindsay, *Cact. Amer.* **38**:196 with figs. (1966); *MSJ* **14**:61 (1974); *Int Newer Mamm.* 22 with fig. (1973)

Series **Supertextae** M. SUPERTEXTA Group

This comparatively recently described species seems to have found acceptance with collectors, mainly because of its white spines, which give the plant from a distance the appearance of a snow-white ball of short spines. In cultivation it seems to retain the whiteness, not readily discolouring on the lower part of the stem, as many *Mammillarias* will. It resembles a less columnar *M. albilanata*. Often simple, it will sometimes offset in cultivation; stems about 6 cm across and to 7 or 8 cm tall. Axils have white wool. Radial spines number 18 to 24, 2 to 4 mm long, white, needle-like. Central spines number 4 sometimes to 6, 3 to 7 mm, long, stronger than the radials, white to pale yellow with dark brown tips. Flowers are 13 mm long, purplish-pink, stigma-lobes 3, small, yellow, Fruit is red, seeds golden-brown, pitted.

Reported from Chiapas route 190, 16 km west of

Ocozocuautla; on the road to El Suspiro; south of San Felipe 3 km before San Cristobal de las Casas, Sierra Ecatipec; Oaxaca, Cerro Lachiguiri, near Tehuantepec. (See colour plate.)

Hunt allies this species to *M. albilanata*.

M. tegelbergiana

M. tenampensis (B. & R.) Berger, *Kakteen* 325 (1929); *The Cact.* **4**:101 (1923); *MSJ* **11**:35 (1971) & **14**:62 (1974)

Hunt refers this name to synonymy with *M. sartorii*.

M. tesopacensis Craig, *Mamm. Handb.* 104 with fig. (1945); *MSJ* **14**:62 (1974)

Hunt refers this species to *M. sonorensis*, from which Craig distinguished it merely by flower colour (cream with pink midstripe as compared with deep pink in *M. sonorensis*). As Hunt points out the species can hardly stand when Craig described *M. tesopacensis* var. *rubriflora* with deep purple-pink flowers, thus negating his differentiation—referred then to *M. sonorensis*.

M. tetracantha Pfeiff., *Enum. Cact.* 18 (1837); *MSJ* **13**:23 (1973) & **14**:62 (1974)

Referred by Hunt to *M. obconella*.

M. tetrancistra Engelm., *Amer. Journ. Sci. Ser.* **2**:14, 337 (1852); *Contr. US. Nat. Herb.* **3**:104 (1894); *Proc. Amer. Acad.* **3**:262 (1856); Benson, *Cacti of Arizona*, **ed. 3**:162 (1969); *Cacti of California* 194 (1970); *Cact. Amer.* **43**:23 with fig. (1971); *MSJ* **9**:4 (1969) & **14**:62 (1974)

Series **Ancistracanthae** M. TETRANCISTRA Group

This is a difficult to grow, hard to come by, large-flowered species. It is very prone to lose its tuberous roots, and few specimens in cultivation get to any size unless they are on a graft. In the American Society's journal (ref. above) an excellent account of a study of this species is given. The species is described as solitary or occasionally clustering, greatly variable in size and spination—from a small form about 3 to 5 cm tall found on the Ord Mountains in California to specimens 25 cm tall and 10 cm wide found near Whitewater, California. All have tuberous roots, the stem cylindric, usually narrowing in the upper part to give a distinctive ovoid-cylindric shape, up to 25 cm tall, from 3 to 5 cm usually (to 10 cm) in diameter, with bristles in the axils and wool also in the growing area. Radial spines 30 to 60 in two series, the outer white, 5 to 10 mm long, thin, bristle-like, the inner stronger and longer, white tipped purple-brown, or completely purple-brown (reported from Sonoita, Sonora with only 18 to 20 radials—this is the most south-easterly occurrence). Central spines number 3 or 4, thicker still, needle-like, brown or blackish, upper 2 or 3 to 14 mm long, straight or 1 or more hooked, the lower stouter, up to 18 mm long, hooked. Flowers are about 2·5 cm long, opening to 2·5 to 3·5 cm wide, lavender edged with white. Fruit is red, seed very distinctive, black with large corky appendage.

Reported variously from USA, California, San Felipe; a wild area of Arizona; southern Nevada; southern Utah; and in Mexico, from Baja California and Sonora, near Sonoita. (See colour plate.)

M. tetrancistra

M. theresae Cutak, *Cact. Amer.* **39**:239 (1967); *Int. Newer Mamm.* 23 with fig. (1973); *MSJ* **14**:63 (1974) & **19**:21 (1979)
Series **Longiflorae** M. SABOAE Group

In the decade following its description this species has found its way into most *Mammillaria* enthusiasts' collections and into a great many more because of its singular beauty of form and large, freely produced flowers. It is easily propagated from cuttings, although seed presents problems, since the fruit forms within the plant body making collection of the seed difficult, though not impossible. It is, in addition, slow from seed, and in my experience seed obtained commercially has a low germination rate. Close relatives are *M. goldii* and *M. saboae* (including *M. haudeana*). *M. theresae* is simple, or sparingly clustering—large clusters are often the result of degrafted plants—to about 4 cm tall and 2 to 3 cm in diameter, areoles and axils sparsely woolly, although in cultivation the golden disc of the areole is most prominent. Only radial spines are present, numbering 22 to 30, only 2 mm long, plumose, translucent white. Flowers are large, 35–45 mm long, opening to about 30 mm wide, violet-purple. Fruit remains embedded in the body, 10 mm long, seeds black, pitted.

Reported from Durango, eastern slope of Coneto Mountains, in rock outcrops, 1 km below Coneto Pass, and from about 21 to 27 km from the junction of Guatimape-Coneto road with the Durango-Santiago Papasquiaro highway at Guatinape, at 2,133 to 2,286 m above sea-level.

M. theresae

M. thornberi Orcutt, *West Amer. Sci* **12**:161 (1902); *The Cact.* **4**:162 (1923); *MSJ* **9**:38 (1969); *The Cacti of Arizona*, 3rd ed.: 155 (1969)
Series **Ancistracanthae** M. MICROCARPA Group

There is a history of confusion with a species of *Echinocereus* with this *Mammillaria* species, known for many years (and still no doubt labelled as such in some collections) as *M. fasciculata*.

It is not an easy plant to keep without some of the stems drying up, although the whole plant rarely collapses once several stems have formed. It forms dense clusters of finger-sized stems, usually about 5 to 8 cm tall, but in habitat sometimes much longer (up to 30 cm), each about 2 to 2·5 cm wide, or wider if taller. Axils are naked. Radial spines are slender, 13 to 20 in number, 5 to 7 mm long, white with dark brown to nearly black tips. There is usually 1 central spine, sometimes 2 or 3, often up to 18 mm long, brownish or black, strongly hooked, sometimes all hooked if more present. Flowers are broad funnel shaped, purplish to lavender-pink, 1·5 to 2 cm wide. Fruits are prominent, fat, red berries, long lasting, seeds black.

Reported from Arizona, near Tucson, in Pinal and Pima counties, largely in the Papago Indian reservation, also from Mexico in northern Sonora. It grows in 'sandy or fine soils under shrubs in flats and washes in the desert at 800 to 2400 feet altitude.'

M. thornberi

M. tiegeliana Schmoll, *Cact. Amer.* **7**:21 (1935) illustration only; *Cacti and other Succ.* 94 (1935); *Die Cact.* **5**:3402 with fig. (1971); *MSJ* **14**:63 (1974)

A name not validly published and referred as long ago as 1945 by Craig to *M. cadereytensis*, and thence by Hunt to *M. perbella*.

M. tolimensis Craig, *Mamm. Handb.* 318 with fig. (1945); *Cact. Amer.* **43**:7 (1971); *MSJ* **14**:63 (1974)

Dismissed by Glass and Foster and by Hunt as a form of *M. compressa*.

M. tomentosa Ehrenb., *Allg. Gartenz.* **17**:262 (1849); *MSJ* **14**:64 (1974)

A doubtful name applying probably to *M. spinosissima*.

M. tonalensis D. R. Hunt, *Cact. GB* **41**: 103 (1979)
Series **Sphacelatae** M. SPHACELATA Group

This is a recently described species with affinities to *M. sphacelata*. It has the same freely clustering habit with slender stems up to about 12 cm long, upright or becoming decumbent, and 2 to 2·5 cm wide, to 3·5 cm in maturity. The axils are naked or have a little wool. Radial spines number 9 to 12, to 1 cm long, straight, chalky-white, the upper spines tipped chestnut-brown. There is 1 central spine, standing straight out from the centre of the areole, to 18 mm long, hooked, chestnut-brown in youth, becoming almost black. Flowers are funnel-shaped, about 15 mm long, 11 mm wide when fully open, carmine with whitish margins and brownish-pink outer petals. Fruit and seed not described, probably scarlet fruit, black seeds.

Reported from Oaxaca, Puente de Tonala, on steep, limestone rocks lightly covered with bushes, with *M. carnea* and *M. dixanthocentron*.

M. tonalensis

M. trichacantha K. Schum., *Gesamt. Kakt. Nachtrag.* 133 with fig. (1903); *MSJ* **14**:64 (1974)

Hunt refers this uncertainly identifiable pubescent spined species to synonymy with *M. nana*.

M. trohartii Hildm. ex K. Schum., *Gesamt. Kakt.* 586 (1898); *MSJ* **14**:64 (1974)

Referred to *M. magnimamma*.

M. uberiformis Zucc., *Enum. Cact.* 34 (1837); *Gesamt. Kakt.* 508 (1898); *Cact. Amer.* **43**:72 with fig. (1971); *MSJ* **14**:64 (1974)

Hunt now refers this species to varietal status with *M. longimamma*.

M. umbrina Ehrenb., *Allg. Gartenz.* **17**:287 (1849); *MSJ* **14**:64 (1974)

An indeterminable species without cited locality, the name turns up in catalogues with a variety of different plants resulting, mostly referrable to the series *Polyacanthae*.

M. uncinata Zucc. ex Pfeiff., *Enum. Cact.* 34 (1837); *Pl. Nov. Monac.* 715 (1837); *MSJ* **14**:65 (1974)
Series **Macrothelae** M. HEYDERI Group

This is a widespread species in habitat and in collections, being frequently and for a long time offered by nurserymen, and indeed a candidate for the less discerning wholesale nurserymen. It is the only member of the series *Macrothelae* with distinctly hooked spines, apart from perhaps aberrant discoveries, referred to by Hunt, linked with *M. gigantea* and *M. heyderi*. It makes large, flat-globular, dark blue-green bodied plants, usually solitary, woolly in the younger axils, although the wool will sometimes persist in cultivation. Radial spines usually number 4, sometimes to 6, about 5 or 6 mm long, the upper stronger and sometimes shorter, pink to reddish-brown, straight or a little curved, the others straight, white tipped brown. There is 1 central spine (unless you count the odd radial referred to above, which is somewhat more central), hooked, to 10 mm long, stronger than the radials, pink to more usually dark purple-brown, tipped darker still. Glass and Foster report that the northernmost form has 4 centrals and 7 radials, a form with 2 hooked centrals (var. *biuncinata* Lemaire) occurs abundantly east of San Luis de la Paz in the state of San Luis Potosi, and a plant with 3 hooked centrals was found north of the city of San Luis Potosi. In the same area they found *M. lloydii*, and Hunt has theorised that this may be a straight-spined form of *M. uncinata*. Cultivated plants flower with similar blooms, reddish-white with brownish mid-stripe, pink-tipped, about 2 cm long and wide, blooming at the same time of year, and there is certainly a strong resemblance in spination, body colour and shape. Fruit is red, seeds light brown.

Reported from a wide area, including Hidalgo, near Pachuca, from the Cerro Ventoso, near Mineral del Monte, near Sinquiluca, from Chihuahua, San Luis Potosi and Queretaro, Guanajuato, Zacatecas, Aguascalientes and north-east Jalisco.

M. uncinata

M. unihamata Boed., *Kakteenk.* 1937:40 with fig. (1937); *MSJ* **14**:66 (1974)

Referred, a little uncomfortably, to *M. weingartiana*.

M. vagaspina Craig, *Mamm. Handb.* 62 with fig. (1945); *MSJ* **12**:40 (1972) & **14**:76 (1974)

Hunt regards this species as a north-easterly race of *M. magnimamma*.

M. varieaculeata F. G. Buchenau, *Cact. Suc. Mex.* **11**:79 with figs. (1966); *MSJ* **14**:76 (1974); *Int. Newer Mamm.* 24 with fig. (1973); *Kakt. u. a. Sukk.* **29**: 208 (1978)
Series **Polyedrae** M. MYSTAX Group

In spite of suggestions that this is a variety of *M. mystax*, it has been maintained, and is indeed worth a place in a collection. Unlike *M. mystax* it clusters fairly early in life, to make clusters up to 25 cm in diameter in time, with individual heads about 9 cm wide and 13 cm or more tall. Axils have wool and many bristles. Radial spines number 17 to 20 or more, 4 to 8 mm long, the lower longer, white. Central spines vary from 4 to 5 in youth to only 1 or 2 in older plants; the younger ones are about 12 mm long, but in age the plants develop very long centrals up to 45 mm in length, dark brown, becoming greyish. Flowers are scarlet, paler at the base, about 15 mm long and wide. Fruit is scarlet, seeds brown.

Reported from Puebla, south of Chilac, at 1,200 m between rocks on stony clay.

M. varieaculeata

M. vaupelii Tiegel, *Deutsch. Gartenz.* **48**:412 with fig. (1933); *MSJ* **14**:76 (1974)

There is little doubt that few collections, if any, include a plant conforming to the original description of this species, although a great many have the label firmly attached to a plant with orange-brown, shortish spines, close to *M. conspicua*. Even allowing for the original description being of a more heavily-spined plant, the central spines of most seen under this name do not come anywhere near the length required. Tiegel described a solitary, globular plant, with wool 'lax almost bristly' in the axils; radial spines 16, 5 to 6 mm long, glassy white; central spines 2, the lower 15 mm long, the upper 10 mm long, stout needle-like, coffee-brown. Flowers were not described, fruit carmine red, 15 mm long, seed yellowish.

Reported without locality from Oaxaca.

M. velthuisiana Hort., *MSJ* 7:48 (1967) & **14**:77 (1974)

Plants raised from seed sold under this name are referrable to *M. petterssonii*.

M. verhaertiana Boed., *Monatsschr. Kakteenk.* **22**:152 with fig. (1912); *MSJ* **14**:77 (1974)

Hunt is of the opinion that this imperfectly described and untypified species is the same as the later described *M. phitauiana*, but prefers the latter name in view of the full description, cited locality and deposited type specimen. The illustration *M. verhaertiana* by Craig is not, in Hunt's opinion, of this species, being closer to *M. angelensis*, itself perhaps a form of *M. dioica*.

M. vetula Mart., *Nov. Act. Nat. Cur.* **16(1)**:338 with fig. (1832); *Hort. Reg. Monac.* 128 (1829) name only; *MSJ* **14**:77 (1974)

Series **Proliferae** M. GRACILIS Group

The differences between this species and *M. magneticola* are minimal, and by precedence *M. vetula* has priority. The description need only be modified as to the central spine count to embrace both names.

It is freely clustering to form flat topped mounds of globose to elongated heads, with occasionally a little wool in the axils, sometimes none. Radial spines at first number 25 to 30, in maturity up to 50, white, thin, bristle-like, about 12 mm long. Central spines are 1 or 2, a little stronger, reddish brown (white-spined forms occur), about 10 mm long. Flowers are about 15 mm long, lemon yellow (or paler) with brownish smudgy stripes on the outer segments. Fruit is whitish to greenish, seeds black.

Reported subsequently (1837) from San Jose del Oro in the state of Hidalgo, 'often covered with snow and ice', and (1846) from the neighbourhood of Encarnacion (near San Jose del Oro) on limestone. Since this latter locality is the cited type locality of *M. magneticola* there can be little doubt that the two are conspecific.

M. viereckii Boed., *Zeitschr. Sukk.* **3**:73 with fig. (1927); *MSJ* **13**:52 (1973) & **14**:78 (1974)

Series **Proliferae** M. PROLIFERA Group

This seems to be a lighter-coloured, more densely spined version of *M. picta*.

The description is of a simple plant, occasionally branching from the base, axils with white wool and 8 to 10 white, hairlike, tortuous bristles, often extending beyond the spines; radial spines 6 to 10, 4 to 5 mm long, white, very fine, straight to somewhat tortuous; central spines not truly central, interspersing with the radials, 9 to 11, 12 mm long, slender, straight, amber yellow, sometimes brown tipped (this gave rise to a subspecific name 'brunispina'); flowers about 12 mm long and wide, whitish cream with pale olive-green midstripe, stigma lobes 6 to 7, white; fruit reddish-brown, small, seeds black.

Reported from Tamaulipas, type locality Nogales.

Plants grown under this name do not accord completely with the description and may be an entirely new species.

M. viereckii

M. villifera Otto, *Enum. Cact.* 18 (1837); *MSJ* **14**:78 (1974)

Referred by Craig to *M. polyedra*, since when it has sunk without trace.

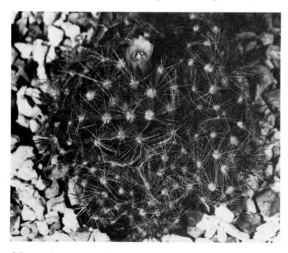

M. vetula

M. viperina J. A. Purpus, *Monatsschr. Kakteenk.* **22**:148 (1912); *MSJ* **14**:78 (1974)

Hunt regards this as a 'more slender, decumbent-stemmed form of *M. sphacelata*. In the valley of Tehuacan every intergradation can be found.'

M. virginis Fittkau & Kladiwa, *Die Kakt. Lfg.* **46**:108c with figs. (1971); *MSJ* **14**:78 (1974)
Series **Polyacanthae** M. SPINOSISSIMA Group
Plants grown from seed which conform to the description, endorse Hunt's opinion that this is yet another member of the *M. spinosissima* complex. The extent to which it should be recognized can be determined only by field study, a difficult task in the terrain where it occurs. The description is as follows: stem cylindric, rarely branching from base, to 25 cm tall, 8 cm in diameter, with naked axils; radial spines 15 to 21, 2 to 7 mm long, white tipped dark red-brown; central spines 2 to 8, 4 to 12 mm long, reddish-brown, the lowermost sometimes hooked, little different in thickness from the radials; flowers 12 to 14 mm long, brownish-red outer segments with pink or white margins, inner segments with violet midstripe and paler margins; fruit olive-green, pink below, seeds brown, pitted.

Reported from Guerrero, near Ancon, 1,800 to 2,100 m altitude on limestone and on leaf-mould-covered ground in shade or half-shade.

M. virginis

M. viridiflora (B. & R.) Boed., *Mamm. Vergl. Schluss.* 36 (1933); *The Cact.* **4**:153 (1923); *Cact. Amer.* **49**:23 & 52 (1977); *MSJ* **14**:79 (1974) & **15**:22 (1975)
Series **Ancistracanthae** M. BARBATA Group

Much valuable work has recently been done in the field on the inter-relationships of this species and *M. wrightii* and *M. wilcoxii*. For the last few years collectors of seed or plants have been reluctant to do more by way of naming the various components of the complex than to describe them as of the *Mammillaria wrightii/wilcoxii/viridiflora* complex from a given locality.

Allan and Dale Zimmerman have clarified the situation, and have maintained *M. wrightii* and *M. viridiflora* as good species, reducing *M. wilcoxii* to varietal status beneath *M. wrightii*, and sinking *M. orestera* (syn. *M. chavezei*) beneath *M. viridiflora*.

As far as *M. viridiflora* is concerned this is a distinctly smaller-flowered species than *M. wrightii*, with generally dusky pink, fringed flowers, and rarely the pale green originally described by Britton and Rose.

The broad description of what it must be remembered is a widespread, variable species is as follows: low-growing globular or short-columnar plant bodies, slow to form small clusters of stems, with naked axils, radial spines thin, white, bristle-like, 13 to 42 or more in number, averaging 21, 6 to 18 mm in length, averaging 10 mm; no sub-centrals (rarely a few, stiffer than radials and reddish-brown when present); central spines 1 to 4, hooked, 8 to 31 mm, average about 15 mm long, reddish-brown, sometimes pubescent; flower fringed and white to transparent at the margins of the petals, extremely variable in colour but lightly coloured, greenish, yellowish, white or varying shades of pink, often markedly differing between the outer and inner petals, but never the purple or magenta of the related *M. wrightii*. This varies too in size from 17 to 35 mm long (averaging 26 mm) and 12 to 42 mm in diameter (averaging 23 mm); stigma-lobes 4 to 11, averaging 6, greenish to yellowish; fruit 6·5 to 22 mm long averaging 13 mm, 4 to 13 mm in diameter averaging about 8 mm; seeds black.

Reported typically in granite outcrops from a wide area in the southern United States—in Arizona and south-west New Mexico.

M. viridiflora

M. voburnensis, Scheer in Hooker, *London Journ. Bot.* **4**:136 (1845); *MSJ* **14**:79 (1974)
Series **Polyedrae**   M. KARWINSKIANA Group

A well-known, widely distributed, fast growing species which shows some reluctance to flower in England. I have seen clumps of this species 30 cm tall and nearly as wide with several hundred heads which have never flowered. Perhaps the almost monstrous growth has something to do with this reluctance to bloom, as this is commonly the case with monstrous forms of other cacti, and certainly the rate of offsetting in plants seen in cultivation is phenomenal. Craig includes a photo in his handbook in flower, however, described as yellow, tinged red; the fruit was described therein as red, clavate, and the seeds brown.

Scheer's description called for a clustering plant with cylindric stems (beneath the surrounding offsets), with milky sap, axils woolly and bristly, tubercles angled above, rounded below, dark green and red towards the apex. Radial spines to 9, nearly equal (about 4 mm), the 4 lower a little longer, ivory-white. Central spines 1 or 2, 12 mm long, rigid, straight, brown in youth, subsequently becoming ivory-white speckled with brown. Reported from Guatemala, originally without locality, but rediscovered near Guatemala City.

The specific name alludes to the gardens at Woburn, whence Kew received and grew the originally described plant. The spelling 'v', rather than the common 'w' at the beginning is correct and follows the original, but is confusing since purist Latin scholars will pronounce the 'v' as though it were a 'w', thus endorsing the misconceived 'w'.

Hunt relates the name to *M. collinsii* and *M. eichlamii*.

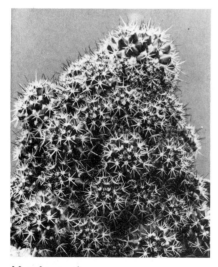

M. voburnensis

M. vonwyssiana Krainz, *Schweiz. Gart.* 170 with figs. (1970); *MSJ* **14**:80 (1974)

The name persists for plants with a goodly amount of wool in the axils, staying solitary and flowering freely with pink, deeper midstriped blooms about 15 mm long and wide. But the application of the name is in doubt, and Hunt refers it in the direction of *M. perbella*.

M. wagnerana Boed., *Monatsschr. Deutsch. Kakt. Ges.* **4**:199 with figs. (1932); *MSJ* **15**:12 (1975)
Series **Macrothelae**   M. HEYDERI Group

This is not a well-known name in collections, although in the last few years seedlings have appeared on the market. The original description was of a simple plant flat-globular 6 cm tall, 10 cm in diameter, with 4-sided tubercles about 7 mm long, axils with dense white wool. Radial spines 9 or 10, unequal, the upper 2 or 3 about 5 to 7 mm long, the lateral twice as long, and the lower three times as long, all whitish-yellow tipped brown. Central spines 2 to 4 coloured reddish yellow, variable in different plants, either 2 cm long and straight, or tortuous, or 4 to 5 cm long. Flowers dirty white with pale pink midstripe. Fruit red, seeds brown.

Reported from Zacatecas, near San Miguel del Mezquital, and from Durango east of Parrilla.

M. wagnerana

M. waltheri Boed., *Zeitschr. Sukk.* 72 with fig. (1927); *MSJ* **15**:12 (1975)

Craig regarded this species as a variety of *M. hemisphaerica*, which with the submergence of the latter name beneath *M. heyderi* reduces its standing still further. It is not known in collections distinct from *M. hemisphaerica*.

M. weingartiana Boed., *Monatsschr. Deutsch. Kakt. Ges.* **4**:219 with fig. (1932); *MSJ* **15**:12 (1975)
Series **Stylothelae**   M. BOMBYCINA Group

Hunt equates with this species the more commonly used name *M. unihamata* reported from the same locality. Described as simple or clustering (plants in cultivation are slow to offset), stems globose 4 to 5 cm in diameter, (with tuberous lower stem) axils naked. Radial spines 20 to 28 (16 to 20 in *M. unihamata*), 6 to 8 mm long, white, smooth. Central spines in young plants only 1, to 12 mm long, hooked, tawny (dark red-brown in *M. unihamata*) later 2 to 3 shorter straight centrals are sometimes present on new growth. Flowers are produced early in the year in England, about 10 mm long, described as pale greenish-yellow (cream-yellow in plants grown as *M. unihamata*) with pinkish-brown midstripe, fringed, stigma-lobes 3 to 5, white or pale pink. Fruit small, red, seeds black.

Reported from Nuevo Leon, near Ascension, in grassy fields.

M. weingartiana

M. wiesingeri Boed., *Kakteenk.* 204 with fig. (1933); *MSJ* **15**:13 (1975)
Series **Heterochlorae** M. DISCOLOR Group
This species has recently become available again through seedlings collected from the unusual type-locality, a belt of forest where it grows often hard up

against the roots of pine-trees amongst pine-needle litter in patches of sharp stones.

It is a solitary species, pronouncedly flat-globose, to 4 cm tall, 8 cm in diameter with thick roots. The tubercles are slender and placed closely together, giving a very spiny appearance to the plants; axils occasionally have bristles. Radial spines number 18 to 20, and are 5 to 6 mm long, very thin, needle-like and glassy-white. Central spines number 4, rarely 5 or 6, 5 to 6 mm long, straight, red-brown, much stronger than the radials. Flowers, unusually for this type of plant, are quite clear carmine-red, about 12 mm long, 10 mm in diameter. Fruit is carmine-red, seeds yellow-brown.

Reported from Hidalgo, near Metztitlan, at 2,000 m altitude among obsidian rocks and pine-needle debris as indicated above.

M. wilcoxii Toumey ex K. Schum., *Gesamt. Kakt.* 545 (1898); *MSJ* **15**:14 & 21 (1975); *Cact. Amer.* **49**:23 & 51 (1977)
This former species is now generally accepted to be a variety of *M. wrightii*—see under that name.

M. wildii A. Dietrich, *Allg. Gartenz.* **4**:137 (1836); *MSJ* **15**:14 (1975)
Series **Stylothelae** M. WILDII Group
A well-known species in collections, forming clusters of variable-sized stems with flabby tubercles easily pulled off with the hooked spines cluster catching in clothing or on unwary fingers. There appear in collections occasionally pink flowered plants, not so vigorously growing (sometimes labelled *M. wildii* var. *rosea*), but it is not known whether these occur in the wild or have been produced in cultivation. The tubercles were described as up to 10 mm long, 4 to 6 mm broad with long hairs in the axils. Radial spines 8 to 10, 6 to 8 mm long, straight bristle-like, white. Central spines 3 to 4, 8 to 10 mm long, 1 hooked pale yellow becoming grey brown. Flowers whitish, with brownish-red midstripe, inner petals transparent

M. wiesingeri

M. wildii

white, stigma-lobes 5 yellowish-green. Fruit brownish-red, seeds black.

Reported from Hidalgo around the Barranca of Metztitlan.

M. winterae Boed., *Monatsschr. Deutsch. Kakt. Ges.* **1**:119 with fig. (1929); *Cact. Amer.* **42**:265 with fig. (1970); *MSJ* **15**:14 (1975)
Series **Macrothelae** M. MAGNIMAMMA Group

Hunt equates with this species *M. zahniana*, which differs only in shorter, subulate spines and pure yellow flowers.

M. winterae is described as solitary, depressed globose, up to 20 to 30 cm in diameter, although in cultivation specimens 15 cm are about the largest seen. The tubercles are quadrangular, to 15 mm long, 15 to 25 mm wide, with axils at first naked, later densely white-woolled. Spines are only central, 4, upper and lower to 30 mm long, those at the side to 15 mm, stout, needle-like, straight or somewhat curved, pale grey or faintly reddish, brownish near the tip. Flowers are about 3 cm long, 2·5 cm wide, yellowish-white with sulphur-yellow midstripe and brownish-red stripe on outer petals, stigma-lobes 5 to 9 greenish-yellow. Fruit is pale red, seeds pale red-brown.

Reported from Nuevo Leon, near Monterrey, and at Coahuila near Saltillo.

M. winterae

M. woburnensis Muehlenpfordt—see under *M. voburnensis*.

M. woodsii Craig, *Cact. Amer.* **15**:33 (1943); *MSJ* **15**:15 (1975)

Hunt equates this name to *M. hahniana*—see under that name.

M. wrightii Engelm., *Proc. Amer. Acad.* **3**:262 (1856); *Rep. Pacific Railr.* **4**:27 (1856); *Cact. Bound.* 7 with fig. (1859); *Cact. Amer.* **49**:23 & 51 (1977); *MSJ* **15**:21 (1975)
Series **Ancistracanthae** M. BARBATA Group

Allan and Dale Zimmerman have recently published the results of extensive field study of this species and *M. viridiflora*, as well as *M. wilcoxii*, which is reduced to varietal status under *M. wrightii*.

The fundamental difference between *M. wrightii* and *M. viridiflora* is in the flower size, shape and colour: while *M. wrightii* with its sparser spination is fairly easily distinguishable from *M. viridiflora*, var. *wilcoxii* often closely resembles *M. viridiflora* in body and spination until the large, purple to magenta reflexing-petalled flower appears on the former, or on the latter the smaller, paler coloured, more erect, flower.

The descriptions of *M. wrightii* and var. *wilcoxii* as modified by the Zimmermans' field studies over a wide area of their occurrence are as follows:

M. wrightii Engelm. var. *wrightii*—usually solitary, forming flat-globular to short-columnar bodies about 5 or 6 cm in diameter with naked axils; radial spines 8 to 20, average 13, white, thin, bristle-like, 6 to 19 mm, average about 11 mm; central spines 1 to 7, average 2 or 3, 1 or more hooked, 5 to 21 mm long, average 12 mm brown to dark-brown. Flower deeply coloured, purple to magenta, the margins purple to pink, 25 to 52 mm long, 27 to 75 mm broad, usually broader than long, petals widely reflexing, stigma-lobes greenish, yellowish or rarely reddish. Fruit large, 14 to 28 mm long, average about 19 mm, 11 to 26 mm wide, average about 15 mm, seeds black, pitted.

M. wrightii var. *wrightii*

var. *wilcoxii* Toumey ex K. Schumann—as for the type, but with generally more radial spines, 12 to 30, average about 20, and smaller fruit, 9 to 20 mm long, average 15 mm, 6 to 15 mm wide, average 11 mm.

Reported from a wide area in Arizona and southwest New Mexico.

var. *wolfii* Schreier, *Kakt. u. a. Sukk.* **27**:9 with fig. (1976)—an invalidly published name according to Hunt, see below.

fa. *wolfii* D. R. Hunt, *Cact. GB* **41**:97 (1979)

Hunt prefers the status *forma* to describe this flower-

M. wrightii var. *wilcoxii*

colour variant. It differs from the type only in having white flowers, and is the result of a single collection.

For detailed information on this species the Zimmermans' papers in the American Society's journal should be studied. There is no doubt that this is a most difficult species in cultivation, being very prone to rot off at any age. A very gritty compost, with pure grit round the base of the plant, seems to be best, with a light hand on the watering-can, and plenty of sunlight.

M. wrightii fa. *wolfii*

M. wuthenauiana Backeb., *Beitr. Sukk. u. -pflege* 5 (1941); Fedde, *Rep. Spec. Nov.* **51**:64 (1942); *Stachlige Wildnis.* 368 (1942); *Die Cact.* **5**:3444 with fig. (1961); *Int. Newer Mamm.* 25 with fig. (1973); *MSJ* **15**:25 (1975)

Hunt equates this name with *M. bella* or *M. nunezii*.

M. xaltianguensis Sanchez-Mejorada, *An. Inst. Biol. Mex.* **44**, *Bot. Ser.* (1) 30 with figs (1975); *MSJ* **15**:51 (1975); *Cact. GB* **39**:74 (1977); *Kakt. u. a. Sukk.* **29**:231 (1978)

Series **Polyacanthae**   M. NUNEZII Group

This recent discovery is close to *M. duoformis*, differing according to Sanchez-Mejorada in its stronger body, the setting, shape and colour (green rather than bluish-green) of the tubercles, smaller number of spirals, fewer bristles in the axils, fewer radials (always white), with reddish to chestnut-brown to brownish-yellow centrals, a flowering zone closer to the centre, and smooth-edged petals. He seems determined to convince the reader of the difference!

The description is of a simple or somewhat clustering plant with cylindrical stems to 20 cm tall, 7 to 8 cm wide. Axils have a little wool and bristles, 8 to 12 mm long, in youth. Radial spines are 16 to 20 in number, 5 or 6 mm long, bristle-like, translucent white. Centrals number 4, the upper 7 to 8 mm long, the lowest 8 to 12 mm long, occasionally hooked, needle-like, purplish or yellowish-brown, reddish tipped, later whitish. Flowers are small, 12 mm long, yellowish with purple-red stripes on the outer petals. Fruit is green, later yellow above, seeds brown.

Reported from Guerrero, Municipio de Acapulco, 1 km north of Zaltianguis, growing on sandy, granite hills on the right hand bank of the Rio Xaltianguis, by the Mexico to Acapulco highway, at 500 m altitude, in low pasture at the edge of deciduous woodland.

M. xaltianguensis

M. xanthina (B. & R.) Boed., *Mamm. Vergl. Schluss.* 47 (1933); *The Cact.* **4**:164 with fig. (1923); *Cact. Amer.* **42**:109 (1970); *MSJ* **15**:30 (1975)

It is doubtful if this species is known in cultivation. Reported from Durango, nothing like it is known from this now well-explored area, and Hunt questions whether it might perhaps have been from further west or north in Mexico.

It was described as depressed, globose, type 7 cm tall, 8 to 9 cm wide, dull bluish-green, axils woolly in youth. Radial spines number 10 to 12, up to 4 mm long white, needle-like. Central spines number 2, brownish, stronger and a little longer than the radials. Flowers are pale lemon yellow.

As mentioned above, reported dubiously from Durango, near Monte Mercado.

M. yaquensis Craig, *Mamm. Handb.* 320 with fig. (1945); *Die Kakteen Lfg.* 3 (1957); *MSJ* **15**:30 (1975)
Series **Ancistracanthae** M. MICROCARPA Group

A well-known freely clustering species, widely distributed in collections, sometimes accidentally, as the short stems are easily detached when the hooked spines leap at anything approaching them unwarily. It is worth growing for the large, pink flowers with the wonderfully colour-matched long stigma-lobes in purple-red.

It was described as having stems to 7 cm tall and 1·5 cm in diameter, with faintly woolly axils. Radial spines number 18, 5 to 6 mm long, fine, needle-like, cream tipped light brown. There is 1 central spine, 1·7 mm long, hooked, reddish-brown tipped dark brown to black, (thicker than the radials). Flowers are 2 cm long and wide, whitish-pink with pink midstripe; stigma-lobes 6, 5 to 7 mm long, purple-red. Fruit is scarlet, seeds black.

Reported from Sonora, Rio Yaqui in flat lowlands near Fort Pithaya.

Hunt allies this species to *M. thornberi*.

M. yaquensis

M. yucatanensis (B. & R.) Orcutt, *Cactog.* 8 (1926); *The Cact.* **4**:114 with fig. (1923); *MSJ* **15**:30 (1975)
Series **Supertextae** M. SUPERTEXTA Group

There is little to distinguish this species from *M. columbiana*, and it may well be that this and *M. ruestii*, which differs only in having dark red-brown centrals should be sunk under the prior name, *M. columbiana*.

It was described as clustering, with stems 10 to 15 cm tall, 3 to 6 cm wide, with woolly axils. Radial spines are about 20 in number (Craig says up to 30, averaging 25), white, fine needle-like. Central spines number 4 (rarely there are 5, and Craig says 3 to 6) stronger than the radials, 6 to 8 mm long, yellowish-brown. The flowers are very small, deep pink, and barely protrude through the dense axillary wool. The fruit is bright red, the seeds brown. Reported from Yucatan, Progreso.

M. yucatanensis

M. zacatecasensis Shurly, *Cact. GB* **22**:51 with fig. (1960); *Cact. Amer.* **42**:142 (1970); *MSJ* **15**:31 (1975); *Int. Newer Mamm.* 26 with fig. (1973)
Series **Stylothelae** M. BOMBYCINA Group

This is an early flowering species, close to *M. rettigiana* in appearance.

It was described as solitary, and, surprisingly for this series, seems to remain so in cultivation for some years at least. It makes a short-cylindric plant in time, 6 to 7 cm wide and up to 10 or 12 cm tall. Axils are naked. Radial spines number 20 to 24, 3 to 5 mm long,

M. zacatecasensis

yellowish, thin and bristle-like. Central spines number 3 or 4 (more in older plants), the upper 2 or 3 straight and 10 mm long, the lower more central, 15 mm long and hooked, all smooth, yellow below, pale red above, giving an overall pinkish cast to the plant; the lower tubercles in time become compressed and the spines densely packed and darker. Flowers are 14 mm wide, white with pink midstripes. Fruit is red, the seeds black with a corky base.

Reported subsequent to Shurly's description, from the mountains south of the city of Zacatecas, on grassy hillsides.

Hunt has suggested that it may be conspecific with *M. gilensis* and *M. jaliscana*.

M. zahniana Boed., *Monatsschr. Deutsch. Kakt. Ges.* **1**:120 with fig. (1929); *MSJ* **15**:31 (1975)
Hunt refers this species to *M. winterae*.

M. zapilotensis Craig, *Mamm. Handb.* 132 with fig. (1945)
The hooked-spine form of *M. guerreronis*; sometimes straight and hooked spined stems occur on the same plant. Not upheld as a species or at any level.

M. zeilmanniana Boed., *Monatsschr. Deutsch. Kakt. Ges.* **3**:227 with fig. (1931); *MSJ* **5**:11 (1965) & **15**:31 (1975)
Series **Stylothelae** M. BOMBYCINA Group

A well-known, wonderfully floriferous species, often grown by the florist trade, this is worth a place in any collection. There are more heavily petalled forms, as well as white-flowered (known as var. *alba* or var. *albiflora*) and pink-flowered, compared with the more typical purple or pinkish-violet. It has a reputation of suddenly dying without apology, but it really presents no cultural problems.

Plants are heavily clustering, each head is about 4·5 cm wide and 6 cm or more tall, axils naked. Radial spines number about 15 to 18, finely bristle-like, white, pubescent, about 10 mm long. Central spines

number 4, the upper 3 straight, 8 mm long, the lowermost hooked and a little longer, all reddish-brown. Flowers are up to 2 cm long as stated, purple, pinkish-violet, pink or white. Fruit is small, almost hidden by the spines, 7 mm long, 4 mm wide, pale pink (whitish-green according to Boedeker), seeds black.

Reported from Guanajuato, near San Miguel Allende, among rocks in leaf mould.

M. zeilmanniana (white flowered)

M. zephyranthoides Scheidw., *Allg. Gartenz.* **9**:41 (1841); *MSJ* **15**:32 (1975)
Series **Ancistracanthae** M. ZEPHYR-ANTHOIDES Group

Hunt has recently referred this species from its long association with *Dolichothele*, where it has been an odd bedfellow, to the series *Ancistracanthae*, where in fact Schumann put it. In common with that series it presents some difficulty in cultivation, being liable to lose its roots if overwatered and recover slowly. It tends to shrivel in the winter months and make little

M. zeilmanniana

M. zephyranthoides

growth each year, unless the right balance of conditions is achieved.

It remains solitary and flattish, to 10 cm wide and to 8 cm tall, although plants this size are rarely seen. The tubercles are long, to 25 mm, flabby with naked axils. Radial spines number 12 to 18, very thin, 8 to 10 mm long, white. There is 1 central spine, to 14 mm long, stronger than radials, hooked, yellowish to red-brown. Flowers are 4 cm wide, white with red midstripes. Fruit is red, ovoid, seeds black.

Reported from Oaxaca at 2,300 m altitude; Puebla, near Tehuacan; Hidalgo, near Tisayuca and near Tula; Queretaro, El Lans.

M. zeyerana Haage ex. K. Schum., *Gesamt. Kakt.* 574 (1898); *MSJ* **15**:32 (1975)
Series **Macrothelae**   M. HEYDERI Group

This is a close ally of *M. grusonii*, but said by Glass and Foster to be distinct.

It is a large, solitary species, to 10 cm (or more in cultivation), flat globular, naked in the axils. Radial spines number 10, white, stiff, needle-like, on the upper part of the areole. Central spines number 4, the lower 3 nearly radial, to 15 mm long, the uppermost longer, to 20 mm long, chestnut brown. Flowers, fruit and seed were undescribed, but the specimen pictured has flowers creamy-yellow with wide reddish-yellow midstripe. Fruit is red, seeds brown.

Reported by Boedeker from north-east Durango and by Craig from Viesca in Coahuila.

M. zuccariniana Mart., *Nov. Act. Nat. Cur.* **16(1)**:331 with fig. (1832); *MSJ* **15**:33 (1975)
Series **Macrothelae**   M. MAGNIMAMMA Group

Hunt asserts that Britton and Rose's identification of plants from San Luis Potosi, later followed by Craig and others is doubtful, and offers as a more likely candidate plants occurring in the mountains between Zimapan and Encarnacion, which are accepted as this species by Sr. Otero and others in the Mexican Cactus Society.

Seeds from these plants have been distributed by the Mammillaria Society in the last few years and have yielded plants according very well with Martius's description, as follows: solitary, cylindric, type about 20 cm high (5 cm wide at 3 years old from seed, promising to become 10 cm or more), dark, glaucous green body, axils naked except in the flowering area where some wool is present and some long white hairs; radial spines 3 to 4, 2 to 6 mm long, white, often deciduous, i.e. lacking in older growth; central spines 2, the upper about 25 mm, the lower somewhat longer, whitish tipped purple at first, later ashy grey; flowers 25 mm long, rose-purple, stigma-lobes 4 to 5, yellow. (Fruit on recent seed-grown plants is scarlet to purplish-red and seed light brown).

Reported originally by early writers (but not the author of the description) to have come from Hidalgo, Ixmiquilpan, but this is doubted. Present accepted plants of this species, as stated above, come from the mountains between Zimapan and Encarnacion.

M. zeyerana

M. zuccariniana

FLOWERS, FRUIT AND SEED

The flowers, fruit and seed of *Mammillarias* bear study in relation to the separation of the various species into their subgenera, series and groups, as evidenced by David Hunt's classification (page 13).

Already we have seen in the last few years the means of using modern methods to classify, or help classify, plants. In particular the scanning electron microscope (SEM) has opened the window to a new world of plant beauty, and photographs have been published showing the incredible structure of seeds and pollen grains, as well as the surface texture of different parts of plants. A few photographs illustrate this beauty, and give some indication of the very different seed-surface textures and make-up.

Differences in the flowers are shown in the photographs accompanying the commentary on species.

Apart from obvious colour difference, the shape and size of *Mammillaria* flowers differs remarkably: from the large, red or yellow flowers of the subgenera *Cochemiea*, *Mamillopsis* and some of the *Dolichothele*, through the large pink flowers of the series *Longifiorae*, the intermediate in size and variously coloured *Ancistracanthae*, and often as large flowered *Macrothelae*, to the smaller flowers of other series.

The fruit too, tends to reflect the different series, and some idea of the different shapes of fruit is given in the line drawings; the colour varies from deep purple-red, to red, orange, green and yellow, to white and sometimes translucent. In identifying an unknown plant it is not a factor to be overlooked, along with all the other means of identification.

Drawings of *Mammillaria* fruits, representative of the different subgenera and sections

Subgenus	Section	Series
Mammilloydia		
Oehmea		
Dolichothele		
Cochemiea		
Mamillopsis		
Mammillaria		
	Hydrochylus	
		Longiflorae
		Ancistracanthae
		Stylothelae
		Proliferae
		Lasiacanthae
		Sphacelatae
		Leptocladodae
		Decipientes
	Subhydrochylus	
		Heterochlorae
		Polyacanthae
		Supertextae
	Mammillaria (syn. Galactochylus)	
		Leucocephalae
		Macrothelae
		Polyedrae

1 *M. candida*	8 *M. guelzowiana*	15 *M. oteroi*	22 *M. camptotricha*	29 *M. hahniana*
2 *M. beneckei*	9 *M. sheldonii*	16 *M. gracilis*	23 *M. backebergiana*	30 *M. mammillaris*
3 *M. uberiformis*	10 *M. thornberi*	17 *M. prolifera*	24 *M. rhodantha*	31 *M. grusonii*
4 *M. longimamma*	11 *M. mainiae*	18 *M. magallanii*	25 *M. spinosissima*	32 *M. marksiana*
5 *M. halei*	12 *M. wrightii*	19 *M. schiedeana*	26 *M. haageana*	33 *M. scrippsiana*
6 *M. senilis*	13 *M. bocasana*	20 *M. sphacelata*	27 *M. crucigera*	34 *M. polyedra*
7 *M. longiflora*	14 *M. glassii*	21 *M. elongata*	28 *M. parkinsonii*	

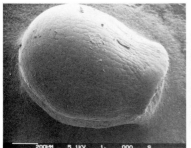

Seed of *M. candida* of the subgenus *Mammilloydia* magnified 36 times

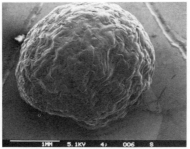

Seed of *M. beneckei* of the subgenus *Oehmea* magnified 13 times

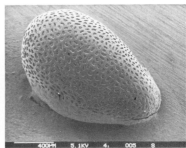

Seed of *M. senilis* of the subgenus *Mamillopsis* magnified 28 times

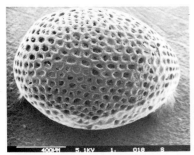

Seed of *M. wrightii* of the subgenus *Mammillaria*, series *Ancistracanthae* magnified 34 times

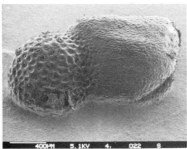

Seed of *M. pennispinosa* of the subgenus *Mammillaria*, series *Stylothelae* magnified 25 times

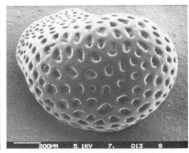

Seed of *M. prolifera* of the subgenus *Mammillaria*, series *Proliferae* magnified 38 times

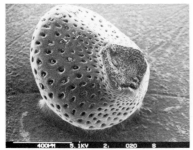

Seed of *M. pottsii* of the subgenus *Mammillaria*, series *Leptocladodae* magnified 40 times

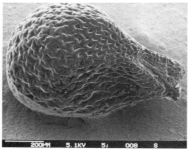

Seed of *M. dixanthocentron* of the subgenus *Mammillaria*, series *Supertextae* magnified 52 times

Seed of *M. parkinsonii* of the subgenus *Mammillaria*, series *Leucocephalae* magnified 38 times

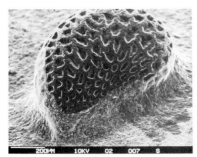

Seed of *M. camptotricha* of the subgenus *Mammillaria*, series *Decipientes* magnified 46 times

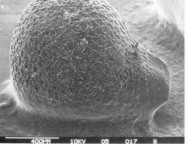

Seed of *M. solisioides* of the subgenus *Mammillaria*, series *Lasiacanthae* magnified 36 times

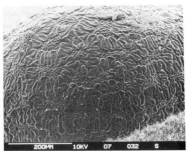

Seed of *M. magnimamma* of the subgenus *Mammillaria*, series *Macrothelae* magnified 88 times

GLOSSARY OF TERMS WITH PARTICULAR REFERENCE TO MAMMILLARIA

To help the reader to pronounce and understand what some collectors regard as the most daunting part of collecting these plants, i.e. the names of the plants, the following glossary of terms is offered.

Most specific *Mammillaria* names are made up of a person's or a place's name with the suffix -ensis, -iana, -ii or -i and -iae or -ae. If these endings are seen the preceding part of the species name will indicate either the species' origins, e.g. *M. zacatecasensis*, from Zacatecas, or the person for whom the plant is named, e.g. *M. laui*, for Alfred Lau, or *M. theresae*, for Theresa Bock. Note that either surname or first name may be used; the ending -ii or -i indicates a male person, -iae or -ae a female.

Specific names other than these are generally descriptive either of the plant, e.g. *M. dixanthocentron*, with two (di-), yellow (xantho-) centrals (centron), or of its habitat, e.g. *M. glareosa*, from stony places. As can be seen the word is often compound, and needs breaking up to be comprehended.

Pronunciation is a difficult subject to be dogmatic about, since different languages have different interpretations of words which are essentially of Latin or Greek origin. But there are rules to be followed, which will give a good idea of what is generally accepted to be the correct way to tackle the problem.

Firstly the accentuated syllable should usually be the penultimate one if it is a 'long' syllable or if the word has only two syllables; otherwise it falls on the syllable before the penultimate, e.g. *M. albilanāta*, but *M. ālbicans*. Most letters are sounded individually, but that *M. oteroi* has four syllables in the specific name; as far as possible the original pronunciation of the place name or person's name is followed, but this does lead to difficulties with such names as *M. jaliscana*, where the Spanish 'j' is an 'h' in the back of the throat. Most collectors sacrifice the proper pronunciation rather than risk a sore throat.

The most important vowels and consonants which pose problems in pronunciation are listed below, and most are generally accepted, but as with all 'rules' there are exceptions:

ae = ee as in keep
au = a as in ball

c is hard (k) before a, o and u, and soft (s) before e, i and y
ch is either hard (k) or soft, as in chimney
ei = i as in bite
g is hard, as in game, before a, o and u, and soft (as in gentle) before e, i and y
oe = ee as in keep
ui is pronounced as two syllables, not as in suit.

acantha	spine
aculeata	prickly, spiny
-ae	named for female, e.g. *carmenae, theresae*
albi	white
albicans	white
albidula	whitish
-alis	pertaining to
alpina	alpine, from high mountains
amoena	pleasing, amenable
ancistro	hooked, like a fish-hook
angularis	angular, angled
anther	part of the stamen bearing pollen
antho	flower
-ana	belonging to
applanata	flattened
appressed	lying flat
arachn-	pertaining to spiders, i.e. spider or web like
areole	felty pad on apex of tubercle from which spines arise
arida	dry
armata	armed, spined
armillata	edged or fringed
arroyo	water-course, especially one which is dry at times
atro	dark
aureo	golden-yellow
axil	junction at tubercles' bases from which flowers, fruits and offsets arise
barbata	bearded
bella	beautiful
bi-	two
-bilis	capacity for
bombycina	silken
brevi-	short

bristle	stiff hair occurring usually in the axils
caerulea	sky blue
caespitose	growing in clumps
cal-	beautiful
calix	outer envelope of flower, made up of sepals
callus	corky tissue formed after wounding
campto-	bent, curved
candida	white
capensis	from the cape, *M. capensis* is from the cape of Baja California
caput	head
carnea	flesh-coloured, pale pink
carpa	fruit
central spines	those spines (usually less in number and stronger than the radial spines)-coming from the centre of the areole and not lying flat to the body of the plant
centri	central
cephalo	head
ceras	horn
chiono-	white, snowy
chloro-	green, yellowish-green
chrys	golden-yellow
-chylus	sap
ciliate	fringed
cirrha	having tendril-like spines or bristles
citri-	lemon-yellow
clad-	branch
co-	with, together
collina	growing on a hill
color	colour
coma	hair
compressa	flattened, compressed
concolor	of the same colour
confusa	confused, disordered, untidy
conspecific	belonging to the same species
conspicua	striking, distinguished
cornuta	horned
coronaria	wreathed, crowned
crinita	having long, soft hairs
crispa	curled
cristate	having fasciated growth, where the growing point has become multiplied and elongated and remains so; not to be confused with dichotomous dividing
crocidata	deep orange
crucigera	cross bearing
dasy-	very hairy, thick
dealbata	whitened
decipiens	deceiving
decumbent	lying flat, but with tip ascending
densi-	dense, closely set
denudata	uncovered, naked

di-	two
dia-	through, between
dich-	twofold
dichotomous	branching by production of dividing growing point, as in *M. parkinsonii, M. perbella* and a few other species
digitata	spreading from one point, finger-like
dioica	with unisexual flowers on separate plants
discolor	of differing colours
dolicho	long
dumosa	pertaining to bushes
duo-	two
dura	hard
e-	out of, from
ebena	black, like ebony
ec-	out of, from
echino-	spiny, bristly; a hedgehog
-edra	base
egregia	excellent
elegans	elegant, beautiful
elongata	elongated, long
-ensis	belonging to, usually referring to habitat locality
epiphyte	plant which grows on other plants, but not necessarily parasitically
epithet	name
erecta	erect, upright
erio	woolly
erythro	red
-escens	tending towards
eu-	good, well
ex-	out of, from
exserted	projecting from, sticking out
falsi-	deceptive, false
fasciate	producing cristate growth
fasciculata	arranged in dense bunches
fera	bearing
fertilis	fruitful
filament	that part of the stamen to which the anther is attached
flat-globular	like a globe that has been flattened from above
flavescens	becoming yellow
flavi-	yellow
-flora	flower
form, forma, fa.	shape; plant or group of plants below specific level and below variety level, not sufficiently distinct to justify varietal status
formosa	beautiful
fragilis	fragile, brittle, easily broken or detached
fruit	mature ovary, berry
fuliginosa	dirty brown, sooty
fusca	grey-brown
galact-	milky

gastro-	stomach-shaped	**litoralis**	of the sea-shore
gemini	paired, in twos	**longi-**	long
genus	a taxonomic category containing species with some characters in common	**lumper**	botanist or collector who inclines to the view that broader categories of classification are preferable, cf. splitter
gigantea	vary large, gigantic		
glareosa	frequenting gravelly places	**macro-**	long, large
globose	like a globe in shape	**magni-**	large
glochid	barbed or hooked bristle or spine	**magnificus**	magnificent
glochidiata	bearing glochids	**major**	larger, greater
gona	angle	**mammilla**	nipple
gracilis	slender, graceful	**maritimus**	growing by the sea
graft	plant produced by vegetatively uniting one plant (the scion) on top of another (the stock)	**maximus**	greatest, largest
		medi-	the middle
		meia-	small, few
grandis	large	**mela-, melano-**	black, dark
gummifera	having gum, or thick sap		
habit	general appearance, mode of growth	**micro-**	small
		minor	smaller
habitat	wild locality where a species grows	**mon, mono**	one, single
hair	slender bristle with characteristics of hair	**montana**	of mountains
		multi-	many, much
hamata	with hooked tip	**mutabilis**	changeable
hastifera	beset with spears, or spines	**myrio-**	a great many
head	a stem or the top of a stem	**mystax**	moustache
helia	of the sun	**nana**	dwarf, small
hemi	half	**napina**	turnip-shaped, referring to the large rootstock
herbarium	an establishment where plant material, usually dried, is preserved, like the herbarium at the Royal Botanic Gardens, Kew		
		ne-	not, without
		neck	where the stem and root join, usually at soil level
hirsuta	hairy, hirsute, with long hair	**neo-**	new
hyaline	translucent, glass-like	**nigra**	dark, black
hybrid	the progeny of cross-fertilisation between two different species	**nivea, nivosa**	snow white
		nobilis	noble
hydro	water	**nomen nudum, nom. nud., n.n.**	name published without a proper description
-iana	suffix for species names added usually to someone's name as a tribute to that person		
		ob-	inverse, inverted, against
-ica	suffix often added to place names to indicate the origin of the species	**obconella**	inversely conic
		obscura	uncertain, obscure
-ifera	suffix denoting many or much	**obvallata**	surrounded with a wall
im-	in, not	**occidentalis**	western
in-	in, not	**ochr-**	ochre-coloured, pale yellowish-brown
ingens	very large, enormous		
insularis	of islands, isolated	**octo-**	eight
inter-	among, between	**-odes**	similar to, with the appearance of
intra-	within	**offset**	growing stems which appear other than at the main growing point, often around the base of the main stem but sometimes from the sides; not applied usually to dichotomously produced side-stems
intro-	into, towards		
-ina	belonging to		
-issima	superlative, most, e.g. *M. spinosissima*, most spiny		
lactea	milky		
laeta	bright		
lanata	woolly	**-oides**	similar to, with the appearance of
lasio	pubescent, with short, soft hairs	**-ola**	diminutive suffix
lenta	adhesive, pliant	**-opsis**	like, similar to
lepto-	slender	**oreo-**	of mountains
leuco-	white		

-osa	full of
pachy-	thick, stout
pacifica	pertaining to the Pacific Ocean
pectinata	comb-like
penni-	feather-like
penta	five
per-	entirely, through, very
perbella	very beautiful
petra	pertaining to rocks or stones
phae-	brown, greyish-brown
philo-	growing in, liking, loving
phlegma	heat
-phorus	bearing, carrying
phymato	warty, tumour-like
picta	painted, patterned
pili-, pilo-	pertaining to hairs
pilifera	bearing hairs
plumosa	feathery
poly-	many
prolifera	producing many offsets
pseudo-	false
pubescens	covered with short, soft hairs, pubescent
pubi-	pubic, downy, finely hairy
pulchella	small and beautiful
pulli-	brown or blackish and shining
pusilla	small, weak
pygmaea	very small
pyrrho-	fire-red
quadri-	four
radial spines	those spines spreading laterally from the areole
recti-	straight
-rhiza	root
rhodo-	rose-red
roseo-	rose-coloured, deep pink
rubro-	red
rutilans	orange, red mixed with yellow
saeta	hair, bristle
scion	top part of graft
section	division below subgenus containing species with characteristics in common but not distinct enough to be termed subgenus
semi-	half
semper	continuous, forever
senilis	aged, white-haired
serpenti-	snake-like
seta	hair, bristle
simple, simplex	consisting of one stem, unbranched
sinistro-	turned to the left
species	a population of individuals which breeds true within its own limits of variation, and shows distinct discontinuity from other species
sperma	seed
sphacelata	dark and shrunken

sphaero	globular, spherical
spine	hard or woody growth from a stem, apparently a modified leaf. Very thin or flexuous spines are usually referred to as bristles or hairs
splendens	splendid, glittering
splitter	botanist or collector who takes the view on the classification of genera and species etc. which tends towards breaking down large groups into small ones, e.g. apart from controversial subgenera like *Cochemiea* or *Mamillopsis*, a splitter might also argue for the retention of separate genera for *Bartschella*, *Solisia, Porfiria* etc. A lumper would regard them all as falling beneath *Mammillaria*.
stamen	filament bearing the anther
stella	star
stem	the main growing part of a plant
stigma	the tip of the style, where pollen is received
stigma-lobes	end divisions of stigma, usually coloured cream, green, pink, purple or yellow in *Mammillarias*
stock	the lower part of a graft
strobilina	having form of pine-cone
style	stigma-bearing female part of the flower
sub-	somewhat, nearly
subgenus	subdivision of a genus, a category used to contain a group of species having characters in common, but not distinct enough to be recognised at the rank of genus
super	above, over
surculosa	producing suckers, underground shoots
synonym, syn.	a name which is equivalent but subordinate to another, e.g. a later name for what is regarded the same as an earlier described species
taxon, (plural taxa)	a name in taxonomy for any one of any rank
taxonomy	the study of classification of organisms
terete	cylindrical, circular in transverse section
tetra	four
thele	nipple
tomentosa	densely woolly
tri-	three
tricha	hairy

tubercle — another name for the nipple-like parts of *Mammillarias* at the apices of which are the areoles and spine clusters; the make-up of the outer part of the stem in this way enables expansion in times of water-plenty and contraction in times of drought

type — in taxonomy this means a member of a taxon to which the name of that taxon is permanently attached, e.g. *Mammillaria mammillaris* is the type species of the genus *Mammillaria*. A type-plant is the plant which formed the basis for the first description.

uberi- — fruitful, luxuriant

-ula — diminutive suffix

umbrina — dark brown

uncinata — hooked, with hooked tips

uni — one

vaga- — wandering

varia — of different forms

variety, varietas, var. — taxonomic category within a species of plants which have distinguishing features from others of the same species, but not sufficiently distinct to justify species status

vetula — old

villi- — long soft haired

viperina — like a viper, snake-like, long and thin

virginis — white, virginal

viridi — green

wool — mass of soft hairs

xantho — yellow

zephyr — western

SOCIETIES

At the time of writing there are the following societies for collectors of cactus and succulent plants, which embrace to a greater or lesser degree an interest in Mammillaria.

GREAT BRITAIN

The Mammillaria Society
26 Glenfield Road
Banstead
Surrey

Publishes six journals a year with four photographs in each issue, on the subject of Mammillaria and allied genera; distributes seed to members.
Basic annual subscription (1981) £3.
Membership secretary: Eric Double, Bramble Cottage, Milton Street, Polegate, Sussex.

The National Cactus & Succulent Society
Secretary: Miss W. E. Dunn
43 Dewar Drive
Sheffield.

Publishes four journals a year, over 100 branches throughout UK, which usually meet monthly. Seed distribution annually.
Basic annual subscription (1981) £5.

The Cactus & Succulent Society of Great Britain
67a Gloucester Court
Kew Road
Richmond
Surrey

Publishes four journals a year (with at present a strong flavour of *Mammillaria*); seed distribution annually.
Basic annual subscription (1981) £6.50.

UNITED STATES OF AMERICA

The Cactus & Succulent Society of America, Inc.
Abbey Garden Press,
1675 Las Canoas Road
Santa Barbara,
California 93105, USA

Publishes six journals a year.
Basic annual subscription (1981) $16.

WEST GERMANY

Kakteen und andere Sukkulenten
Deutsche Kakteen-Gesellschaft e.V.
Moorkamp 22
D-3008 Garbsen 5
West Germany

Publishes 12 journals a year (in German).
Basic annual subscription (1981) DM34, joining fee DM8.

Arbeitskreis für Mammillarien-Freunde e.V.
Secretary: Horst Berk,
Marientalstrasse 70/72,
D-4400, Münster
West Germany

Publishes six journals a year (in German), devoted to the study of Mammillaria.
Basic annual subscription (1981) DM30, joining fee DM20.

MEXICO

Sociedad Cactaceas y Suculentes de Mexico
Secretary: Dudley B. Gold
Apartado Postal 979
Cuernavaca
Morelos
Mexico

Publishes four journals a year.
Basic annual subscription (1981) $6

BIBLIOGRAPHY

Allan Hancock Foundation Occasional Papers, 1948, Craig & Dawson — *Allan Hancock Found. Occ. Papers*

American Journal of Science — *Amer. Journ. Sci.*

Allgemeinen Gartenzeitung, 1835–56 — *Allg. Gartenz.*

Anales del Instituto de Biología de la Universidad Nacional de Mexico — *An. Inst. Biol. Mex.*

(Journal) *Arbeitskreis für Mammillarien-Freunde* — *Mitteil. des Arbeits.*

Beitrage zur Sukkulentenkunde und -pflege, 1938–43 — *Beitr. Sukk.*

Beschreibung und Synonymik, 1837, Pfeiffer — *Beschr. und Synon.*

Blätter für Kakteenforschung, 1934–38 — *Blatt. f. Kakteenf.*

Blätter für Sukkulentenkunde, 1949, Backeberg — *Blatt. Sukk.*

Boletín de la Academia de Ciencias Físicas, Matemáticas y Naturales, 1934 – — *Bol. Acad. Cienc. Fis. Mat. y Nat. Venez.*

Alianza Científica Universal (Boletín del Comité Regional del Estado de Durango), 1910 — *Bol. Alianza Cient. Univ. Durango*

Boletín de la Dirección de Estudios Biológicas, 1918 — *Bol. Dir. Estud. Biol.*

Boston Journal of Natural History, 1845–50 — *Boston Journ. Nat. Hist.*

Botany of the Voyage of H.M.S. Herald, 1852–57, Seeman — *Bot. Voy. Herald*

Botanisches Zeitschrift, Ehrenberg — *Bot. Zeit.*

Botanisches Zeitung — *Bot. Zeitung*

Bulletins de L'Académie Royale des Sciences et Belles Lettres de Bruxelles — *Bull. Acad. Sci. Brux.*

The Cactaceae, 1920–23, Britton and Rose — *The Cact.*

Die Cactaceae, 1961–63 (vol. 5 & 6), Backeberg — *Die Cact.*

Cactearum Aliquot Novarum en Horto Monvill, 1838, Lemaire — *Cact. Aliq. Nov.*

Cactaceae of the Boundary Survey, 1859, Engelmann — *Cact. Mex. Bound.* or *Cact. Bound.*

Las Cactácéas de Mexico, 1937, Bravo — *Las Cact. Mex.*

Cacteae en Horto Dyckensis Cultae en anno 1849, Salm-Dyck, 1850 — *Cact. Hort. Dyck*

Cactearum Genera Nova et Species Nova en Horto Monvill, 1839, Lemaire — *Cact. Gen. Nov.*

Cacti, 1937, Borg — *Cacti*

Cacti of Arizona, 1940, Benson — *Cacti of Arizona*

Cacti and other Succulents, 1935, Neale — *Cact. and other Succ.*

Cacti of the South-West, 1972, Weniger — *Cacti of the South-West*

Cactography, 1926, Orcutt — *Cactog.*

Cactus (French Society Journal) — *Cactus (France)* or *Cactus (Paris)*

Cactus Culture based on Biology, 1958, Buxbaum — —

Cactus Journal (London) 1898–1900 — *Cact. Journ.*

Cactus Lexicon, 1977, Backeberg (English trans.) — *Cact. Lex.*

Journal of the Cactus & Succulent Society of America, 1929 – — *Cact. Amer.*

Journal of the Cactus & Succulent Society of Great Britain (formerly *Cactus Journal*) 1932 – including: 'Schumann & Buxbaum Reconciled', 1971, Hunt; 'Schumann & Buxbaum Recompiled', 1977, Hunt; 'Recent Mammillaria Discoveries', 1979, Hunt — *Cact. GB.*

(Journal) Cactus y Suculentas Sociedad Mexico, 1955 – — *Cact. Suc. Mex*

Carolinae Naturae Curiosorum, 1932, Martius — *Carol. Nat. Cur.*

Catalogus Plantarum Horti Botanici Monspeliensis, 1813, de Candolle — *Cat. Pl. Hort. Monsp.*

Commentarii Phytographici, 1839 — *Comm. Phyt.*

Contributions from the United States National Herbarium, 1890 – — *Contr. US. Nat. Herb.*

Delectus Seminum Horto Hamburgensium Botanico, 1833 — *Del. Sem. Hort. Hamb.*

Description of the Cactaceae collected en route near the Thirty-Fifth Parallel (Whipple), 1856, Engelmann and Bigelow — *Descr. Cact.*

Descriptiones Cactacearum Novarum, 1961, Backeberg — *Descr. Cact. Nov.*

Desert Plant Life, 1929–52 — *Des. Pl. Life*

Deutsche Flora, 1882, Karsten — *Deutsche Fl.*

Deutsche Gartenzeitung, 1926–33, Moeller — *Deutsch. Gartenz.*

(Jahrbuch) *Deutschen Kakteen Gesellschaft in der Deutschen Gesellschaft fur Gartenkultur*, 1935–38 — *Jahrb. Deutsch. Kakt. Ges.*

Dictionaire d'Horticulture, 1893–99, Bois (Weber) — *Dict. Hort.*

Encyclopedie Methodique, 1783, Lamarck — *Encycl.*

Enumeratio Cactacearum, 1837, Pfeiffer — *Enum. Cact.*

Erythea, 1893–1938 (not 1900–21) — *Erythea*

Gardener's Dictionary, 1768, Miller — *Gard. Dict.*

Schweizerische Gärtnerzeitung, 1951– — *Gart.*

Gartenflora, 1852, 1862, 1885, 1889 — *Gartenflora*

Gartenwelt, Berlin, 1897–1933 — *Gartenwelt*

Gentes Herbarum, 1953, Moran — *Gentes Herbarum*

Gesamtbeschreibung der Kakteen (Monographia Cactacearum), 1897–99 (13 parts). *Nachtrage* 1898–1902. l.c. 1903, Schumann — *Gesamt. Kakt.* or *Gesamt. Kakt.*

Handbuch der Kakteenkunde, 1846, Foerster — *Handb. Kakt.*

Fuaux Herbarium Bulletin, Victoria, Australia, 1949–53 — *Herb. Bull.*

Hortus Brittanicus, 1830, Loudon — *Hort. Brit.*

Horti Medici Amstelodamensis, 1697, Commelin — —

Hortus Regius Monacensis, 1829, Schwank and Martius — *Hort. Reg. Monac.*

L'Horticulteur Belge, 1837–38 — *Hort. Belge*

Hortus Dyckensis, 1834, Salm-Dyck — *Hort. Dyck.*

Icones Plantarum Rariorum Horti Regni Botanici Berolinensis, 1828, Link & Friedrich — *Ic. Pl. Rar. Hort. Berol.*

Interesting Newer Mammillarias, 1973, Maddams — *Int. Newer Mamm.*

International Code of Botanical Nomenclature, 1978 — ICBN

Just's Botanischer Jahresbericht, 1885–1944 — *Just. Bot. Jahresb.*

Kakteen, 1929–33 — *Kakteen*

Die Kakteen: eine gesamtdarstellung der eingeführten Arten nebst Anzucht- und Pflege-anweisungen, 1956–75 — *Die Kakt. Lfg.*

(Journal) *Kakteen und andere Sukkulenten*, 1950– — *Kakt. u. a. Sukk*

Kakteenkunde, 1933–39 — *Kakteenk.*

Kakteenlexicon, 1966, Backeberg — *Kakteenlex.*

Kaktus ABC, 1935, Backeberg & Knuth — *Kaktus ABC*

Kaktusy — *Kaktusy*

Linnaea. Institut Botanique de l'Université de Genève, 1915–20 — *Linnaea*

London Journal of Botany, 1842–48 — *London Journ. Bot.*

Mammillaria, 1957, Marsden — *Mammillaria*

The Mammillaria Handbook, 1945, Craig — *Mamm. Handb.*

Journal of The Mammillaria Society, 1960– — *MSJ*

Ein Mammillarien Vergleichs Schlüssel, 1933, Boedeker — *Mamm. Vergl. Schluss.*

Manual de Campo de las Cactáceas y Suculentas de la Barranca de Metztitlan, 1978, Sánchez Mejorada — —

Memoir of a Tour of Northern Mexico, 1846–47, Wislizenus, 1848 — *Mem. Tour North Mex.*

Mémoires Muséum d'Histoire Naturalis, 1828–38 de Candolle — *Mem. Mus. Nat. Hist. Paris*

Mémoires sur Quelques Espèces des Cactées, 1834, de Candolle — *Mem. Cact.*

Notes of a Military Reconnaisance, 1848, Emory. Cactaceae by Engelmann. — *Mil. Rec.*

Monatsschrift der Deutschen Kakteen Gesellschaft, 1929–32 — *Monatsschr. Deutsch. Kakt. Ges.*

Monatsschrift fur Kakteenkunde, 1891–1922 — *Monatsschr. Kakteenk.*

Journal of the National Cactus & Succulent Society, 1946– — *Nat. Cact.*

Die Naturlichen Pflanzenfamilien, 1925, Engler — *Nat. Pflanzenfam.*

Native Cacti of California, 1970, Benson — *Cacti of California*

Neue Kakteen, 1931, Backeberg — *Neue Kakt.*

Notizblatt des Botanischen Garten und Museums zu Berlin-Dahlem, 1931 — *Notizbl. Bot. Gard. Mus.*

Nova Acta Physico Medica Academiae Caesareae Leopoldino Carolinae Naturae Curiosorum, 1932, Martius — *Nov. Act. Nat. Cur.*

Philosophical Magazine, 1824–30 — *Phil. Mag.*

Pittonia, 1887–1905 — *Pittonia*

Plantes Grasses, 1799–1829, de Candolle & Redouté — *Pl. Grasses*

Plantarum Novarum Horto Botanico Regio Monacensi, 1837, Zuccarini — *Pl. Nov. Monac.*

Proceedings of American Academy of Arts and Sciences, 1889 — *Proc. Amer. Acad.*

Proceedings of California Academy of Science, 1889 — *Proc. Calif. Acad.*

Prodromus Systematis Naturalis Regni Vegetabilis, 1828, de Candolle — *Prodr.*

Repertorium novarum Specierum Regni Vegetabilis, 1905–40, Fedde — *Repert. Spec. Nov.*

Repertorium Plantarum Succulentarum, 1960–, Rowley and Newton — *Repert. Pl. Succ.*

Reviso Generum Plantarum, 1891, Kuntze — *Rev. Gen. Pl.*

Revisiones Plantarum Succulentarum, 1821, Haworth — *Rev. Pl. Succ.*

Saguaroland Bulletin, 1972 — *Saguaroland Bull.*

Species Plantarum, 1753, Linnaeus — *Sp. Pl.*

Stachlige Wildnis ed. 2, 1943, Backeberg — *Stachl. Wildnis*

Standard Cyclopedia of Horticulture,
  Bailey — *Stand. Cycl. Hort.*

*Succulents—A Glossary of Terms and
  Descriptions* R. B. Ivimey-Cook,
  1974 — —

Sukkulentenkunde, 1948 — *Sukkulentenk.*

*Supplementum Plantarum
  Succulentarum,* 1819, Haworth — *Suppl. Pl. Succ.*

*Swiat Kaktusów (The World of
  Cacti),* Poland, 1966 – — *Swiat Kakt.*

Synopsis Plantarum Succulentarum,
  1812, Haworth — *Syn. Pl. Succ.*

West American Scientist, 1887, 1894,
  1899, 1900, 1902 — *West Amer. Sci.*

*Wochenschrift für Gärtnerei und
  Pflanzenkunde,* 1858–59 — *Wochenschrift*

Zeitschrift für Sukkulentenkunde,
  1923–28 — *Zeitschr. Sukk.*

Zoe, 1891–1900 — *Zoe*

INDEX